"If you are looking for a job ... before you go to the newspapers and the help-wanted ads, listen to Bob Adams, publisher of *The Metropolitan New York JobBank.*"

   -Tom Brokaw, *NBC*

"Help on the job hunt ... Anyone who is job-hunting in the New York area can find a lot of useful ideas in a new paperback called *The Metropolitan New York JobBank ...*"

   -Angela Taylor, *New York Times*

"One of the better publishers of employment almanacs is Adams Media Corporation ... publisher of *The Metropolitan New York JobBank* and similarly named directories of employers in Texas, Boston, Chicago, Northern and Southern California, and Washington DC. A good buy ..."

   -Wall Street Journal's
   National Business Employment Weekly

"For those graduates whose parents are pacing the floor, conspicuously placing circled want ads around the house and typing up resumes, [*The Carolina JobBank*] answers job-search questions."

   -Greensboro News and Record

"A timely book for Chicago job hunters follows books from the same publisher that were well received in New York and Boston ... [*The Chicago JobBank* is] a fine tool for job hunters ..."

   -Clarence Peterson, *Chicago Tribune*

"Because our listing is seen by people across the nation, it generates lots of resumes for us. We encourage unsolicited resumes. We'll always be listed [in *The Chicago JobBank*] as long as I'm in this career."

   -Tom Fitzpatrick, Director of Human Resources
   Merchandise Mart Properties, Inc.

"Job-hunting is never fun, but this book can ease the ordeal ... [*The Los Angeles JobBank*] will help allay fears, build confidence, and avoid wheel-spinning."

   -Robert W. Ross, *Los Angeles Times*

"Job hunters can't afford to waste time. *The Minneapolis-St. Paul JobBank* contains information that used to require hours of research in the library."

   -Carmella Zagone
   Minneapolis-based Human Resources Administrator

"*The Boston JobBank* provides a handy map of employment possibilities in greater Boston. This book can help in the initial steps of a job search by locating major employers, describing their business activities, and for most firms, by naming the contact person and listing typical professional positions. For recent college graduates, as well as experienced professionals, *The Boston JobBank* is an excellent place to begin a job search."

-Juliet F. Brudney, Career Columnist
Boston Globe

"No longer can jobseekers feel secure about finding employment just through want ads. With the tough competition in the job market, particularly in the Boston area, they need much more help. For this reason, *The Boston JobBank* will have a wide and appreciative audience of new graduates, job changers, and people relocating to Boston. It provides a good place to start a search for entry-level professional positions."

-Journal of College Placement

"*The Phoenix JobBank* is a first-class publication. The information provided is useful and current."

-Lyndon Denton
Director of Human Resources and Materials Management
Apache Nitrogen Products, Inc.

"*The Seattle JobBank* is an essential resource for job hunters."

-Gil Lopez, Staffing Team Manager
Battelle Pacific Northwest Laboratories

"I read through the 'Basics of Job Winning' and 'Resumes' sections [in *The Dallas-Fort Worth JobBank*] and found them to be very informative, with some positive tips for the job searcher. I believe the strategies outlined will bring success to any determined candidate."

-Camilla Norder, Professional Recruiter
Presbyterian Hospital of Dallas

"Through *The Dallas-Fort Worth JobBank,* we've been able to attract high-quality candidates for several positions."

-Rob Bertino, Southern States Sales Manager
CompuServe

"Packed with helpful contacts, *The Houston JobBank* empowers its reader to launch an effective, strategic job search in the Houston metropolitan area."

-Andrew Ceperley, Director
College of Communication Career Services
The University of Texas at Austin

What makes the
JobBank series
the nation's premier
line of employment guides?

With vital employment information on thousands of employers across the nation, the JobBank series is the most comprehensive and authoritative set of career directories available today.

Each book in the series provides information on **dozens of different industries** in a given city or area, with the primary employer listings providing contact information, telephone and fax numbers, e-mail addresses, Websites, a summary of the firm's business, internships, and in many cases descriptions of the firm's typical professional job categories.

All of the reference information in the JobBank series is as up-to-date and accurate as possible. Every year, the entire database is thoroughly researched and verified by mail and by telephone. Adams Media Corporation publishes **more local employment guides more often** than any other publisher of career directories.

The JobBank series offers **28 regional titles**, from Minneapolis to Houston, and from Boston to San Francisco as well as **two industry-specific titles**. All of the information is organized geographically, because most people look for jobs in specific areas of the country.

A condensed, but thorough, review of the entire job search process is presented in the chapter **The Basics of Job Winning**, a feature which has received many compliments from career counselors. In addition, each JobBank directory includes a section on **resumes and cover letters** the *New York Times* has acclaimed as "excellent."

The JobBank series gives job hunters the most comprehensive, timely, and accurate career information, organized and indexed to facilitate your job search. An entire career reference library, JobBank books are designed to help you find optimal employment in any market.

Top career publications from Adams Media Corporation

The JobBank Series:
each JobBank book is $16.95

The Atlanta JobBank, 14th Ed.
The Austin/San Antonio JobBank, 3rd Ed.
The Boston JobBank, 19th Ed.
The Carolina JobBank, 6th Ed.
The Chicago JobBank, 18th Ed.
The Colorado JobBank, 13th Ed.
The Connecticut JobBank, 2nd Ed.
The Dallas-Fort Worth JobBank, 13th Ed.
The Detroit JobBank, 9th Ed.
The Florida JobBank, 15th Ed.
The Houston JobBank, 11th Ed.
The Indiana JobBank, 3rd Ed.
The Las Vegas JobBank, 2nd Ed.
The Los Angeles JobBank, 17th Ed.
The Minneapolis-St. Paul JobBank, 11th Ed.
The Missouri JobBank, 3rd Ed.
The New Jersey JobBank, 1st Ed.
The Metropolitan New York JobBank, 18th Ed.
The Ohio JobBank, 10th Ed.
The Greater Philadelphia JobBank, 14th Ed.
The Phoenix JobBank, 8th Ed.
The Pittsburgh JobBank, 2nd Ed.
The Portland JobBank, 3rd Ed.
The San Francisco Bay Area JobBank, 16th Ed.
The Seattle JobBank, 12th Ed.
The Tennessee JobBank, 5th Ed.
The Virginia JobBank, 3rd Ed.
The Metropolitan Washington DC JobBank, 15th Ed.

The JobBank Guide to Computer & High-Tech Companies, 2nd Ed. ($17.95)
The JobBank Guide to Health Care Companies, 2nd Ed. ($17.95)

The National JobBank, 2003 (Covers the entire U.S.: $450.00 hc)

Other Career Titles:

The Adams Cover Letter Almanac ($12.95)
The Adams Internet Job Search Almanac, 6th Ed. ($12.95)
The Adams Executive Recruiters Almanac, 2nd Ed. ($17.95)
The Adams Job Interview Almanac ($12.95)
The Adams Jobs Almanac, 8th Ed. ($16.95)
The Adams Resume Almanac ($10.95)
Business Etiquette in Brief ($7.95)
Campus Free College Degrees, 8th Ed. ($16.95)
Career Tests ($12.95)
Closing Techniques, 2nd Ed. ($8.95)
Cold Calling Techniques, 4th Ed. ($8.95)
College Grad Job Hunter, 4th Ed. ($14.95)
The Complete Resume & Job Search Book for College Students, 2nd Ed. ($12.95)
Cover Letters That Knock 'em Dead, 5th Ed. ($12.95)
Every Woman's Essential Job Hunting & Resume Book ($11.95)
The Everything Cover Letter Book ($12.95)
The Everything Get-A-Job Book ($12.95)
The Everything Hot Careers Book ($12.95)
The Everything Job Interview Book ($12.95)
The Everything Online Business Book ($12.95)
The Everything Online Job Search Book ($12.95)
The Everything Resume Book ($12.95)
The Everything Selling Book ($12.95)
First Time Resume ($7.95)
How to Start and Operate a Successful Business ($9.95)
Knock 'em Dead, 2003 ($14.95)
Knock 'em Dead Business Presentations ($12.95)
Market Yourself and Your Career, 2nd Ed. ($12.95)
The New Professional Image ($12.95)
The 150 Most Profitable Home Businesses for Women ($9.95)
The Resume Handbook, 3rd Ed. ($7.95)
Resumes That Knock 'em Dead, 5th Ed. ($12.95)
The Road to CEO ($20.00 hc)
The 250 Job Interview Questions You'll Most Likely Be Asked ($9.95)
Your Executive Image ($10.95)

If you cannot find these titles at your favorite book outlet, you may order them directly from the publisher. **BY PHONE:** Call 800/872-5627 (in Massachusetts 508/427-7100). We accept Visa, Mastercard, and American Express. $4.95 will be added to your total for shipping and handling. **BY MAIL:** Write out the full titles of the books you'd like to order and send payment, including $4.95 for shipping and handling to: Adams Media Corporation, 57 Littlefield Street, Avon MA 02322. 30-day money back guarantee.
BY FAX: 800/872-5628.
Discounts available for standing orders.

15th Edition
THE Florida
JobBank

Reference Editor:	Christie L. Barros
Assistant Reference Editor:	Lisa A. Geraghty
Production Manager:	Michelle Roy Kelly

Adams Media Corporation
AVON, MASSACHUSETTS

Published by Adams Media Corporation
57 Littlefield Street, Avon MA 02322. U.S.A.
www.adamsmedia.com

ISBN: 1-58062-820-6
ISSN: 1069-8981
Manufactured in Canada.

*This book is available on standing order
and at quantity discounts for bulk purchases.*

For information, call 800/872-5627 (in Massachusetts, 508/427-7100).

TABLE OF CONTENTS

SECTION ONE: INTRODUCTION

How to Use This Book/12
An introduction to the most effective way to use The Florida JobBank.

SECTION TWO: THE JOB SEARCH

The Basics of Job Winning/16
A review of the elements of a successful job search campaign. Includes advice on developing effective strategies, time planning, and preparing for interviews. Special sections address situations faced by jobseekers who are currently employed, those who have lost a job, and graduates conducting their first job search.

Resumes and Cover Letters/30
Advice on creating strong resumes and cover letters.

SECTION THREE: PRIMARY EMPLOYERS

The Employers/50
The Florida JobBank is organized according to industry. Many listings include the address and phone number of each major firm listed, along with a description of the company's basic product lines and services, and, in many cases, a contact name and other relevant hiring information.

Accounting and Management Consulting/50
Advertising, Marketing, and Public Relations/55
- Direct Mail Marketers, Market Researchers

Aerospace/60
- Aerospace Products and Services
- Aircraft Equipment and Parts

Apparel, Fashion, and Textiles/70
- Broadwoven Fabric Mills, Knitting Mills, and Yarn and Thread Mills
- Curtains and Draperies
- Footwear
- Nonwoven Fabrics
- Textile Goods and Finishing

Architecture, Construction, and Engineering/74
- Architectural and Engineering Services
- Civil and Mechanical Engineering Firms
- Construction Products, Manufacturers, and Wholesalers
- General Contractors/Specialized Trade Contractor

Arts, Entertainment, Sports, and Recreation/82
- Botanical and Zoological Gardens
- Entertainment Groups
- Motion Picture and Video Tape Production and Distribution
- Museums and Art Galleries
- Physical Fitness Facilities
- Professional Sports Clubs; Sporting and Recreational Camps
- Public Golf Courses and Racing and Track Operations
- Theatrical Producers and Services

Automotive/88
- Automotive Repair Shops
- Automotive Stampings

- *Industrial Vehicles and Moving Equipment*
- *Motor Vehicles and Equipment*
- *Travel Trailers and Campers*

Banking/Savings and Loans/92

Biotechnology, Pharmaceuticals, and Scientific R&D/99
- *Clinical Labs*
- *Lab Equipment Manufacturers*
- *Pharmaceutical Manufacturers and Distributors*

Business Services and Non-Scientific Research/105
- *Adjustment and Collection Services*
- *Cleaning, Maintenance, and Pest Control Services*
- *Credit Reporting Services*
- *Detective, Guard, and Armored Car Services/Security Systems Services*
- *Miscellaneous Equipment Rental and Leasing*
- *Secretarial and Court Reporting Services*

Charities and Social Services/110
- *Job Training and Vocational Rehabilitation Services*

Chemicals/Rubber and Plastics/113
- *Adhesives, Detergents, Inks, Paints, Soaps, Varnishes*
- *Agricultural Chemicals and Fertilizers*
- *Carbon and Graphite Products*
- *Chemical Engineering Firms*
- *Industrial Gases*

Communications: Telecommunications and Broadcasting/117
- *Cable/Pay Television Services*
- *Communications Equipment*
- *Radio and Television Broadcasting Stations*
- *Telephone, Telegraph, and Other Message Communications*

Computer Hardware, Software, and Services/124
- *Computer Components and Hardware Manufacturers*
- *Consultants and Computer Training Companies*
- *Internet and Online Service Providers*
- *Networking and Systems Services*
- *Repair Services/Rental and Leasing*
- *Resellers, Wholesalers, and Distributors*
- *Software Developers/Programming Services*

Educational Services/142
- *Business/Secretarial/Data Processing Schools*
- *Colleges/Universities/Professional Schools*
- *Community Colleges/Technical Schools/Vocational Schools*
- *Elementary and Secondary Schools*
- *Preschool and Child Daycare Services*

Electronic/Industrial Electrical Equipment/150
- *Electronic Machines and Systems*
- *Semiconductor Manufacturers*

Environmental and Waste Management Services/164
- *Environmental Engineering Firms*
- *Sanitary Services*

Fabricated/Primary Metals and Products/168
- *Aluminum and Copper Foundries*
- *Die-Castings*
- *Iron and Steel Foundries/Steel Works, Blast Furnaces, and Rolling Mills*

Financial Services/171
- *Consumer Financing and Credit Agencies*
- *Investment Specialists*
- *Mortgage Bankers and Loan Brokers*
- *Security and Commodity Brokers, Dealers, and Exchanges*

Food and Beverages/Agriculture/177
- Crop Services and Farm Supplies
- Dairy Farms
- Food Manufacturers/Processors and Agricultural Producers
- Tobacco Products

Government/185
- Courts
- Executive, Legislative, and General Government
- Public Agencies (Firefighters, Military, Police)
- United States Postal Service

Health Care: Services, Equipment, and Products/188
- Dental Labs and Equipment
- Home Health Care Agencies
- Hospitals and Medical Centers
- Medical Equipment Manufacturers and Wholesalers
- Offices and Clinics of Health Practitioners
- Residential Treatment Centers/Nursing Homes
- Veterinary Services

Hotels and Restaurants/215

Insurance/221

Legal Services/225

Manufacturing: Miscellaneous Consumer/227
- Art Supplies
- Batteries
- Cosmetics and Related Products
- Household Appliances and Audio/Video Equipment
- Jewelry, Silverware, and Plated Ware
- Miscellaneous Household Furniture and Fixtures
- Musical Instruments
- Tools
- Toys and Sporting Goods

Manufacturing: Miscellaneous Industrial/232
- Ball and Roller Bearings
- Commercial Furniture and Fixtures
- Fans, Blowers, and Purification Equipment
- Industrial Machinery and Equipment
- Motors and Generators/Compressors and Engine Parts
- Vending Machines

Mining/Gas/Petroleum/Energy Related/239
- Anthracite, Coal, and Ore Mining
- Mining Machinery and Equipment
- Oil and Gas Field Services
- Petroleum and Natural Gas

Paper and Wood Products/242
- Forest and Wood Products and Services
- Lumber and Wood Wholesale
- Millwork, Plywood, and Structural Members
- Paper and Wood Mills

Printing and Publishing/246
- Book, Newspaper, and Periodical Publishers
- Commercial Photographers
- Commercial Printing Services
- Graphic Designers

Real Estate/261
- Land Subdividers and Developers
- Real Estate Agents, Managers, and Operators
- Real Estate Investment Trusts

Retail/267

Stone, Clay, Glass, and Concrete Products/278
- Cement, Tile, Sand, and Gravel
- Crushed and Broken Stone
- Glass and Glass Products
- Mineral Products

Transportation/Travel/282
- Air, Railroad, and Water Transportation Services
- Courier Services
- Local and Interurban Passenger Transit
- Ship Building and Repair
- Transportation Equipment
- Travel Agencies
- Trucking
- Warehousing and Storage

Utilities: Electric/Gas/Water/290

Miscellaneous Wholesaling/293
- Exporters and Importers

SECTION FOUR: INDEX

Index of Primary Employers by Industry/296

INTRODUCTION

HOW TO USE THIS BOOK

Right now, you hold in your hands one of the most effective job-hunting tools available anywhere. In *The Florida JobBank*, you will find valuable information to help you launch or continue a rewarding career. But before you open to the book's employer listings and start calling about current job openings, take a few minutes to learn how best to use the resources presented in *The Florida JobBank*.

The Florida JobBank will help you to stand out from other jobseekers. While many people looking for a new job rely solely on newspaper help-wanted ads, this book offers you a much more effective job-search method – direct contact. The direct contact method has been proven twice as effective as scanning the help-wanted ads. Instead of waiting for employers to come looking for you, you'll be far more effective going to them. While many of your competitors will use trial and error methods in trying to set up interviews, you'll learn not only how to get interviews, but what to expect once you've got them.

In the next few pages, we'll take you through each section of the book so you'll be prepared to get a jump-start on your competition.

Basics of Job Winning

Preparation. Strategy. Time management. These are three of the most important elements of a successful job search. *Basics of Job Winning* helps you address these and all the other elements needed to find the right job.

One of your first priorities should be to define your personal career objectives. What qualities make a job desirable to you? Creativity? High pay? Prestige? Use *Basics of Job Winning* to weigh these questions. Then use the rest of the chapter to design a strategy to find a job that matches your criteria.

In *Basics of Job Winning,* you'll learn which job-hunting techniques work, and which don't. We've reviewed the pros and cons of mass mailings, help-wanted ads, and direct contact. We'll show you how to develop and approach contacts in your field; how to research a prospective employer; and how to use that information to get an interview and the job.

Also included in *Basics of Job Winning*: interview dress code and etiquette, the "do's and don'ts" of interviewing, sample interview questions, and more. We also deal with some of the unique problems faced by those jobseekers who are currently employed, those who have lost a job, and college students conducting their first job search.

Resumes and Cover Letters

The approach you take to writing your resume and cover letter can often mean the difference between getting an interview and never being noticed. In this section, we discuss different formats, as well as what to put on (and what to leave off) your resume. We review the benefits and drawbacks of professional resume writers, and the importance of a follow-up letter. Also included in this section are sample resumes and cover letters you can use as models.

The Employer Listings

Employers are listed alphabetically by industry. When a company does business under a person's name, like "John Smith & Co.," the company is usually listed by the surname's spelling (in this case "S"). Exceptions occur when a company's name is widely recognized, like "JCPenney" or "Howard Johnson Motor Lodge." In those cases, the company's first name is the key ("J" and "H" respectively).

The Florida JobBank covers a very wide range of industries. Each company profile is assigned to one of the industry chapters listed below.

Accounting and Management Consulting
Advertising, Marketing, and Public Relations
Aerospace
Apparel, Fashion, and Textiles
Architecture, Construction, and Engineering
Arts, Entertainment, Sports, and Recreation
Automotive
Banking/Savings and Loans
Biotechnology, Pharmaceuticals, and
    Scientific R&D
Business Services and Non-Scientific
    Research
Charities and Social Services
Chemicals/Rubber and Plastics
Communications: Telecommunications and
    Broadcasting
Computer Hardware, Software, and Services
Educational Services
Electronic/Industrial Electrical Equipment
Environmental and Waste Management
    Services

Fabricated/Primary Metals and Products
Financial Services
Food and Beverages/Agriculture
Government
Health Care: Services, Equipment, and
    Products
Hotels and Restaurants
Insurance
Legal Services
Manufacturing: Miscellaneous Consumer
Manufacturing: Miscellaneous Industrial
Mining/Gas/Petroleum/Energy Related
Paper and Wood Products
Printing and Publishing
Real Estate
Retail
Stone, Clay, Glass, and Concrete Products
Transportation/Travel
Utilities: Electric/Gas/Water
Miscellaneous Wholesaling

Many of the company listings offer detailed company profiles. In addition to company names, addresses, and phone numbers, these listings also include contact names or hiring departments, and descriptions of each company's products and/or services. Many of these listings also feature a variety of additional information including:

Common positions - A list of job titles that the company commonly fills when it is hiring, organized in alphabetical order from Accountant to X-ray Technician. Note: Keep in mind that *The Florida JobBank* is a directory of major employers in the area, not a directory of openings currently available. Many of the companies listed will be hiring, others will not. However, since most professional job openings are filled without the placement of help-wanted ads, contacting the employers in this book directly is still a more effective method than browsing the Sunday papers.

Special programs - Does the company offer training programs, internships, or apprenticeships? These programs can be important to first time jobseekers and college students looking for practical work experience. Many employer profiles will include information on these programs.

Parent company - If an employer is a subsidiary of a larger company, the name of that parent company will often be listed here. Use this information to supplement your company research before contacting the employer.

Number of employees - The number of workers a company employs.

Company listings may also include information on other U.S. locations and any stock exchanges the firm may be listed on.

A note on all employer listings that appear in *The Florida JobBank*: This book is intended as a starting point. It is not intended to replace any effort that you, the jobseeker, should devote to your job hunt. Keep in mind that while a great deal of effort has been put into collecting and verifying the company profiles provided in this book, addresses and contact names change regularly. Inevitably, some contact names listed herein have changed even before you read this. We recommend you contact a company before mailing your resume to ensure nothing has changed.

Index

   The Florida JobBank index is listed alphabetically by industry.

THE JOB SEARCH

THE BASICS OF JOB WINNING: A CONDENSED REVIEW

This chapter is divided into four sections. The first section explains the fundamentals that every jobseeker should know, especially first-time jobseekers. The next three sections deal with special situations faced by specific types of jobseekers: those who are currently employed, those who have lost a job, and college students.

THE BASICS:
Things Everyone Needs to Know

Career Planning

The first step to finding your ideal job is to clearly define your objectives. This is better known as career planning (or life planning if you wish to emphasize the importance of combining the two). Career planning has become a field of study in and of itself.

If you are thinking of choosing or switching careers, we particularly emphasize two things. First, choose a career where you will enjoy most of the day-to-day tasks. This sounds obvious, but most of us have at some point found the idea of a glamour industry or prestigious job title attractive without thinking of the key consideration: Would we enjoy performing the everyday tasks the position entails?

The second key consideration is that you are not merely choosing a career, but also a lifestyle. Career counselors indicate that one of the most common problems people encounter in jobseeking is that they fail to consider how well-suited they are for a particular position or career. For example, some people, attracted to management consulting by good salaries, early responsibility, and high-level corporate exposure, do not adapt well to the long hours, heavy travel demands, and constant pressure to produce. Be sure to ask yourself how you might adapt to the day-to-day duties and working environment that a specific position entails. Then ask yourself how you might adapt to the demands of that career or industry as a whole.

Choosing Your Strategy

Assuming that you've established your career objectives, the next step of the job search is to develop a strategy. If you don't take the time to develop a plan, you may find yourself going in circles after several weeks of randomly searching for opportunities that always seem just beyond your reach.

The most common jobseeking techniques are:

- following up on help-wanted advertisements (in the newspaper or online)
- using employment services
- relying on personal contacts
- contacting employers directly (the Direct Contact method)

Each of these approaches can lead to better jobs. However, the Direct Contact method boasts twice the success rate of the others. So unless you have specific reasons to employ other strategies, Direct Contact should form the foundation of your job search.

If you choose to use other methods as well, try to expend at least half your energy on Direct Contact. Millions of other jobseekers have already proven that Direct Contact has been twice as effective in obtaining employment, so why not follow in their footsteps?

Setting Your Schedule

Okay, so now that you've targeted a strategy it's time to work out the details of your job search. The most important detail is setting up a schedule. Of course, since job searches aren't something most people do regularly, it may be hard to estimate how long each step will take. Nonetheless, it is important to have a plan so that you can monitor your progress.

When outlining your job search schedule, have a realistic time frame in mind. If you will be job-searching full-time, your search could take at least two months or more. If you can only devote part-time effort, it will probably take at least four months.

You probably know a few people who seem to spend their whole lives searching for a better job in their spare time. Don't be one of them. If you are presently working and don't feel like devoting a lot of energy to jobseeking right now, then wait. Focus on enjoying your present position, performing your best on the job, and storing up energy for when you are really ready to begin your job search.

> **The first step in beginning your job search is to clearly define your objectives.**

Those of you who are currently unemployed should remember that *job-hunting is tough work, both physically and emotionally.* It is also intellectually demanding work that requires you to be at your best. So don't tire yourself out by working on your job campaign around the clock. At the same time, be sure to discipline yourself. The most logical way to manage your time while looking for a job is to keep your regular working hours.

If you are searching full-time and have decided to choose several different strategies, we recommend that you divide up each week, designating some time for each method. By trying several approaches at once, you can evaluate how promising each seems and alter your schedule accordingly. Keep in mind that the *majority of openings are filled without being advertised.* Remember also that positions advertised on the Internet are just as likely to already be filled as those found in the newspaper!

If you are searching part-time and decide to try several different contact methods, we recommend that you try them sequentially. You simply won't have enough time to put a meaningful amount of effort into more than one method at once. Estimate the length of your job search, and then allocate so many weeks or months for each contact method, beginning with Direct Contact. The purpose of setting this schedule is not to rush you to your goal but to help you periodically evaluate your progress.

The Direct Contact Method

Once you have scheduled your time, you are ready to begin your search in earnest. Beginning with the Direct Contact method, the first step is to develop a checklist for categorizing the types of firms for which you'd like to work. You might categorize firms by product line, size, customer type (such as industrial or consumer), growth prospects, or geographical location. Keep in mind, the shorter the list the easier it will be to locate a company that is right for you.

Next you will want to use this *JobBank* book to assemble your list of potential employers. Choose firms where *you* are most likely to be able to find a job. Try matching your skills with those that a specific job demands. Consider where your skills might be in demand, the degree of competition for employment, and the employment outlook at each company.

Separate your prospect list into three groups. The first 25 percent will be your primary target group, the next 25 percent will be your secondary group, and the remaining names will be your reserve group.

After you form your prospect list, begin working on your resume. Refer to the Resumes and Cover Letters section following this chapter for more information.

Once your resume is complete, begin researching your first batch of prospective employers. You will want to determine whether you would be happy working at the firms you are researching and to get a better idea of what their employment needs might be. You also need to obtain enough information to sound highly informed about the company during phone conversations and in mail correspondence. But don't go all out on your research yet! You probably won't be able to arrange interviews with some of these firms, so save your big research effort until you start to arrange interviews. Nevertheless, you should plan to spend several hours researching each firm. Do your research in batches to save time and energy. Start with this book, and find out what you can about each of the firms in your primary target group. For answers to specific questions, contact any pertinent professional associations that may be able to help you learn more about an employer. Read industry publications looking for articles on the firm. (Addresses of associations and names of important publications are listed after each section of employer listings in this book.) Then look up the company on the Internet or try additional resources at your local library. Keep organized, and maintain a folder on each firm.

> **The more you know about a company, the more likely you are to catch an interviewer's eye. (You'll also face fewer surprises once you get the job!)**

Information to look for includes: company size; president, CEO, or owner's name; when the company was established; what each division does; and benefits that are important to you. An abundance of company information can now be found electronically, through the World Wide Web or commercial online services. Researching companies online is a convenient means of obtaining information quickly and easily. If you have access to the Internet, you can search from your home at any time of day.

You may search a particular company's Website for current information that may be otherwise unavailable in print. In fact, many companies that maintain a site update their information daily. In addition, you may also search articles written about the company online. Today, most of the nation's largest newspapers, magazines, trade publications, and regional business periodicals have online versions of their publications. To find additional resources, use a search engine like Yahoo! or Alta Vista and type in the keyword "companies" or "employers."

If you discover something that really disturbs you about the firm (they are about to close their only local office), or if you discover that your chances of getting a job there are practically nil (they have just instituted a hiring freeze), then cross them off your prospect list. If possible, supplement your research efforts by contacting individuals who know the firm well. Ideally you should make an informal contact with someone at that particular firm, but often a direct competitor or a major customer will be able to supply you with just as much information. At the very least, try to obtain whatever printed information the company has available -- not just annual reports, but product brochures, company profiles, or catalogs. This information is often available on the Internet.

Getting the Interview

Now it is time to make Direct Contact with the goal of arranging interviews. If you have read any books on job-searching, you may have noticed that most of these books tell you to avoid the human resources office like the plague. It is said that the human resources office never hires people; they screen candidates. Unfortunately, this is often the case. If you can identify the appropriate manager with the authority to hire you, you should try to contact that person directly.

The obvious means of initiating Direct Contact are:

- Mail (postal or electronic)
- Phone calls

Mail contact is a good choice if you have not been in the job market for a while. You can take your time to prepare a letter, say exactly what you want, and of course include your resume. Remember that employers receive many resumes every day. Don't be surprised if you do not get a response to your inquiry, *and don't spend weeks waiting for responses that may never come.* If you do send a letter, follow it up (or precede it) with a phone call. This will increase your impact, and because of the initial research you did, will underscore both your familiarity with and your interest in the firm. Bear in mind that your goal is to make your name a familiar one with prospective employers, so that when a position becomes available, your resume will be one of the first the hiring manager seeks out.

DEVELOPING YOUR CONTACTS: NETWORKING

Some career counselors feel that the best route to a better job is through somebody you already know or through somebody to whom you can be introduced. These counselors recommend that you build your contact base beyond your current acquaintances by asking each one to introduce you, or refer you, to additional people in your field of interest.

The theory goes like this: You might start with 15 personal contacts, each of whom introduces you to three additional people, for a total of 45 additional contacts. Then each of these people introduces you to three additional people, which adds 135 additional contacts. Theoretically, you will soon know every person in the industry.

Of course, developing your personal contacts does not work quite as smoothly as the theory suggests because some people will not be able to introduce you to anyone. The further you stray from your initial contact base, the weaker your references may be. So, if you do try developing your own contacts, try to begin with as many people that you know personally as you can. Dig into your personal phone book and your holiday greeting card list and locate old classmates from school. Be particularly sure to approach people who perform your personal business such as your lawyer, accountant, banker, doctor, stockbroker, and insurance agent. These people develop a very broad contact base due to the nature of their professions.

If you send a fax, always follow with a hard copy of your resume and cover letter in the mail. Often, through no fault of your own, a fax will come through illegibly and employers do not often have time to let candidates know.

Another alternative is to make a "cover call." Your cover call should be just like your cover letter: concise. Your first statement should interest the employer in you. Then try to subtly mention your familiarity with the firm. Don't be overbearing; keep your introduction to three sentences or less. Be pleasant, self-confident, and relaxed. This will greatly increase the chances of the person at the other end of the line developing the conversation. But don't press. If you are asked to follow up with "something in the mail," this signals the conversation's natural end. Don't try to prolong the conversation once it has ended, and don't ask what they want to receive in the mail. Always send your resume and a highly personalized follow-up letter, reminding the addressee of the phone conversation. *Always* include a cover letter if you are asked to send a resume, and treat your resume and cover letter as a total package. Gear your letter toward the specific position you are applying for and prove why you would be a "good match" for the position.

> **Always include a cover letter if you are asked to send a resume.**

Unless you are in telephone sales, making smooth and relaxed cover calls will probably not come easily. Practice them on your own, and then with your friends or relatives.

DON'T BOTHER WITH MASS MAILINGS OR BARRAGES OF PHONE CALLS

Direct Contact does not mean burying every firm within a hundred miles with mail and phone calls. Mass mailings rarely work in the job hunt. This also applies to those letters that are personalized -- but dehumanized -- on an automatic typewriter or computer. Don't waste your time or money on such a project; you will fool no one but yourself.

The worst part of sending out mass mailings, or making unplanned phone calls to companies you have not researched, is that you are likely to be remembered as someone with little genuine interest in the firm, who lacks sincerity -- somebody that nobody wants to hire.

If you obtain an interview as a result of a telephone conversation, be sure to send a thank-you note reiterating the points you made during the conversation. You will appear more professional and increase your impact. However, unless specifically requested, don't mail your resume once an interview has been arranged. Take it with you to the interview instead.

You should never show up to seek a professional position without an appointment. Even if you are somehow lucky enough to obtain an interview, you will appear so unprofessional that you will not be seriously considered.

HELP WANTED ADVERTISEMENTS

Only a small fraction of professional job openings are advertised. Yet the majority of jobseekers -- and quite a few people not in the job market -- spend a lot of time studying the help wanted ads. As a result, the competition for advertised openings is often very severe.

A moderate-sized employer told us about their experience advertising in the help wanted section of a major Sunday newspaper:

It was a disaster. We had over 500 responses from this relatively small ad in just one week. We have only two phone lines in this office and one was totally knocked out. We'll never advertise for professional help again.

If you insist on following up on help wanted ads, then research a firm before you reply to an ad. Preliminary research might help to separate you from all of the other professionals responding to that ad, many of whom will have only a passing interest in the opportunity. It will also give you insight about a particular firm, to help you determine if it is potentially a good match. That said, your chances of obtaining a job through the want ads are still much smaller than they are with the Direct Contact method.

Preparing for the Interview

As each interview is arranged, begin your in-depth research. You should arrive at an interview knowing the company upside-down and inside-out. You need to know the company's products, types of customers, subsidiaries, parent company, principal locations, rank in the industry, sales and profit trends, type of ownership, size, current plans, and much more. By this time you have probably narrowed your job search to one industry. Even if you haven't, you should still be familiar with common industry terms, the trends in the firm's industry, the firm's principal competitors and their relative performance, and the direction in which the industry leaders are headed.

Dig into every resource you can! Surf the Internet. Read the company literature, the trade press, the business press, and if the company is public, call your stockbroker (if you have one) and ask for additional information. If possible, speak to someone at the firm before the interview, or if not, speak to someone at a competing firm. The more time you spend, the better. Even if you feel extremely pressed for time, you should set aside several hours for pre-interview research.

> **You should arrive at an interview knowing the company upside-down and inside-out.**

If you have been out of the job market for some time, don't be surprised if you find yourself tense during your first few interviews. It will probably happen every time you re-enter the market, not just when you seek your first job after getting out of school.

Tension is natural during an interview, but knowing you have done a thorough research job should put you more at ease. Make a list of questions that you think might be asked in each interview. Think out your answers carefully and practice them with a friend. Tape record your responses to the problem questions. (See also in this chapter: Informational Interviews.) If you feel particularly unsure of your interviewing skills, arrange your first interviews at firms you are not as interested in. (But remember it is common courtesy to seem enthusiastic about the possibility of working for any firm at which you interview.) Practice again on your own after these first few interviews. Go over the difficult questions that you were asked.

Take some time to really think about how you will convey your work history. Present "bad experiences" as "learning experiences." Instead of saying "I hated my position as a salesperson because I had to bother people on the phone," say "I realized that cold-calling was not my strong suit. Though I love working with people, I decided my talents would be best used in a more face-to-face atmosphere." Always find some sort of lesson from previous jobs, as they all have one.

Interview Attire

How important is the proper dress for a job interview? Buying a complete wardrobe, donning new shoes, and having your hair styled every morning are not enough to guarantee you a career position as an investment banker. But on the other hand, if you can't find a clean, conservative suit or won't take the time to wash your hair, then you are just wasting your time by interviewing at all.

Personal grooming is as important as finding appropriate clothes for a job interview. Careful grooming indicates both a sense of thoroughness and self-confidence. This is not the time to make a statement – take out the extra earrings and avoid any garish hair colors not found in nature. Women should not wear excessive makeup, and both men and women should refrain from wearing any perfume or cologne (it only takes a small spritz to leave an allergic interviewer with a fit of sneezing and a bad impression of your meeting). Men should be freshly shaven, even if the interview is late in the day, and men with long hair should have it pulled back and neat.

Men applying for any professional position should wear a suit, preferably in a conservative color such as navy or charcoal gray. It is easy to get away with wearing the same dark suit to consecutive interviews at the same company; just be sure to wear a different shirt and tie for each interview.

Women should also wear a business suit. Professionalism still dictates a suit with a skirt, rather than slacks, as proper interview garb for women. This is usually true even at companies where pants are acceptable attire for female employees. As much as you may disagree with this guideline, the more prudent time to fight this standard is after you land the job.

The final selection of candidates for a job opening won't be determined by dress, of course. However, inappropriate dress can quickly eliminate a first-round candidate. So while you shouldn't spend a fortune on a new wardrobe, you should be sure that your clothes are adequate. The key is to dress at least as formally or slightly more formally and more conservatively than the position would suggest.

What to Bring

Be complete. Everyone needs a watch, a pen, and a notepad. Finally, a briefcase or a leather-bound folder (containing extra, *unfolded*, copies of your resume) will help complete the look of professionalism.

Sometimes the interviewer will be running behind schedule. Don't be upset, be sympathetic. There is often pressure to interview a lot of candidates and to quickly fill a demanding position. So be sure to come to your interview with good reading material to keep yourself occupied and relaxed.

The Interview

The very beginning of the interview is the most important part because it determines the tone for the rest of it. Those first few moments are especially crucial. Do you smile when you meet? Do you establish enough eye contact, but not too much? Do you walk into the office with a self-assured and confident stride? Do you shake hands firmly? Do you make small talk easily without being garrulous? It is

---

BE PREPARED:
Some Common Interview Questions

Tell me about yourself.

Why did you leave your last job?

What excites you in your current job?

Where would you like to be in five years?

How much overtime are you willing to work?

What would your previous/present employer tell me about you?

Tell me about a difficult situation that you
faced at your previous/present job.

What are your greatest strengths?

What are your weaknesses?

Describe a work situation where you took initiative
and went beyond your normal responsibilities.

Why should we hire you?

---

human nature to judge people by that first impression, so make sure it is a good one. But most of all, try to be yourself.

Often the interviewer will begin, after the small talk, by telling you about the company, the division, the department, or perhaps, the position. Because of your detailed research, the information about the company should be repetitive for you, and the interviewer would probably like nothing better than to avoid this regurgitation of the company biography. So if you can do so tactfully, indicate to the interviewer that you are very familiar with the firm. If he or she seems intent on providing you with background information, despite your hints, then acquiesce.

But be sure to remain attentive. If you can manage to generate a brief discussion of the company or the industry at this point, without being forceful, great. It will help to further build rapport, underscore your interest, and increase your impact.

> **The interviewer's job is to find a reason to turn you down; your job is to not provide that reason.**
>
> -John L. LaFevre, author,
> *How You Really Get Hired*
>
> Reprinted from the 1989/90 *CPC Annual,* with permission of the National Association of Colleges and Employers (formerly College Placement Council, Inc.), copyright holder.

Soon (if it didn't begin that way) the interviewer will begin the questions, many of which you will have already practiced. This period of the interview usually falls into one of two categories (or somewhere in between): either a structured interview, where the interviewer has a prescribed set of questions to ask; or an unstructured interview, where the interviewer will ask only leading questions to get you to talk about yourself, your experiences, and your goals. Try to sense as quickly as possible in which direction the interviewer wishes to proceed. This will make the interviewer feel more relaxed and in control of the situation.

Remember to keep attuned to the interviewer and make the length of your answers appropriate to the situation. If you are really unsure as to how detailed a response the interviewer is seeking, then ask.

As the interview progresses, the interviewer will probably mention some of the most important responsibilities of the position. If applicable, draw parallels between your experience and the demands of the position as detailed by the interviewer. Describe your past experience in the same manner that you do on your resume: emphasizing results and achievements and not merely describing activities. But don't exaggerate. Be on the level about your abilities.

The first interview is often the toughest, where many candidates are screened out. If you are interviewing for a very competitive position, you will have to make an impression that will last. Focus on a few of your greatest strengths that are relevant to the position. Develop these points carefully, state them again in different words, and then try to summarize them briefly at the end of the interview.

Often the interviewer will pause toward the end and ask if you have any questions. Particularly in a structured interview, this might be the one chance to really show your knowledge of and interest in the firm. Have a list prepared of specific questions that are of real interest to you. Let your questions subtly show your research and your knowledge of the firm's activities. It is wise to have an extensive list of questions, as several of them may be answered during the interview.

Do not turn your opportunity to ask questions into an interrogation. Avoid reading directly from your list of questions, and ask questions that you are fairly certain the interviewer can answer (remember how you feel when you cannot answer a question during an interview).

Even if you are unable to determine the salary range beforehand, do not ask about it during the first interview. You can always ask later. Above all, don't ask about fringe benefits until you have been offered a position. (Then be sure to get all the details.)

Try not to be negative about anything during the interview, particularly any past employer or any previous job. Be cheerful. Everyone likes to work with someone who seems to be happy. Even if you detest your current/former job or manager, do not make disparaging comments. The interviewer may construe this as a sign of a potential attitude problem and not consider you a strong candidate.

Don't let a tough question throw you off base. If you don't know the answer to a question, simply say so – do not apologize. Just smile. Nobody can answer every question – particularly some of the questions that are asked in job interviews.

Before your first interview, you may be able to determine how many rounds of interviews there usually are for positions at your level. (Of course it may differ quite a bit even within the different levels of one firm.) Usually you can count on attending at least two or three interviews, although some firms are known to give a minimum of six interviews for all professional positions. While you should be more relaxed as you return for subsequent interviews, the pressure will be on. The more prepared you are, the better.

Depending on what information you are able to obtain, you might want to vary your strategy quite a bit from interview to interview. For instance, if the first interview is a screening interview, then be sure a few of your strengths really stand out. On the other hand, if later interviews are primarily with people who are in a position to veto your hiring, but not to push it forward, then you should primarily focus on building rapport as opposed to reiterating and developing your key strengths.

If it looks as though your skills and background do not match the position the interviewer was hoping to fill, ask him or her if there is another division or subsidiary that perhaps could profit from your talents.

After the Interview

Write a follow-up letter immediately after the interview, while it is still fresh in the interviewer's mind (see the sample follow-up letter format found in the Resumes and Cover Letters chapter). Not only is this a thank-you, but it also gives you the chance to provide the interviewer with any details you may have forgotten (as long as they can be tactfully added in). If you haven't heard back from the interviewer within a week of sending your thank-you letter, call to stress your continued interest in the firm and the position. If you lost any points during the interview for any reason, this letter can help you regain footing. Be polite and make sure to stress your continued interest and competency to fill the position. Just don't forget to proofread it thoroughly. If you are unsure of the spelling of the interviewer's name, call the receptionist and ask.

THE BALANCING ACT:
Looking for a New Job While Currently Employed

For those of you who are still employed, job-searching will be particularly tiring because it must be done in addition to your normal work responsibilities. So don't overwork yourself to the point where you show up to interviews looking exhausted or start to slip behind at your current job. On the other hand, don't be tempted to quit your present job! The long hours are worth it. Searching for a job while you have one puts you in a position of strength.

Making Contact

If you must be at your office during the business day, then you have additional problems to deal with. How can you work interviews into the business day? And if you work in an open office, how can you even call to set up interviews? Obviously, you should keep up the effort and the appearances on your present job. So maximize your use of the lunch hour, early mornings, and late afternoons for calling. If you keep trying, you'll be surprised how often you will be able to reach the executive you are trying to contact during your out-of-office hours. You can catch people as early as 8 a.m. and as late as 6 p.m. on frequent occasions.

Scheduling Interviews

Your inability to interview at any time other than lunch just might work to your advantage. If you can, try to set up as many interviews as possible for your lunch hour. This will go a long way to creating a relaxed atmosphere. But be sure the interviews don't stray too far from the agenda on hand.

Lunchtime interviews are much easier to obtain if you have substantial career experience. People with less experience will often find no alternative to taking time off for interviews. If you have to take time off, you have to take time off. But try to do this as little as possible. Try to take the whole day off in order to avoid being blatantly obvious about your job search, and try to schedule two to three interviews for the same day. (It is very difficult to maintain an optimum level of energy at more than three interviews in one day.) Explain to the interviewer why you might have to juggle your interview schedule; he/she should honor the respect you're showing your current employer by minimizing your days off and will probably appreciate the fact that another prospective employer is interested in you.

> **Try calling as early as 8 a.m. and as late as 6 p.m. You'll be surprised how often you will be able to reach the executive you want during these times of the day.**

References

What do you tell an interviewer who asks for references from your current employer? Just say that while you are happy to have your former employers contacted, you are trying to keep your job search confidential and would rather that your current employer not be contacted until you have been given a firm offer.

IF YOU'RE FIRED OR LAID OFF:
Picking Yourself Up and Dusting Yourself Off

If you've been fired or laid off, you are not the first and will not be the last to go through this traumatic experience. In today's changing economy, thousands of professionals lose their jobs every year. Even if you were terminated with just cause, do not lose heart. Remember, being fired is not a reflection on you as a person. It is usually a reflection of your company's staffing needs and its perception of your recent job performance and attitude. And if you were not performing up to par or enjoying your work, then you will probably be better off at another company anyway.

Be prepared for the question "Why were you fired?" during job interviews.

A thorough job search could take months, so be sure to negotiate a reasonable severance package, if possible, and determine to what benefits, such as health insurance, you are still legally entitled. Also, register for unemployment compensation immediately. Don't be surprised to find other professionals collecting unemployment compensation – it is for everyone who has lost their job.

Don't start your job search with a flurry of unplanned activity. Start by choosing a strategy and working out a plan. Now is not the time for major changes in your life. If possible, remain in the same career and in the same geographical location, at least until you have been working again for a while. On the other hand, if the only industry for which you are trained is leaving, or is severely depressed in your area, then you should give prompt consideration to moving or switching careers.

Avoid mentioning you were fired when arranging interviews, but be prepared for the question "Why were you fired?" during an interview. If you were laid off as a result of downsizing, briefly explain, being sure to reinforce that your job loss was not due to performance. If you were in fact fired, be honest, but try to detail the reason as favorably as possible and portray what you have learned from your mistakes. If you are confident one of your past managers will give you a good reference, tell the interviewer to contact that person. Do not to speak negatively of your past employer and try not to sound particularly worried about your status of being temporarily unemployed.

Finally, don't spend too much time reflecting on why you were let go or how you might have avoided it. Think positively, look to the future, and be sure to follow a careful plan during your job search.

THE COLLEGE STUDENT:
Conducting Your First Job Search

While you will be able to apply many of the basics covered earlier in this chapter to your job search, there are some situations unique to the college student's job search.

THE GPA QUESTION
You are interviewing for the job of your dreams. Everything is going well: You've established a good rapport, the interviewer seems impressed with your qualifications, and you're almost positive the job is yours. Then you're asked about your GPA, which is pitifully low. Do you tell the truth and watch your dream job fly out the window?

Never lie about your GPA (they may request your transcript, and no company will hire a liar). You can, however, explain if there is a reason you don't feel your grades reflect your abilities, and mention any other impressive statistics. For example, if you have a high GPA in your major, or in the last few semesters (as opposed to your cumulative college career), you can use that fact to your advantage.

Perhaps the biggest problem college students face is lack of experience. Many schools have internship programs designed to give students exposure to the field of their choice, as well as the opportunity to make valuable contacts. Check out your school's career services department to see what internships are available. If your school does not have a formal internship program, or if there are no available internships that appeal to you, try contacting local businesses and offering your services. Often, businesses will be more than willing to have an extra pair of hands (especially if those hands are unpaid!) for a day or two each week. Or try contacting school alumni to see if you can "shadow" them for a few days, and see what their daily duties are like.

Informational Interviews

Although many jobseekers do not do this, it can be extremely helpful to arrange an informational interview with a college alumnus or someone else who works in your desired industry. You interview them about their job, their company, and their industry with questions you have prepared in advance. This can be done over the phone but is usually done in person. This will provide you with a contact in the industry who may give you more valuable information -- or perhaps even a job opportunity -- in the future. Always follow up with a thank you letter that includes your contact information.

The goal is to try to begin building experience and establishing contacts as early as possible in your college career.

What do you do if, for whatever reason, you weren't able to get experience directly related to your desired career? First, look at your previous jobs and see if there's anything you can highlight. Did you supervise or train other employees? Did you reorganize the accounting system, or boost productivity in some way? Accomplishments like these demonstrate leadership, responsibility, and innovation -- qualities that most companies look for in employees. And don't forget volunteer activities and school clubs, which can also showcase these traits.

On-Campus Recruiting

Companies will often send recruiters to interview on-site at various colleges. This gives students a chance to interview with companies that may not have interviewed them otherwise. This is particularly true if a company schedules "open" interviews, in which the only screening process is who is first in line at the sign-ups. Of course, since many more applicants gain interviews in this format, this also means that many more people are rejected. The on-campus interview is generally a screening interview, to see if it is worth the company's time to invite you in for a second interview. So do everything possible to make yourself stand out from the crowd.

The first step, of course, is to check out any and all information your school's career center has on the company. If the information seems out of date, check out the company on the Internet or call the company's headquarters and ask for any printed information.

Many companies will host an informational meeting for interviewees, often the evening before interviews are scheduled to take place. DO NOT MISS THIS MEETING. The recruiter will almost certainly ask if you attended. Make an effort to stay after the meeting and talk with the company's representatives. Not only does this give you an opportunity to find out more information about both the company and the position, it also makes you stand out in the recruiter's mind. If there's a particular company that you had your heart set on, but you weren't able to get an interview with them, attend the information session anyway. You may be able to persuade the recruiter to squeeze you into the schedule. (Or you may discover that the company really isn't the right fit for you after all.)

Try to check out the interview site beforehand. Some colleges may conduct "mock" interviews that take place in one of the standard interview rooms. Or you may be able to convince a career counselor (or even a custodian) to let you sneak a peek during off-hours. Either way, having an idea of the room's setup will help you to mentally prepare.

Arrive at least 15 minutes early to the interview. The recruiter may be ahead of schedule, and might meet you early. But don't be surprised if previous interviews have run over, resulting in your 30-minute slot being reduced to 20 minutes (or less). Don't complain or appear anxious; just use the time you do have as efficiently as possible to showcase the reasons *you* are the ideal candidate. Staying calm and composed in these situations will work to your advantage.

LAST WORDS

A parting word of advice. Again and again during your job search you will face rejection. You will be rejected when you apply for interviews. You will be rejected after interviews. For every job offer you finally receive, you probably will have been rejected many times. Don't let rejections slow you down. Keep reminding yourself that the sooner you go out, start your job search, and get those rejections flowing in, the closer you will be to obtaining the job you want.

RESUMES AND COVER LETTERS

When filling a position, an employer will often have 100-plus applicants, but time to interview only a handful of the most promising ones. As a result, he or she will reject most applicants after only briefly skimming their resumes.

Unless you have phoned and talked to the employer – which you should do whenever you can – you will be chosen or rejected for an interview entirely on the basis of your resume and cover letter. *Your cover letter must catch the employer's attention, and your resume must hold it.* (But remember – a resume is no substitute for a job search campaign. *You* must seek a job. Your resume is only one tool, albeit a critical one.)

RESUME FORMAT:
Mechanics of a First Impression

The Basics

Employers dislike long resumes, so unless you have an unusually strong background with many years of experience and a diversity of outstanding achievements, keep your resume length to one page. If you must squeeze in more information than would otherwise fit, try using a smaller typeface or changing the margins. Watch also for "widows" at the end of paragraphs. You can often free up some space if you can shorten the information enough to get rid of those single words taking up an entire line. Another tactic that works with some word processing programs is to decrease the font size of your paragraph returns and changing the spacing between lines.

Print your resume on standard 8 1/2" x 11" paper. Since recruiters often get resumes in batches of hundreds, a smaller-sized resume may be lost in the pile. Oversized resumes are likely to get crumpled at the edges, and won't fit easily in their files.

First impressions matter, so make sure the recruiter's first impression of your resume is a good one. Never hand-write your resume (or cover letter)! Print your resume on quality paper that has weight and texture, in a conservative color such as white, ivory, or pale gray. Good resume paper is easy to find at many stores that sell stationery or office products. It is even available at some drug stores. Use *matching* paper and envelopes for both your resume and cover letter. One hiring manager at a major magazine throws out all resumes that arrive on paper that differs in color from the envelope!

Do not buy paper with images of clouds and rainbows in the background or anything that looks like casual stationery that you would send to your favorite aunt. Do not spray perfume or cologne on your resume. Do not include your picture with your resume unless you have a specific and appropriate reason to do so.

Another tip: Do a test print of your resume (and cover letter), to make sure the watermark is on the same side as the text so that you can read it. Also make sure it is right-side up. As trivial as this may sound, some recruiters check for this! One recruiter at a law firm in New Hampshire sheepishly admitted this is the first thing he checks. *"I open each envelope and check the watermarks on the resume and cover letter. Those candidates that have it wrong go into a different pile."*

Getting it on Paper

Modern photocomposition typesetting gives you the clearest, sharpest image, a wide variety of type styles, and effects such as italics, bold-facing, and book-like justified margins. It is also too expensive for many jobseekers. The quality of today's laser printers means that a computer-generated resume can look just as impressive as one that has been professionally typeset.

A computer with a word processing or desktop publishing program is the most common way to generate your resume. This allows you the flexibility to make changes almost instantly and to store different drafts on disk. Word processing and desktop publishing programs also offer many different fonts to choose from, each taking up different amounts of space. (It is generally best to stay between 9-point and 12-point font size.) Many other options are also available, such as bold-facing or italicizing for emphasis and the ability to change and manipulate spacing. It is generally recommended to leave the right-hand margin unjustified as this keeps the spacing between the text even and therefore easier to read. It is not wrong to justify both margins of text, but if possible try it both ways before you decide.

For a resume on paper, the end result will be largely determined by the quality of the printer you use. Laser printers will generally provide the best quality. Do not use a dot matrix printer.

Many companies now use scanning equipment to screen the resumes they receive, and certain paper, fonts, and other features are more compatible with this technology. White paper is preferable, as well as a standard font such as Courier or Helvetica. You should use at least a 10-point font, and avoid bolding, italics, underlining, borders, boxes, or graphics.

Household typewriters and office typewriters with nylon or other cloth ribbons are *not* good enough for typing your resume. If you don't have access to a quality word processing program, hire a professional with the resources to prepare your resume for you. Keep in mind that businesses such as Kinko's (open 24 hours) provide access to computers with quality printers.

Don't make your copies on an office photocopier. Only the human resources office may see the resume you mail. Everyone else may see only a copy of it, and copies of copies quickly become unreadable. Furthermore, sending photocopies of your resume or cover letter is completely unprofessional. Either print out each copy individually, or take your resume to a professional copy shop, which will generally offer professionally-maintained, extra-high-quality photocopiers and charge fairly reasonable prices. You want your resume to represent you with the look of polished quality.

Proof with Care

Whether you typed it or paid to have it produced professionally, mistakes on resumes are not only embarrassing, but will usually remove you from consideration (particularly if something obvious such as your name is misspelled). No matter how much you paid someone else to type, write, or typeset your resume, *you* lose if there is a mistake. So proofread it as carefully as possible. Get a friend to help you. Read your draft aloud as your friend checks the proof copy. Then have your friend read aloud while you check. Next, read it letter by letter to check spelling and punctuation.

If you are having it typed or typeset by a resume service or a printer, and you don't have time to proof it, pay for it and take it home. Proof it there and bring it back later to get it corrected and printed.

If you wrote your resume with a word processing program, use the built-in spell checker to double-check for spelling errors. Keep in mind that a spell checker will not find errors such as "to" for "two" or "wok" for "work." Many spell check programs do not recognize missing or misused punctuation, nor are they set to check the spelling of capitalized words. It's important that you still proofread your resume to check for grammatical mistakes and other problems, even <u>after</u> it has been spellchecked. If you find mistakes, do not make edits in pen or pencil or use white-out to fix them on the final copy!

Electronic Resumes

As companies rely increasingly on emerging technologies to find qualified candidates for job openings, you may opt to create an electronic resume in order to remain competitive in today's job market. Why is this important? Companies today sometimes request that resumes be submitted by e-mail, and many hiring managers regularly check online resume databases for candidates to fill unadvertised job openings. Other companies enlist the services of electronic employment database services, which charge jobseekers a nominal fee to have their resumes posted to the database to be viewed by potential employers. Still other companies use their own automated applicant tracking systems, in which case your resume is fed through a scanner that sends the image to a computer that "reads" your resume, looking for keywords, and files it accordingly in its database.

Whether you're posting your resume online, e-mailing it directly to an employer, sending it to an electronic employment database, or sending it to a company you suspect uses an automated applicant tracking system, you must create some form of electronic resume to take advantage of the technology. Don't panic! An electronic resume is simply a modified version of your conventional resume. An electronic resume is one that is sparsely formatted, but filled with keywords and important facts.

In order to post your resume to the Internet -- either to an online resume database or through direct e-mail to an employer -- you will need to change the way your resume is formatted. Instead of a Word, WordPerfect, or other word processing document, save your resume as a plain text, DOS, or ASCII file. These three terms are basically interchangeable, and describe text at its simplest, most basic level, without the formatting such as boldface or italics that most jobseekers use to make their resumes look more interesting. If you use e-mail, you'll notice that all of your messages are written and received in this format. First, you should remove all formatting from your resume including boldface, italics, underlining, bullets, differing font sizes, and graphics. Then, convert and save your resume as a plain text file. Most word processing programs have a "save as" feature that allows you to save files in different formats. Here, you should choose "text only" or "plain text."

Another option is to create a resume in HTML (hypertext markup language), the text formatting language used to publish information on the World Wide Web. However, the real usefulness of HTML resumes is still being explored. Most of the major online databases do not accept HTML resumes, and the vast majority of companies only accept plain text resumes through their e-mail.

Finally, if you simply wish to send your resume to an electronic employment database or a company that uses an automated applicant tracking system, there is no need to convert your resume to a plain text file. The only change you need to make is to organize the information in your resume by keywords. Employers are likely to do keyword searches for information, such as degree held or knowledge of particular types of software. Therefore, using the right keywords or key phrases in your resume is critical to its ultimate success. Keywords are usually nouns or short phrases that the computer searches for which refer to experience, training, skills, and abilities. For example, let's say an employer searches an employment database for a sales representative with the following criteria:

BS/BA
exceeded quota
cold calls
high energy
willing to travel

Even if you have the right qualifications, neglecting to use these keywords would result in the computer passing over your resume. Although there is no way to know for sure which keywords employers are most likely to search for, you can make educated guesses by checking the help-wanted ads or online job postings for your type of job. You should also arrange keywords in a keyword summary, a paragraph listing your qualifications that immediately follows your name and address (see sample letter in this chapter). In addition, choose a nondecorative font with clear, distinct characters, such as Helvetica or Times. It is more difficult for a scanner to accurately pick up the more unusual fonts. Boldface and all capital letters are best used only for major section headings, such as "Experience" and "Education." It is also best to avoid using italics or underlining, since this can cause the letters to bleed into one another.

For more specific information on creating and sending electronic resumes, see *The Adams Internet Job Search Almanac.*

Types of Resumes

The most common resume formats are the functional resume, the chronological resume, and the combination resume. (Examples can be found at the end of this chapter.) A functional resume focuses on skills and de-emphasizes job titles, employers, etc. A functional resume is best if you have been out of the work force for a long time or are changing careers. It is also good if you want to highlight specific skills and strengths, especially if all of your work experience has been at one company. This format can also be a good choice if you are just out of school or have no experience in your desired field.

Choose a chronological format if you are currently working or were working recently, and if your most recent experiences relate to your desired field. Use reverse chronological order and include dates. To a recruiter your last job and your latest schooling are the most important, so put the last first and list the rest going back in time.

A combination resume is perhaps the most common. This resume simply combines elements of the functional and chronological resume formats. This is used by many jobseekers with a solid track record who find elements of both types useful.

Organization

Your name, phone number, e-mail address (if you have one), and a complete mailing address should be at the top of your resume. Try to make your name stand out by using a slightly larger font size or all capital letters. Be sure to spell out everything. Never abbreviate St. for Street or Rd. for Road. If you are a college student, you should also put your home address and phone number at the top.

Change your message on your answering machine if necessary -- RUSH blaring in the background or your sorority sisters screaming may not come across well to all recruiters. If you think you may be moving within six months then include a second address and phone number of a trusted friend or relative who can reach you no matter where you are.

Remember that employers will keep your resume on file and may contact you months later if a position opens that fits your qualifications. All too often, candidates are unreachable because they have moved and had not previously provided enough contact options on their resume.

Next, list your experience, then your education. If you are a recent graduate, list your education first, unless your experience is more important than your education. (For example, if you have just graduated from a teaching school, have some business experience, and are applying for a job in business, you would list your business experience first.)

Keep everything easy to find. Put the dates of your employment and education on the left of the page. Put the names of the companies you worked for and the schools you attended a few spaces to the right of the dates. Put the city and state, or the city and country, where you studied or worked to the right of the page.

The important thing is simply to break up the text in some logical way that makes your resume visually attractive and easy to scan, so experiment to see which layout works best for your resume. However you set it up, *stay consistent*. Inconsistencies in fonts, spacing, or tenses will make your resume look sloppy. Also, be sure to use tabs to keep your information vertically lined up, rather than the less precise space bar.

RESUME CONTENT:
Say it with Style
Sell Yourself

You are selling your skills and accomplishments in your resume, so it is important to inventory yourself and know yourself. If you have achieved something, say so. Put it in the best possible light, but avoid subjective statements, such as "I am a hard worker" or "I get along well with my coworkers." Just stick to the facts.

While you shouldn't hold back or be modest, don't exaggerate your achievements to the point of misrepresentation. Be honest. Many companies will immediately drop an applicant from consideration (or fire a current employee) upon discovering inaccurate or untrue information on a resume or other application material.

Write down the important (and pertinent) things you have done, but do it in as few words as possible. Your resume will be scanned, not read, and short, concise phrases are much more effective than long-winded sentences. Avoid the use of "I" when emphasizing your accomplishments. Instead, use brief phrases beginning with action verbs.

While some technical terms will be unavoidable, you should try to avoid excessive "technicalese." Keep in mind that the first person to see your resume may be a human resources person who won't necessarily know all the jargon -- and how can they be impressed by something they don't understand?

Keep it Brief

Also, try to hold your paragraphs to six lines or less. If you have more than six lines of information about one job or school, put it in two or more paragraphs. A short resume will be examined more carefully. Remember: Your resume usually has between eight and 45 seconds to catch an employer's eye. So make every second count.

Job Objective

A functional resume may require a job objective to give it focus. One or two sentences describing the job you are seeking can clarify in what capacity your skills will be best put to use. Be sure that your stated objective is in line with the position you're applying for.

Examples:

> An entry-level editorial assistant position in the publishing industry.
> A senior management position with a telecommunications firm.

Don't include a job objective on a chronological resume unless your previous work experiences are <u>completely</u> unrelated to the position for which you're applying. The presence of an overly specific job objective might eliminate you from consideration for other positions that a recruiter feels are a better match for your qualifications. But even if you don't put an objective on paper, having a career goal in mind as you write can help give your resume a solid sense of direction.

USE ACTION VERBS

How you write your resume is just as important as *what* you write. In describing previous work experiences, the strongest resumes use short phrases beginning with action verbs. Below are a few you may want to use. (This list is not all-inclusive.)

achieved	developed	integrated	purchased
administered	devised	interpreted	reduced
advised	directed	interviewed	regulated
arranged	distributed	launched	represented
assisted	established	managed	resolved
attained	evaluated	marketed	restored
budgeted	examined	mediated	restructured
built	executed	monitored	revised
calculated	expanded	negotiated	scheduled
collaborated	expedited	obtained	selected
collected	facilitated	operated	served
compiled	formulated	ordered	sold
completed	founded	organized	solved
computed	generated	participated	streamlined
conducted	headed	performed	studied
consolidated	identified	planned	supervised
constructed	implemented	prepared	supplied
consulted	improved	presented	supported
controlled	increased	processed	tested
coordinated	initiated	produced	trained
created	installed	proposed	updated
determined	instructed	published	wrote

Some jobseekers may choose to include both "Relevant Experience" and "Additional Experience" sections. This can be useful, as it allows the jobseeker to place more emphasis on certain experiences and to de-emphasize others.

Emphasize continued experience in a particular job area or continued interest in a particular industry. De-emphasize irrelevant positions. It is okay to include one opening line providing a general description of each company you've worked at. Delete positions that you held for less than four months (unless you are a very recent college grad or still in school). Stress your <u>results</u> and your achievements, elaborating on how you contributed in your previous jobs. Did you increase sales, reduce costs, improve a product, implement a new program? Were you promoted? Use specific numbers (i.e., quantities, percentages, dollar amounts) whenever possible.

Education

Keep it brief if you have more than two years of career experience. Elaborate more if you have less experience. If you are a recent college graduate, you may choose to include any high school activities that are directly relevant to your career. If you've been out of school for a while you don't need to list your education prior to college.

Mention degrees received and any honors or special awards. Note individual courses or projects you participated in that might be relevant for employers. For example, if you are an English major applying for a position as a business writer, be sure to mention any business or economics courses. Previous experience such as Editor-in-Chief of the school newspaper would be relevant as well.

If you are uploading your resume to an online job hunting site such as CareerCity.com, action verbs are still important, but the key words or key nouns that a computer would search for become more important. For example, if you're seeking an accounting position, key nouns that a computer would search for such as "Lotus 1-2-3" or "CPA" or "payroll" become very important.

Highlight Impressive Skills

Be sure to mention any computer skills you may have. You may wish to include a section entitled "Additional Skills" or "Computer Skills," in which you list any software programs you know. An additional skills section is also an ideal place to mention fluency in a foreign language.

Personal Data

This section is optional, but if you choose to include it, keep it brief. A one-word mention of hobbies such as fishing, chess, baseball, cooking, etc., can give the person who will interview you a good way to open up the conversation.

Team sports experience is looked at favorably. It doesn't hurt to include activities that are somewhat unusual (fencing, Akido, '70s music) or that somehow relate to the position or the company to which you're applying. For instance, it would be worth noting if you are a member of a professional organization in your industry of interest. Never include information about your age, alias, date of birth, health, physical characteristics, marital status, religious affiliation, or political/moral beliefs.

References

The most that is needed is the sentence "References available upon request" at the bottom of your resume. If you choose to leave it out, that's fine. This line is not really necessary. It is understood that references will most likely be asked for and provided by you later on in the interviewing process. Do not actually send references with your resume and cover letter unless specifically requested.

HIRING A RESUME WRITER:
Is it the Right Choice for You?

If you write reasonably well, it is to your advantage to write your own resume. Writing your resume forces you to review your experiences and figure out how to explain your accomplishments in clear, brief phrases. This will help you when you explain your work to interviewers. It is also easier to tailor your resume to each position you're applying for when you have put it together yourself.

If you write your resume, everything will be in your own words; it will sound like you. It will say what you want it to say. If you are a good writer, know yourself well, and have a good idea of which parts of your background employers are looking for, you should be able to write your own resume better than someone else. If you decide to write your resume yourself, have as many people as possible review and proofread it. Welcome objective opinions and other perspectives.

When to Get Help

If you have difficulty writing in "resume style" (which is quite unlike normal written language), if you are unsure which parts of your background to emphasize, or if you think your resume would make your case better if it did not follow one of the standard forms outlined either here or in a book on resumes, then you should consider having it professionally written.

Even some professional resume writers we know have had their resumes written with the help of fellow professionals. They sought the help of someone who could be objective about their background, as well as provide an experienced sounding board to help focus their thoughts.

If You Hire a Pro

The best way to choose a writer is by reputation: the recommendation of a friend, a personnel director, your school placement officer, or someone else knowledgeable in the field.

Important questions:
· "How long have you been writing resumes?"
· "If I'm not satisfied with what you write, will you go over it with me and change it?"
· "Do you charge by the hour or a flat rate?"

There is no sure relation between price and quality, except that you are unlikely to get a good writer for less than $50 for an uncomplicated resume and you shouldn't have to pay more than $300 unless your experience is very extensive or complicated. There will be additional charges for printing. Assume nothing no matter how much you pay. It is your career at stake if there are mistakes on your resume!

Few resume services will give you a firm price over the phone, simply because some resumes are too complicated and take too long to do for a predetermined price. Some services will quote you a price that applies to almost all of their customers. Once you decide to use a specific writer, you should insist on a firm price quote *before* engaging their services. Also, find out how expensive minor changes will be.

COVER LETTERS:
Quick, Clear, and Concise

Always mail a cover letter with your resume. In a cover letter you can show an interest in the company that you can't show in a resume. You can also point out one or two of your skills or accomplishments the company can put to good use.

Make it Personal

The more personal you can get, the better, so long as you keep it professional. If someone known to the person you are writing has recommended that you contact the company, get permission to include his/her name in the letter. If you can get the name of a person to send the letter to, address it directly to that person (after first calling the company to verify the spelling of the person's name, correct title, and mailing address). Be sure to put the person's name and title on both the letter and the envelope. This will ensure that your letter will get through to the proper person, even if a new person now occupies this position. It will not always be possible to get the name of a person. Always strive to get at least a title.

Be sure to mention something about why you have an interest in the company - - *so many candidates apply for jobs with no apparent knowledge of what the company does!* This conveys the message that they just want any job.

Type cover letters in full. Don't try the cheap and easy ways, like using a computer mail merge program or photocopying the body of your letter and typing in the inside address and salutation. You will give the impression that you are mailing to a host of companies and have no particular interest in any one.

Print your cover letter on the same color and same high-quality paper as your resume.

Cover letter basic format

Paragraph 1: State what the position is that you are seeking. It is not always necessary to state how you found out about the position – often you will apply without knowing that a position is open.

Paragraph 2: Include what you know about the company and why you are interested in working there. Mention any prior contact with the company or someone known to the hiring person if relevant. Briefly state your qualifications and what you can offer. (Do not talk about what you cannot do).

Paragraph 3: Close with your phone number and where/when you can be reached. Make a request for an interview. State when you will follow up by phone (or mail or e-mail if the ad requests no phone calls). Do not wait long – generally five working days. If you say you're going to follow up, then actually do it! This phone call can get your resume noticed when it might otherwise sit in a stack of 225 other resumes.

Cover letter do's and don'ts

- *Do* keep your cover letter brief and to the point.
- *Do* be sure it is error-free.
- *Do* accentuate what you can offer the company, not what you hope to gain.
- *Do* be sure your phone number and address is on your cover letter just in case it gets separated from your resume (this happens!).
- *Do* check the watermark by holding the paper up to a light — be sure it is facing forward so it is readable — on the same side as the text, and right-side up.
- *Do* sign your cover letter (or type your name if you are sending it electronically). Blue or black ink are both fine. Do not use red ink.
- *Don't* just repeat information verbatim from your resume.
- *Don't* overuse the personal pronoun "I."
- *Don't* send a generic cover letter — show your personal knowledge of and interest in that particular company.

THANK YOU LETTERS:
Another Way to Stand Out

As mentioned earlier, *always* send a thank you letter after an interview (see the sample later in this section). So few candidates do this and it is yet another way for you to stand out. Be sure to mention something specific from the interview and restate your interest in the company and the position.

It is generally acceptable to handwrite your thank you letter on a generic thank you card (but *never* a postcard). Make sure handwritten notes are neat and legible. However, if you are in doubt, typing your letter is always the safe bet. If you met with several people it is fine to send them each an individual thank you letter. Call the company if you need to check on the correct spelling of their names.

Remember to:
- Keep it short.
- Proofread it carefully.
- Send it *promptly*.

FUNCTIONAL RESUME

C.J. RAVENCLAW
129 Pennsylvania Avenue
Washington DC 20500
202/555-6652
e-mail: ravenclaw@dcpress.net

Objective
A position as a graphic designer commensurate with my acquired skills and expertise.

Summary
Extensive experience in plate making, separations, color matching, background definition, printing, mechanicals, color corrections, and personnel supervision. A highly motivated manager and effective communicator. Proven ability to:

- **Create Commercial Graphics**
- **Produce Embossed Drawings**
- **Color Separate**
- **Control Quality**
- **Resolve Printing Problems**
- **Analyze Customer Satisfaction**

Qualifications
Printing:
Knowledgeable in black and white as well as color printing. Excellent judgment in determining acceptability of color reproduction through comparison with original. Proficient at producing four- or five-color corrections on all media, as well as restyling previously reproduced four-color artwork.

Customer Relations:
Routinely work closely with customers to ensure specifications are met. Capable of striking a balance between technical printing capabilities and need for customer satisfaction through entire production process.

Specialties:
Practiced at creating silk screen overlays for a multitude of processes including velo bind, GBC bind, and perfect bind. Creative design and timely preparation of posters, flyers, and personalized stationery.

Personnel Supervision:
Skillful at fostering atmosphere that encourages highly talented artists to balance high-level creativity with maximum production. Consistently beat production deadlines. Instruct new employees, apprentices, and students in both artistry and technical operations.

Experience
Graphic Arts Professor, Ohio State University, Columbus OH (1992-1996).
Manager, Design Graphics, Washington DC (1997-present).

Education
Massachusetts Conservatory of Art, Ph.D. 1990
University of Massachusetts, B.A. 1988

CHRONOLOGICAL RESUME

HARRY SEABORN
557 Shoreline Drive
Seattle, WA 98404
(206) 555-6584
e-mail: hseaborn@centco.com

EXPERIENCE

THE CENTER COMPANY   Seattle, WA
Systems Programmer   1996-present
- Develop and maintain customer accounting and order tracking database using a Visual Basic front end and SQL server.
- Plan and implement migration of company wide transition from mainframe-based dumb terminals to a true client server environment using Windows NT Workstation and Server.
- Oversee general local and wide area network administration including the development of a variety of intranet modules to improve internal company communication and planning across divisions.

INFO TECH, INC.   Seattle, WA
Technical Manager   1994-1996

- Designed and managed the implementation of a network providing the legal community with a direct line to Supreme Court cases across the Internet using SQL Server and a variety of Internet tools.
- Developed a system to make the entire library catalog available on line using PERL scripts and SQL.
- Used Visual Basic and Microsoft Access to create a registration system for university registrar.

EDUCATION

SALEM STATE UNIVERSITY   Salem, OR
        M.S. in Computer Science.   1993
        B.S. in Computer Science.   1991

COMPUTER SKILLS

- Programming Languages: Visual Basic, Java, C++, SQL, PERL
- Software: SQL Server, Internet Information Server, Oracle
- Operating Systems: Windows NT, UNIX, Linux

FUNCTIONAL RESUME

Donna Hermione Moss
703 Wizard's Way
Chicago, IL 60601
(312) 555-8841
e-mail: donna@cowfire.com

OBJECTIVE:
To contribute over five years of experience in promotion, communications, and administration to an entry-level position in advertising.

SUMMARY OF QUALIFICATIONS:
- Performed advertising duties for small business.
- Experience in business writing and communications skills.
- General knowledge of office management.
- Demonstrated ability to work well with others, in both supervisory and support staff roles.
- Type 75 words per minute.

SELECTED ACHIEVEMENTS AND RESULTS:
Promotion:
Composing, editing, and proofreading correspondence and public relations materials for own catering service. Large-scale mailings.

Communication:
Instruction; curriculum and lesson planning; student evaluation; parent-teacher conferences; development of educational materials. Training and supervising clerks.

Computer Skills:
Proficient in MS Word, Lotus 1-2-3, Excel, and Filemaker Pro.

Administration:
Record-keeping and file maintenance. Data processing and computer operations, accounts receivable, accounts payable, inventory control, and customer relations. Scheduling, office management, and telephone reception.

PROFESSIONAL HISTORY:
Teacher; Self-Employed (owner of catering service); Floor Manager; Administrative Assistant; Accounting Clerk.

EDUCATION:
Beloit College, Beloit, WI, BA in Education, 1991

CHRONOLOGICAL RESUME

PERCY ZIEGLER
16 Josiah Court
Marlborough CT 06447
203/555-9641 (h)
203/555-8176, x14 (w)

EDUCATION

Keene State College, Keene NH
Bachelor of Arts in Elementary Education, 1998
- Graduated *magna cum laude*
- English minor
- Kappa Delta Pi member, inducted 1996

EXPERIENCE
September 1998-
Present

Elmer T. Thienes Elementary School, Marlborough CT
Part-time Kindergarten Teacher
- Instruct kindergartners in reading, spelling, language arts, and music.
- Participate in the selection of textbooks and learning aids.
- Organize and supervise class field trips and coordinate in-class presentations.

Summers
1995-1997

Keene YMCA, Youth Division, Keene NH
Child-care Counselor
- Oversaw summer program for low-income youth.
- Budgeted and coordinated special events and field trips, working with Program Director to initiate variations in the program.
- Served as Youth Advocate in cooperation with social worker to address the social needs and problems of participants.

Spring 1997

Wheelock Elementary School, Keene NH
Student Teacher
- Taught third-grade class in all elementary subjects.
- Designed and implemented a two-week unit on Native Americans.
- Assisted in revision of third-grade curriculum.

Fall 1996

Child Development Center, Keene NH
Daycare Worker
- Supervised preschool children on the playground and during art activities.
- Created a "Wishbone Corner," where children could quietly look at books or take a voluntary "time-out."

ADDITIONAL INTERESTS
Martial arts, Pokemon, politics, reading, skiing, writing.

ELECTRONIC RESUME

GRIFFIN DORE
69 Dursley Drive
Cambridge, MA 02138
(617) 555-5555

KEYWORD SUMMARY

Senior financial manager with over ten years experience in Accounting and Systems Management, Budgeting, Forecasting, Cost Containment, Financial Reporting, and International Accounting. MBA in Management. Proficient in Lotus, Excel, Solomon, and Windows.

EXPERIENCE

COLWELL CORPORATION, Wellesley, MA
Director of Accounting and Budgets, 1990 to present
    Direct staff of twenty in General Ledger, Accounts Payable, Accounts Receivable, and International Accounting.
    Facilitate month-end closing process with parent company and auditors.
    Implemented team-oriented cross-training program within accounting group, resulting in timely month-end closings and increased productivity of key accounting staff.
    Developed and implemented a strategy for Sales and Use Tax Compliance in all fifty states.
    Prepare monthly financial statements and analyses.

FRANKLIN AND DELANEY COMPANY, Melrose, MA
Senior Accountant, 1987-1990
    Managed Accounts Payable, General Ledger, transaction processing, and financial reporting. Supervised staff of five.

Staff Accountant, 1985-1987
    Managed Accounts Payable, including vouchering, cash disbursements, and bank reconciliation.
    Wrote and issued policies.
    Maintained supporting schedules used during year-end audits.
    Trained new employees.

EDUCATION

MBA in Management, Northeastern University, Boston, MA, 1989
BS in Accounting, Boston College, Boston, MA, 1985

ASSOCIATIONS

National Association of Accountants

GENERAL MODEL
FOR A COVER LETTER

Your mailing address
Date

Contact's name
Contact's title
Company
Company's mailing address

Dear Mr./Ms. _____:

Immediately explain why your background makes you the best candidate for the position that you are applying for. Describe what prompted you to write (want ad, article you read about the company, networking contact, etc.). Keep the first paragraph short and hard-hitting.

Detail what you could contribute to this company. Show how your qualifications will benefit this firm. Describe your interest in the corporation. Subtly emphasizing your knowledge about this firm and your familiarity with the industry will set you apart from other candidates. Remember to keep this letter short; few recruiters will read a cover letter longer than half a page.

If possible, your closing paragraph should request specific action on the part of the reader. Include your phone number and the hours when you can be reached. Mention that if you do not hear from the reader by a specific date, you will follow up with a phone call. Lastly, thank the reader for their time, consideration, etc.

Sincerely,

(signature)

Your full name (typed)

Enclosure (use this if there are other materials, such as your resume, that are included in the same envelope)

SAMPLE COVER LETTER

16 Josiah Court
Marlborough CT 06447
January 16, 2000

Ms. Leona Malfoy
Assistant Principal
Laningham Elementary School
43 Mayflower Drive
Keene NH 03431

Dear Ms. Malfoy:

Toby Potter recently informed me of a possible opening for a third grade teacher at Laningham Elementary School. With my experience instructing third-graders, both in schools and in summer programs, I feel I would be an ideal candidate for the position. Please accept this letter and the enclosed resume as my application.

Laningham's educational philosophy that every child can learn and succeed interests me, since it mirrors my own. My current position at Elmer T. Thienes Elementary has reinforced this philosophy, heightening my awareness of the different styles and paces of learning and increasing my sensitivity toward special needs children. Furthermore, as a direct result of my student teaching experience at Wheelock Elementary School, I am comfortable, confident, and knowledgeable working with third-graders.

I look forward to discussing the position and my qualifications for it in more detail. I can be reached at 203/555-9641 evenings or 203/555-8176, x14 weekdays. If I do not hear from you before Tuesday of next week, I will call to see if we can schedule a time to meet. Thank you for your time and consideration.

Sincerely,

Percy Ziegler

Percy Ziegler

Enclosure

GENERAL MODEL FOR A
THANK YOU/FOLLOW-UP LETTER

Your mailing address
Date

Contact's name
Contact's title
Company
Company's mailing address

Dear Mr./Ms._____:

Remind the interviewer of the reason (i.e., a specific opening, an informational interview, etc.) you were interviewed, as well as the date. Thank him/her for the interview, and try to personalize your thanks by mentioning some specific aspect of the interview.

Confirm your interest in the organization (and in the opening, if you were interviewing for a particular position). Use specifics to re-emphasize that you have researched the firm in detail and have considered how you would fit into the company and the position. This is a good time to say anything you wish you had said in the initial meeting. Be sure to keep this letter brief; a half page is plenty.

If appropriate, close with a suggestion for further action, such as a desire to have an additional interview, if possible. Mention your phone number and the hours you can be reached. Alternatively, you may prefer to mention that you will follow up with a phone call in several days. Once again, thank the person for meeting with you, and state that you would be happy to provide any additional information about your qualifications.

Sincerely,

(signature)

Your full name (typed)

PRIMARY EMPLOYERS

ACCOUNTING AND MANAGEMENT CONSULTING

You can expect to find the following types of companies in this chapter:

Consulting and Research Firms
Industrial Accounting Firms
Management Services
Public Accounting Firms
Tax Preparation Companies

ARTHUR ANDERSEN

1111 Brickell Avenue, Suite 1700, Miami FL 33131. 305/374-3700. **Contact:** Human Resources. **World Wide Web address:** http://www.arthurandersen.com. **Description:** One of the largest certified public accounting firms in the world. Arthur Andersen's four key practice areas are Audit and Business Advisory, Tax and Business Advisory, Business Consulting, and Economic and Financial Consulting. **NOTE:** This firm does not accept unsolicited resumes. Please check the Website for available positions. **Corporate headquarters location:** Chicago IL. **Other U.S. locations:** Nationwide. **Parent company:** Arthur Andersen Worldwide Organization is one of the leading providers of professional services in the world. With over 380 worldwide locations, the global practice of its member firms is conducted through two business units: Arthur Andersen and Andersen Consulting, which provides global management and technology consulting. **Number of employees worldwide:** 91,000.

ARTHUR ANDERSEN

101 East Kennedy Boulevard, Suite 2200, Tampa FL 33602-5150. 813/222-4600. **Contact:** Human Resources Department. **World Wide Web address:** http://www.arthurandersen.com. **Description:** One of the largest certified public accounting firms in the world. Arthur Andersen's four key practice areas are Audit and Business Advisory, Tax and Business Advisory, Business Consulting, and Economic and Financial Consulting. **NOTE:** This firm does not accept unsolicited resumes. Please check the Website for available positions. **Corporate headquarters location:** Chicago IL. **Other U.S. locations:** Nationwide. **Parent company:** Arthur Andersen Worldwide Organization is one of the leading providers of professional services in the world. With over 380 worldwide locations, the global practice of its member firms is conducted through two business units: Arthur Andersen and Andersen Consulting, which provides global management and technology consulting. **Number of employees worldwide:** 91,000.

DELOITTE & TOUCHE

One Independent Drive, Suite 2801, Jacksonville FL 32202-5034. 904/356-0011. **Contact:** Human Resources Department. **World Wide Web address:** http://www.us.deloitte.com. **Description:** An international firm of certified public accountants providing professional accounting, auditing, tax, and management consulting services to widely diversified clients. The company has a specialized program consisting of national industry groups and functional groups that cross industry lines. Groups are involved in various disciplines including accounting, auditing, taxation management advisory services, small and growing businesses, mergers and acquisitions, and computer applications. **International locations:** Worldwide.

DELOITTE & TOUCHE
201 East Kennedy Boulevard, Suite 1200, Tampa FL 33602-5821. 813/273-8300. **Contact:** Human Resources Department. **World Wide Web address:** http://www.us.deloitte.com. **Description:** An international firm of certified public accountants providing professional accounting, auditing, tax, and management consulting services to widely diversified clients. The company has a specialized program consisting of national industry groups and functional groups that cross industry lines. Groups are involved in various disciplines including accounting, auditing, taxation management advisory services, small and growing businesses, mergers and acquisitions, and computer applications. **International locations:** Worldwide.

ERNST & YOUNG LLP
390 North Orange Avenue, Suite 1700, Orlando FL 32801. 407/872-6600. **Contact:** Human Resources. **World Wide Web address:** http://www.ey.com. **Description:** A certified public accounting firm that also provides management consulting services. Services include data processing, financial modeling, financial feasibility studies, production planning and inventory management, management sciences, health care planning, human resources, cost accounting, and budgeting systems. **Other U.S. locations:** Nationwide. **International locations:** Worldwide.

ERNST & YOUNG LLP
100 North Tampa Street, Suite 2200, Tampa FL 33602. 813/225-4800. **Contact:** Human Resources. **World Wide Web address:** http://www.ey.com. **Description:** A certified public accounting firm that also provides management consulting services. Services include data processing, financial modeling, financial feasibility studies, production planning and inventory management, management sciences, health care planning, human resources, cost accounting, and budgeting systems. **Other U.S. locations:** Nationwide. **International locations:** Worldwide.

KPMG
One Biscayne Tower, 2 South Biscayne Boulevard, Suite 2800, Miami FL 33131-1802. 305/358-2300. **Contact:** Human Resources. **World Wide Web address:** http://www.kpmg.com. **Description:** KPMG delivers a wide range of value-added assurance, tax, and consulting services. **Corporate headquarters location:** Montvale NJ. **International locations:** Worldwide. **Parent company:** KPMG International has more than 85,000 employees worldwide including 6,500 partners and 60,000 professional staff, serving clients in 844 cities in 155 countries. KPMG International is a leader among professional services firms engaged in capturing, managing, assessing, and delivering information to create knowledge that will help its clients maximize shareholder value.

KPMG
450 East Las Olas Boulevard, Suite 750, Fort Lauderdale FL 33301-3503. 954/524-6000. **Contact:** Human Resources. **World Wide Web address:** http://www.kpmg.com. **Description:** KPMG delivers a wide range of value-added assurance, tax, and consulting services. **Corporate headquarters location:** Montvale NJ. **Other U.S. locations:** Nationwide. **Parent company:** KPMG International has more than 85,000 employees worldwide including 6,500 partners and 60,000 professional staff, serving clients in 844 cities in 155 countries. KPMG International is a leader among professional services firms engaged in capturing, managing, assessing, and delivering information to create knowledge that will help its clients maximize shareholder value.

O'SULLIVAN HICKS PATTON, LLP
P. O. Box 12646, Pensacola FL 32574. 850/435-7400. **Fax:** 850/435-2888. **Contact:** Kathy Anthony, Firm Administrator. **World Wide Web address:** http://www.ohp-cpas.com. **Description:** A full-service accounting and business consulting firm. Founded in 1981. **Common positions include:** Accountant/Auditor; Administrative Assistant. **Special programs:** Co-ops. **Corporate headquarters location:** This location. **Listed on:** Privately held. **Annual sales/revenues:** $5 - $10 million.

PRICEWATERHOUSECOOPERS
3109 West Dr. Martin Luther King Jr. Boulevard, Tampa FL 33607. 813/348-7000. **Fax:** 813/348-8502. **Contact:** Human Resources Department. **World Wide Web address:** http://www.pricewaterhousecoopers.com. **Description:** One of the largest certified public accounting firms in the world.

PricewaterhouseCoopers provides public accounting, business advisory, management consulting, and taxation services. **Corporate headquarters location:** New York NY. **Other U.S. locations:** Nationwide.

PRICEWATERHOUSECOOPERS
101 East Kennedy Boulevard, Suite 1500, Tampa FL 33602. 813/223-7577. **Contact:** Personnel. **World Wide Web address:** http://www.pricewaterhousecoopers.com. **Description:** One of the largest certified public accounting firms in the world. PricewaterhouseCoopers provides public accounting, business advisory, management consulting, and taxation services. **Corporate headquarters location:** New York NY. **Other U.S. locations:** Nationwide.

PRICEWATERHOUSECOOPERS
First Union Financial Center, 200 South Biscayne Boulevard, Suite 1900, Miami FL 33131. 305/375-7400. **Contact:** Tammy Kline, Human Resources Director. **World Wide Web address:** http://www.pricewaterhousecoopers.com. **Description:** One of the largest certified public accounting firms in the world. PricewaterhouseCoopers provides public accounting, business advisory, management consulting, and taxation services. **Corporate headquarters location:** New York NY. **Other U.S. locations:** Nationwide.

ADVERTISING, MARKETING, AND PUBLIC RELATIONS

You can expect to find the following types of companies in this chapter:

Advertising Agencies
Direct Mail Marketers
Market Research Firms
Public Relations Firms

BBDO

2 Alhambra Plaza, Suite 600, Coral Gables FL 33134. 305/446-6006. **Contact:** Human Resources. **World Wide Web address:** http://www.bbdo.com. **Description:** Part of a worldwide network of advertising agencies with related businesses in public relations, direct marketing, sales promotion, graphic arts, and printing. **Corporate headquarters location:** New York NY. **Other U.S. locations:** Los Angeles CA; San Francisco CA; Atlanta GA; Chicago IL; Wellesley MA; Southfield MI. **Parent company:** BBDO Worldwide operates 83 subsidiaries, affiliates, and associates engaged solely in advertising and related operations.

CATALINA MARKETING CORPORATION

200 Carillon Parkway, St. Petersburg FL 33716. 727/579-5000. **Contact:** Human Resources. **World Wide Web address:** http://www.catmktg.com. **Description:** Provides marketing services for consumer product manufacturers and supermarket retailers. The company's point-of-scan electronic marketing network delivers checkout coupons to consumers at supermarket checkouts based on their purchases. The company also provides Internet information on retail grocery promoters. **NOTE:** Entry-level positions are offered. **Common positions include:** Accountant/Auditor; Clerical Supervisor; Computer Programmer; Customer Service Representative; Electrical/Electronics Engineer; Financial Analyst; Human Resources Manager; Market Research Analyst; Purchasing Agent/Manager; Systems Analyst. **Corporate headquarters location:** This location. **Other U.S. locations:** Nationwide. **International locations:** Europe; Japan. **Subsidiaries include:** Catalina Electronic Clearing Services; Health Resource Publishing Company. **Operations at this facility include:** Administration; Divisional Headquarters. **Listed on:** New York Stock Exchange. **Stock exchange symbol:** POS. **Annual sales/revenues:** $51 - $100 million. **Number of employees at this location:** 170. **Number of employees nationwide:** 500. **Number of employees worldwide:** 1,650.

W.B. DONER & COMPANY

6200 Courtney Campbell Causeway, Suite 1050, Tampa FL 33607. 813/289-6909. **Contact:** Human Resources. **Description:** A full-service advertising agency that provides strategic planning, sales promotion, direct marketing, and public relations. **Corporate headquarters location:** Detroit MI. **Other U.S. locations:** Baltimore MD; Boston MA; Cleveland OH; Dallas TX. **International locations:** Australia; Belgium;

Canada; England. **Annual sales/revenues:** More than $100 million. **Number of employees worldwide:** 600.

FITZGERALD ADVERTISING AND PUBLIC RELATIONS
5950 Hazeltine National Drive, Suite 460, Orlando FL 32822. 407/251-1020. **Fax:** 407/251-1042. **Contact:** Personnel. **World Wide Web address:** http://www.fitzcom.com. **Description:** A full-service advertising and public relations agency that specializes in business-to-business marketing communications for the high-tech industry. **Common positions include:** Account Manager; Account Representative; Accountant; Administrative Assistant; Advertising Executive; Graphic Artist; Graphic Designer; Production Manager; Public Relations Specialist; Technical Writer/Editor. **Special programs:** Internships. **Corporate headquarters location:** This location. **Operations at this facility include:** Administration; Sales. **Annual sales/revenues:** $5 - $10 million. **Number of employees at this location:** 10.

HUSK JENNINGS ADVERTISING
6 East Bay Street, Suite 600, Jacksonville FL 32202. 904/354-2600. **Fax:** 904/354-7226. **Contact:** Personnel. **World Wide Web address:** http://www.huskjennings.com. **Description:** An advertising, marketing, and public relations agency. **Common positions include:** Administrative Manager; Public Relations Specialist. **Corporate headquarters location:** This location. **Number of employees at this location:** 15.

LANDERS AND PARTNERS, INC.
2857 Executive Drive, Suite 210, Clearwater FL 33762. 727/572-5228. **Contact:** Cliff Jones, President. **E-mail address:** cjones@landersandpartners.com. **World Wide Web address:** http://www.landersandpartners.com.**Description:** A marketing firm.

NATIONWIDE ADVERTISING SERVICE INC.
3510 Bay to Bay Boulevard, Tampa FL 33629. 813/831-1085. **Contact:** Office Manager. **World Wide Web address:** http://www.hrads.com. **Description:** With offices in 36 major U.S. and Canadian cities, Nationwide Advertising Service is one of the largest and oldest independent, full-service advertising agencies exclusively specializing in human resources communications, promotions, and advertising. The company offers consultation, campaign planning, ad placement, research, and creative production. **Corporate headquarters location:** Cleveland OH. **Other U.S. locations:** Detroit MI; St. Louis MO; Houston TX.

SHAKER ADVERTISING AGENCY
4920 West Cypress Street, Suite 104, Tampa FL 33607. 813/289-1100. **Contact:** Lee Ann Foster, Office Manager. **E-mail address:** hr@shaker.com. **World Wide Web address:** http://www.shaker.com. **Description:** An advertising agency. **Corporate headquarters location:** Oak Park IL. **Other area locations:** Miami/Ft. Lauderdale FL. **Other U.S. locations:** Oak Park IL; Bloomington IN; Boston MA; East Brunswick NJ; Pittsburgh PA; Milwaukee WI. **Number of employees nationwide:** 243.

TULLY-MENARD, INC.
4919 Bayshore Boulevard, Tampa FL 33611. 813/832-6602. **Contact:** Mr. Joe Tully, President. **World Wide Web address:** http://www.tullymenard.com. **Description:** An advertising agency. **NOTE:** Part-time jobs are offered. **Common positions include:** Advertising Executive; Secretary. **Office hours:** Monday - Friday, 8:30 a.m. - 5:00 p.m. **Corporate headquarters location:** This location. **Listed on:** Privately held. **Annual sales/revenues:** Less than $5 million.

VAL-PAK DIRECT MARKETING
8575 Largo Lakes Drive, Largo FL 33773. 727/399-3189. **Toll-free phone:** 800/237-2871. **Fax:** 727/399-3085. **Recorded jobline:** 727/399-3012. **Contact:** LaToy Black, Recruiting Specialist. **E-mail address:** latoy_black@valpak.com. **World Wide Web address:** http://www.valpak.com. **Description:** An international direct mail advertising company that designs, prints, and mails more than 15 billion coupons annually. **NOTE:** Entry-level positions and second and third shifts are offered. **Common positions include:** Account Manager; Account Representative; Accountant; Administrative Assistant; Blue-Collar Worker Supervisor; Buyer; Chief Financial Officer; Computer Operator; Computer Programmer; Computer Support Technician; Computer Technician; Controller; Credit Manager; Customer Service Representative; Database Administrator; Database Manager; Desktop Publishing Specialist; Financial Analyst; Graphic Artist; Graphic Designer; Human Resources Manager; Internet Services Manager; Market Research Analyst; Marketing Manager; MIS Specialist; Network/Systems Administrator; Paralegal; Production Manager; Project Manager; Purchasing Agent/Manager; Registered Nurse; Sales Representative; Secretary; Systems Analyst; Systems Manager; Technical Writer/Editor. **Special programs:** Internships. **Office hours:** Monday - Friday, 8:00 a.m. - 5:00 p.m. **Corporate headquarters location:** This location. **Parent company:** Cox Enterprises, Inc. is one of the

nation's largest privately held media companies with major holdings in the newspaper, television, radio, and cable industries. **Listed on:** Privately held. **President:** Joseph Bourdow. **Annual sales/revenues:** More than $100 million. **Number of employees at this location:** 1,100. **Number of employees nationwide:** 1,500.

WESTWAYNE, INC.
401 East Jackson Street, Suite 3600, Tampa FL 33602. 813/224-9378. **Contact:** Human Resources Department. **World Wide Web address:** http://www.westwayne.com. **Description:** An advertising and marketing agency.

YESAWICH, PEPPERDINE AND BROWN
423 South Keller, Suite 100, Orlando FL 32810. 407/875-1111. **Contact:** Julie Gochnour, Director of Human Resources. **World Wide Web address:** http://www.ypb.com. **Description:** An advertising agency. **Corporate headquarters location:** This location.

AEROSPACE

You can expect to find the following types of companies in this chapter:

Aerospace Products and Services
Aircraft Equipment and Parts

ABA INDUSTRIES
10260 U.S. Highway 19 North, Pinellas Park FL 33782.
727/546-3571. **Contact:** Human Resources Department.
World Wide Web address: http://www.abaindustries.com.
Description: A manufacturer of aircraft engines.

AEROSONIC CORPORATION
1212 North Hercules Avenue, Clearwater FL 33765. 727/461-
3000. **Fax:** 727/447-5926. **Contact:** Human Resources. **World
Wide Web address:** http://www.aerosonic.com. **Description:**
Manufactures mechanical and microprocessor-based aircraft
instruments. **Common positions include:** Accountant/Auditor;
Administrative Assistant; Aerospace Engineer; Blue-Collar
Worker Supervisor; Buyer; Computer Programmer; Controller;
Customer Service Representative; Draftsperson; Human
Resources Manager; Industrial Engineer; Machinist;
Mechanical Engineer; MIS Specialist; Production Manager;
Purchasing Agent/Manager; Quality Control Supervisor; Sales
Executive; Services Sales Representative; Software Engineer;
Systems Analyst; Technical Writer/Editor. **Corporate
headquarters location:** This location. **Other U.S. locations:**
Wichita KS; Charlottesville VA. **Listed on:** American Stock
Exchange. **Stock exchange symbol:** AIM. **Annual
sales/revenues:** $5 - $10 million. **Number of employees at this
location:** 140. **Number of employees nationwide:** 250.

ARROW AIR, INC.
P.O. Box 523726, Miami FL 33152. 785/265-2300. **Physical
address:** 3401 NW 59th Avenue, Miami FL 33152. **Contact:**
Personnel. **World Wide Web address:** http://www.fineair.com.
Description: An all-cargo air carrier service that serves the
North and South American continents. **Common positions
include:** Administrator; Aerospace Engineer; Flight Attendant;
Mechanical Engineer; Operations/Production Manager; Pilot.

B/E AEROSPACE, INC.
1400 Corporate Center Way, Wellington FL 33414. 561/791-
5000. **Fax:** 561/791-7900. **Contact:** Joseph A. Piegari, Vice
President of Human Resources Department. **World Wide Web
address:** http://www.beaerospace.com. **Description:** Designs,
manufactures, sells, and supports a wide range of commercial
aircraft cabin interior products including seats, passenger
entertainment and service systems, lighting products, oxygen
products, and galley structures and inserts. The company
supplies commercial airlines and airframe manufacturers.
Common positions include: Accountant/Auditor; Attorney;
Credit Manager; Designer; Electrical/Electronics Engineer;

Human Resources Manager; Industrial Engineer; Paralegal; Purchasing Agent/Manager; Technical Writer/Editor. **Special programs:** Internships. **Corporate headquarters location:** This location. **Other U.S. locations:** CA; CT; MN; NC; NY; WA; WV. **International locations:** England; Singapore; Wales. **Subsidiaries include:** Aerospace Lighting Corporation; Aircraft Modular Products; Puritan-Bennett Aero Systems; SMR Aerospace; Sextant In-Flight Systems; C.F. Taylor. **Operations at this facility include:** Administration; Sales. **Listed on:** NASDAQ. **Stock exchange symbol:** BEAV. **CEO:** Robert J. Khoury. **Annual sales/revenues:** More than $100 million. **Number of employees at this location:** 30.

B/E AEROSPACE, INC.
11710 Central Parkway, Jacksonville FL 32224-7626. 904/996-3800. **Fax:** 904/996-3838. **Contact:** Julie Crosby, Manager of Human Resources Department. **World Wide Web address:** http://www.beaerospace.com. **Description:** This location manufactures flight galleys. Overall, B/E Aerospace, Inc. designs, manufactures, sells, and supports a wide range of commercial aircraft cabin interior products including seating products, passenger entertainment and service systems, and galley structures and inserts. The company supplies major airlines and airframe manufacturers. Founded in 1965. **NOTE:** Entry-level positions and second and third shifts are offered. **Common positions include:** Administrative Assistant; Buyer; Electrician; Financial Analyst; General Manager; Human Resources Manager; Industrial Engineer; Manufacturing Engineer; Quality Control Supervisor. **Special programs:** Internships; Training. **Corporate headquarters location:** Wellington FL. **Other U.S. locations:** CA; CT; MN; NY; NC; WA; WV. **International locations:** England; Singapore; Wales. **Listed on:** NASDAQ. **Stock exchange symbol:** BEAV. **Annual sales/revenues:** More than $100 million. **Number of employees at this location:** 310.

B/E AEROSPACE, INC.
12807 Lake Drive, P.O. Box 130, Delray Beach FL 33447-0130. 561/276-6083. **Contact:** Human Resources Department. **World Wide Web address:** http://www.beaerospace.com. **Description:** This location manufactures aircraft galley products. Overall, B/E Aerospace, Inc. designs, manufactures, sells, and provides global support for one of the industry's broadest lines of commercial aircraft cabin interior products, including seating products, passenger entertainment and service systems, and galley structures and inserts. The company supplies major airlines and airframe manufacturers.

Corporate headquarters location: Wellington FL. **Other U.S. locations:** CA; CT; MN; NY; NC; WA; WV. **International locations:** England; Singapore; Wales. **Listed on:** NASDAQ. **Stock exchange symbol:** BEAV. **Annual sales/revenues:** More than $100 million.

BAE SYSTEMS
P.O. Box 1500, Tampa 33684. 813/885-7481. **Contact:** Human Resources. **E-mail address:** careers@baesystems.com. **World Wide Web address:** http://www.baesystems.com. **Description:** Designs, manufactures, and sells flight simulators, weapon systems, tactical air defense systems, small arms, and training devices for the U.S. government, as well as commercial and international customers. BAE SYSTEMS also develops simulation-based devices for the entertainment industry. The company also provides a variety of simulator-related training services at customer-owned facilities, its Tampa training center, and the British Aerospace-owned Dulles training facility. BAE SYSTEMS conducts business through its three primary operating segments: Training Devices, Training Services, and Systems Management. **Common positions include:** Accountant/Auditor; Administrator; Aerospace Engineer; Buyer; Draftsperson; Electrical/Electronics Engineer; Industrial Designer; Mechanical Engineer; Purchasing Agent/Manager; Quality Control Supervisor. **Corporate headquarters location:** This location. **Subsidiaries include:** Reflectone UK Limited. **Number of employees at this location:** 400. **Number of employees nationwide:** 980.

CRESTVIEW AEROSPACE CORPORATION
5486 Fairchild Road, Crestview FL 32539-8157. 850/682-2746. **Contact:** Department of Human Resources. **World Wide Web address:** http://www.crestview-aerospace.com. **Description:** Manufactures aircraft components and is engaged in aircraft modification. **Common positions include:** Accountant/Auditor; Administrator; Aerospace Engineer; Blue-Collar Worker Supervisor; Buyer; Computer Programmer; Department Manager; Draftsperson; Electrical/Electronics Engineer; Financial Analyst; Industrial Engineer; Marketing Specialist; Operations/Production Manager; Purchasing Agent/Manager; Quality Control Supervisor; Systems Analyst. **Corporate headquarters location:** Chantilly VA. **Parent company:** Fairchild Aircraft Corporation.

DAYTON-GRANGER, INC.
3299 SW 9th Avenue, Fort Lauderdale FL 33315. 954/463-3451. **Fax:** 954/761-3172. **Contact:** Human Resources. **World Wide Web address:** http://www.daytongranger.com. **Description:** A manufacturer of aviation communications products. **NOTE:** Entry-level positions are offered. **Common positions include:** Accountant/Auditor; Electrical/Electronics Engineer; Mechanical Engineer; MIS Specialist; Purchasing Agent/Manager; Quality Control Supervisor; Technical Writer/Editor. **Corporate headquarters location:** This location. **Operations at this facility include:** Administration; Manufacturing; Research and Development; Sales; Service. **Listed on:** Privately held. **Number of employees at this location:** 220.

EATON CORPORATION
2250 Whitfield Avenue, Sarasota FL 34243. 941/758-7726. **Contact:** Human Resources Department. **World Wide Web address:** http://www.eaton.com. **Description:** A manufacturer of airplane switches. **Listed on:** New York Stock Exchange. **Stock exchange symbol:** ETN. **Annual Revenue:** More than $100 million. **Number of employees worldwide:** 49,000.

FORT LAUDERDALE JET CENTER
1100 Lee Wagner Boulevard, Fort Lauderdale FL 33315. 954/359-3200. **Contact:** Human Resources. **Description:** A private airport for corporate aircraft. Fort Lauderdale Jet Center is a fixed-base operator.

GABLES ENGINEERING, INC.
247 Greco Avenue, Coral Gables FL 33146. 305/774-4400. **Fax:** 305/774-4465. **Contact:** Cary Reyes, Human Resources. **World Wide Web address:** http://www.gableseng.com. **Description:** Designs, configures, and manufactures aircraft communication and navigation control systems. **Common positions include:** Electrical/Electronics Engineer; Electronics Technician; Software Engineer; Technical Writer/Editor. **Corporate headquarters location:** This location. **Operations at this facility include:** Manufacturing; Research and Development. **Number of employees at this location:** 220.

HEICO AEROSPACE CORPORATION
3000 Taft Street, Hollywood FL 33021. 954/987-6101. **Fax:** 954/987-8228. **Contact:** Human Resources. **World Wide Web address:** http://www.heico.com. **Description:** Manufactures and distributes jet aircraft engine parts and repairs and overhauls engine components. **Parent company:** HEICO

Corporation. **Listed on:** New York Stock Exchange. **Stock exchange symbol:** HEI.

HONEYWELL
1401 W Cypress Creek Road, Fort Lauderdale FL 33309. 954/928-2100. **Fax:** 954/928-2619. **Contact:** Personnel. **World Wide Web address:** http://www.honeywell.com. **Description:** This location designs and manufactures airborne electronic equipment for the commercial airlines and military markets. Overall, Honeywell is engaged in the research, development, manufacture, and sale of advanced technology products and services in the fields of chemicals, electronics, automation, and controls. The company's major businesses are home and building automation and control, performance polymers and chemicals, industrial automation and control, space and aviation systems, and defense and marine systems. **Other U.S. locations:** Nationwide. **Listed on:** New York Stock Exchange. **Stock exchange symbol:** HON.

HOOVER INDUSTRIES INC.
7260 NW 68th Street, Miami FL 33166-2014. 305/888-9791. **Fax:** 305/887-4632. **Contact:** Human Resources. **World Wide Web address:** http://www.hooverindustries.com. **Description:** Manufactures seat covers, cushions, and inflatable survival equipment for the aerospace industry. Founded in 1955. **Common positions include:** Accountant/Auditor; Blue-Collar Worker Supervisor; Cost Estimator; Draftsperson; Human Resources Manager; Purchasing Agent/Manager; Quality Control Supervisor; Software Engineer; Systems Analyst; Transportation/Traffic Specialist. **Corporate headquarters location:** This location. **Listed on:** Privately held. **Number of employees at this location:** 200.

LOCKHEED MARTIN ELECTRONICS & MISSILES
498 Oak Road, Ocala FL 34472-3099. 352/687-2163. **Contact:** Human Resources. **E-mail address:** jobs.lmc@lmco.com. **World Wide Web address:** http://www.lockheedmartin.com. **Description:** Develops, manufactures, and supports advanced combat systems, electro-optics, and air defense technology. **Corporate headquarters location:** Bethesda MD. **Listed on:** New York Stock Exchange. **Stock exchange symbol:** LMT.

METRIC SYSTEMS CORPORATION
645 Anchors Street, Fort Walton Beach FL 32548. 850/302-3000. **Fax:** 850/302-3475. **Contact:** Martha Stevens, Manager of Human Resources Department. **World Wide Web address:** http://www.metricsys.com. **Description:** Designs, develops,

and manufactures aerospace defense products. **Common positions include:** Account Manager; Accountant; Administrative Assistant; Attorney; Blue-Collar Worker Supervisor; Clerical Supervisor; Computer Engineer; Computer Operator; Computer Programmer; Computer Technician; Controller; Cost Estimator; Database Administrator; Design Engineer; Draftsperson; Electrical/Electronics Engineer; Environmental Engineer; Graphic Artist; Graphic Designer; Human Resources Manager; Industrial Engineer; Manufacturing Engineer; Mechanical Engineer; Operations Manager; Production Manager; Project Manager; Purchasing Agent/Manager; Quality Assurance Engineer; Quality Control Supervisor; Secretary; Software Engineer; Systems Analyst; Technical Writer/Editor; Vice President. **Operations at this facility include:** Administration; Manufacturing; Research and Development; Sales; Service. **Listed on:** New York Stock Exchange. **Stock exchange symbol:** TSY. **President/CEO:** Edward R. Epstein. **Purchasing Manager:** Victor Martire. **Annual sales/revenues:** $51 - $100 million. **Number of employees at this location:** 560.

MICRODYNE CORPORATION
491 Oak Road, Ocala FL 34472. 352/687-4633. **Contact:** Eugene Sawyer, Personnel Director. **World Wide Web address:** http://www.microdyne.com. **Description:** As part of the aerospace telemetry division, this location manufactures radio and television transmitters for aircraft. Overall, Microdyne Corporation designs, manufactures, markets, and supports a broad line of data communications hardware products that enable local area network and remote network access communications. The company is also a leading supplier of LAN adapter cards that provide the connection between computers (including personal computers, file servers, minicomputers, and mainframe computers) and the network. The company's products support computer bus structures, wiring systems, and network topologies including ethernet, fast ethernet, and token ring. Microdyne Corporation is divided into three businesses: networking products, which support inter-computer network communications; aerospace telemetry, which manufactures receivers used in a variety of applications involving missiles, aircraft, satellites, and other space vehicles; and manufacturing support services. **Corporate headquarters location:** Alexandria VA. **Other U.S. locations:** Carson CA; San Jose CA; Indianapolis IN. **International locations:** England; Germany. **Listed on:** New York Stock Exchange. **Stock exchange symbol:** LLL. **Number of employees worldwide:** 470.

THE NEW PIPER AIRCRAFT, INC.
2926 Piper Drive, Vero Beach FL 32960. 561/567-4361. **Fax:** 561/778-7860. **Contact:** Rosalie Webster, Vice President of Human Resources. **E-mail address:** jobs@newpiper.com. **World Wide Web address:** http://www.newpiper.com. **Description:** Manufactures personal and business aircraft including the Saratoga II TC, Warrior III, Arrow, Seminole, Saratoga II HP, Archer III, Malibu Mirage, Malibu Meridian, and Seneca V. **Corporate headquarters location:** This location. **Subsidiaries include:** Piper Financial Services, Inc. provides aircraft financing and leasing services.

NORTHROP GRUMMAN CORPORATION
P.O. Drawer 3447, St. Augustine FL 32085. 904/825-3300. **Contact:** Human Resources. **World Wide Web address:** http://www.northgrum.com. **Description:** This location is an aircraft overhaul and modification facility. Overall, Northrop Grumman manufactures military aircraft, commercial aircraft parts, and electronic systems. Northrop Grumman has developed the B-2 Stealth Bomber, parts for the F/A-18 and the 747, and radar equipment. Other operations include computer systems development for management and scientific applications. **Corporate headquarters location:** Los Angeles CA. **Operations at this facility include:** Administration; Manufacturing; Service. **Listed on:** New York Stock Exchange. **Stock exchange symbol:** NOC.

PRATT & WHITNEY
P.O. Box 109600, West Palm Beach FL 33410-9600. 561/796-2000. **Contact:** Human Resources. **World Wide Web address:** http://www.pratt-whitney.com. **Description:** This location is the headquarters for the division of large military engines and space propulsion systems. Primary operations at the facility include the design and testing of turbine and liquid rocket engines and the production of liquid hydrogen-fuel rocket engines. **Corporate headquarters location:** East Hartford CT. **Parent company:** United Technologies Corporation designs and manufactures engines and space propulsion systems for commercial and general aviation. **Number of employees at this location:** 5,000.

ROCKWELL COLLINS
P.O. Box 1060, Melbourne FL 32902-1060. 321/725-0800. **Contact:** Human Resources Department. **World Wide Web address:** http://www.rockwell.com. **Description:** Manufactures aircraft radio transmitters. **Corporate headquarters location:** Milwaukee WI. **Parent company:** Rockwell International

Corporation provides products for the printing, military, automotive, and aerospace industries through its electronics, automotive, and graphics divisions. Products include military and commercial communication equipment, guidance systems, electronics, components for automobiles, and printing presses. Rockwell provides the government with parts and services for bombers, as well as power systems for the space station and is a major contractor for the Space Shuttle Orbiter program. **Listed on:** New York Stock Exchange. **Stock exchange symbol:** ROK. **CEO:** Don H. Davis, Jr. **Annual sales:** More than $100 million. **Number of employees worldwide:** 23,000.

SIGNATURE FLIGHT SUPPORT
4050 SW 11th Terrace, Fort Lauderdale FL 33315. 954/359-0000. **Fax:** 407/648-7390. **Contact:** Brenda Knighton, Department of Human Resources. **E-mail address:** brendaknighton@signatureflight.com. **World Wide Web address:** http://www.signatureflight.com. **Description:** A supplier and distributor of machine parts for corporate jets. The company is also involved in refueling and offers maintenance and inspections of corporate jets. **Common positions include:** Automotive Mechanic; Customer Service Representative. **Corporate headquarters location:** Orlando FL. **Other U.S. locations:** Nationwide. **Parent company:** BBA Aviation. **Operations at this facility include:** Administration; Service. **Number of employees nationwide:** 4,500.

SIKORSKY AIRCRAFT CORPORATION
P.O. Box 109610, West Palm Beach, FL 33410-9600. 561/775-5200. **Contact:** Department of Human Resources. **E-mail address:** sikorskywes@sikorsky.com. **World Wide Web address:** http://www.sikorsky.com. **Description:** Manufactures helicopters for commercial, industrial, and military applications. **Corporate headquarters location:** Stratford CT. **Other U.S. locations:** AL; CT. **Parent company:** United Technologies Corporation designs and manufactures engines and space propulsion systems for commercial and general aviation. **President:** Dean Borgman. **Annual revenues:** More than $100 million.

UNISON INDUSTRIES
7575 Baymeadows Way, Jacksonville FL 32256-8514. 904/739-4000. **Contact:** Bob Owens, Human Resources. **E-mail address:** jobs@unisonindustries.com. **World Wide Web address:** http://www.unisonindustries.com **Description:** Manufactures turbine aircraft ignition systems and piston

products. **Corporate headquarters location:** This location. **Other U.S. locations:** IL; NY; TX. **International locations:** Mexico. **President/CEO:** Frederick Sontag. **Number of employees worldwide:** 1,400.

UNITED SPACE ALLIANCE (USA)
8550 Astronaut Boulevard, Cape Canaveral FL 32920. 321/799-6800. **Contact:** Human Resources. **World Wide Web address:** http://www.unitedspacealliance.com. **Description:** A primary contractor for the NASA space shuttle operations. The company is responsible for ground operations and flight support of the Space Shuttle. **Corporate headquarters location:** Houston TX. **President/CEO:** Russell D. Turner. **Number of employees nationwide:** 10,000.

WORLD FUEL SERVICES, INC.
700 South Royal Poinciana Boulevard, Suite 800, Miami Springs FL 33166. 305/884-2001. **Contact:** Ileana Garcia, Director of Human Resources. **World Wide Web address:** http://www.wfscorp.com. **Description:** Engaged in aviation fuel services for air carriers and provides used oil recycling services in the southeastern United States. **Common positions include:** Accountant/Auditor; Biological Scientist; Chemist; Credit Manager; Geologist/Geophysicist; Petroleum Engineer; Services Sales Representative. **Corporate headquarters location:** This location. **Operations at this facility include:** Administration; Sales. **Listed on:** New York Stock Exchange. **Stock exchange symbol:** INT. **Annual revenues:** More than $100 million.

APPAREL, FASHION, AND TEXTILES

You can expect to find the following types of companies in this chapter:

Broadwoven Fabric Mills
Knitting Mills
Curtains and Draperies
Footwear
Nonwoven Fabrics
Textile Goods and Finishing
Yarn and Thread Mills

AMERICAN WOOLEN COMPANY

P.O. Box 521399, Miami FL 33152-1399. 305/635-4000. **Physical address:** 4000 NW 30th Avenue, Miami FL 33142. **Fax:** 305/633-4997. **Contact:** Richard Marcus, President. **Description:** Manufactures blankets.

CHICO'S FAS

11215 Metro Parkway, Fort Myers FL 33912. 941/277-6200. **Fax:** 941/277-7035. **Contact:** Human Resources. **E-mail address:** humanresources@chicos.com. **World Wide Web address:** http://www.chicos.com. **Description:** A manufacturer and retailer of women's apparel and accessories. Founded in 1983. **Corporate headquarters location:** This location. **Other U.S. locations:** Nationwide. **Listed on:** NASDAQ. **Stock exchange symbol:** CHS. **Annual sales/revenues:** More than $100 million.

DECORATOR INDUSTRIES, INC.

10011 Pines Boulevard, Suite 201, Pembroke Pines FL 33024. 954/436-8909. **Contact:** Human Resources. **Description:** Manufactures draperies, bedspreads, and accessory products.

HOLLANDER HOME FASHIONS CORPORATION

6560 West Rogers Circle, Suite 19, Boca Raton FL 33487. 561/997-6900. **Fax:** 561/997-8738. **Contact:** Human Resources Department. **World Wide Web address:** http://www.hollander.com. **Description:** Manufactures bed pillows, comforters, mattress pads, comforter sets, and specialty bedding products. **Common positions include:** Accountant/Auditor; Administrative Manager; Blue-Collar Worker Supervisor; Clerical Supervisor; Computer Programmer; Credit Manager; Customer Service Representative; Designer; Financial Analyst; General Manager; Human Resources Manager; Industrial Engineer; Industrial Production Manager; Manufacturer's/Wholesaler's Sales Rep.; Mechanical Engineer; Purchasing Agent/Manager; Quality Control Supervisor. **Corporate headquarters location:** This location. **Other U.S. locations:** Nationwide. **Operations at this facility include:** Administration; Manufacturing; Research and Development; Sales. **Listed on:** Privately held. **Number of employees at this location:** 40. **Number of employees nationwide:** 1,200.

INJECTION FOOTWEAR CORPORATION

8730 NW 36th Avenue, Miami FL 33147. 305/696-4611. **Contact:** Human Resources Department. **Description:** Manufactures shoes. **Common positions include:**

Accountant/Auditor; Administrator; Computer Programmer; Credit Manager; Customer Service Representative; General Manager; Industrial Designer; Manufacturer's/Wholesaler's Sales Rep.; Marketing Specialist; Purchasing Agent/Manager; Quality Control Supervisor; Systems Analyst. **Corporate headquarters location:** This location. **Operations at this facility include:** Manufacturing; Sales.

SUPERIOR UNIFORM GROUP
10099 Seminole Boulevard, Seminole FL 33772. 727/397-9611. **Contact:** Jennifer Schmidt, Corporate Manager of Human Resources. **World Wide Web address:** http://www.superiormfg.com. **Description:** A manufacturer and wholesale distributor of uniforms, career apparel, and accessories for the hospital and health care fields, hotels and restaurants, and the public safety, industrial, transportation, and commercial markets. Fashion Seal Uniforms is the company's largest division and a prime supplier to the health care market. Other divisions include Worklon, Martin's Uniforms, Appel Uniforms, Universal Laundry Bags, Lamar Caribbean Sales, D'Armigene Design Center, and Superior Surgical International. **Common positions include:** Accountant/Auditor; Buyer; Commercial Artist; Computer Programmer; Credit Manager; Customer Service Rep.; Human Resources Manager; Industrial Engineer; Industrial Production Manager; Manufacturer's/Wholesaler's Sales Rep.; Quality Control Supervisor; Systems Analyst. **Corporate headquarters location:** This location. **Listed on:** American Stock Exchange. **Stock exchange symbol:** SGC. **President:** Cliff McAlexander.

TROPICAL SPORTSWEAR INTERNATIONAL
4902 West Waters Avenue, Tampa FL 33634. 813/249-4900. **Contact:** Human Resources. **World Wide Web address:** http://www.tsionline.com. **Description:** Manufactures men's and women's denim, twill, and corduroy casual clothing. Brand names include Savane and Bill Blass. Founded in 1927. **NOTE:** Entry-level positions and second and third shifts are offered. **Common positions include:** Administrative Assistant; Blue-Collar Worker Supervisor; Controller; Cost Estimator; Education Administrator; Financial Analyst; Human Resources Manager; Manufacturing Engineer; MIS Specialist; Quality Control Supervisor; Sales Manager; Systems Analyst; Systems Manager. **Special programs:** Internships. **Corporate headquarters location:** This location. **Other U.S. locations:** NY. **International locations:** Dominican Republic; Mexico. **Listed on:** NASDAQ. **Stock exchange symbol:** TSIC. **Annual sales/revenues:** More than $100 million. **Number of**

employees at this location: 640. **Number of employees worldwide:** 1,600.

WESTPOINT STEVENS
P.O. Box 625, Chipley FL 32428. 850/638-4956. **Contact:** Valerie Pettis, Personnel Director. **World Wide Web address:** http://www.westpointstevens.com. **Description:** Manufactures and markets bedroom and bathroom products sold in retail outlets nationwide. **Corporate headquarters location:** NY. **Other U.S. locations:** Nationwide. **International locations:** Canada; England. **Listed on:** New York Stock Exchange. **Stock exchange symbol:** WYS. **Number of employees nationwide:** 15,000.

ARCHITECTURE, CONSTRUCTION, AND ENGINEERING

You can expect to find the following types of companies in this chapter:

Architectural and Engineering Services
Civil and Mechanical Engineering Firms
Construction Products, Manufacturers, and Wholesalers
General Contractors/ Specialized Trade Contractors

AJT & ASSOCIATES, INC.
8910 Astronaut Boulevard, Cape Canaveral FL 32920-4225. 321/783-7989. **Contact:** Human Resources Department. **World Wide Web address:** http://www.ajt-assoc.com. **Description:** Provides environmental science and architectural engineering services. **Common positions include:** Architect; Civil Engineer; Electrical/Electronics Engineer; Environmental Engineer; Mechanical Engineer.

ATC ASSOCIATES
9955 NW 116 Way, Suite 1, Miami FL 33178. 305/882-8200. **Contact:** Human Resources Department. **World Wide Web address:** http://www.atc-enviro.com. **Description:** Performs comprehensive environmental consulting, engineering, and on-site remediation services. Services include assessment of environmental regulations, investigation of contaminated sites, and the design and engineering of methods to correct or prevent the contamination. The company also performs remedial actions, and emergency response actions in cases of spills and accidental releases of hazardous waste. ATC Associates addresses hazardous and nonhazardous contaminants in municipal and industrial water supplies; in wastewater and storm water from municipal, industrial, and military installations; and in groundwater, soils, and air space. Customers include federal, state, and local government agencies.

ALUMA SYSTEMS
6402 East Hanna Avenue, Tampa FL 33610. 813/626-1133. **Toll-free phone:** 800/282-9199. **Contact:** Personnel. **World Wide Web address:** http://www.aluma.com. **Description:** Supplies forming, shoring, and scaffolding products to the industrial maintenance and concrete construction industries. **Common positions include:** Manufacturer's/Wholesaler's Sales Rep. **Operations at this facility include:** Sales.

APAC INC.
14299 Alico Road, Fort Myers FL 33913. 941/267-7767. **Contact:** Ms Elaine Paserella, Personnel Manager. **World Wide Web address:** http://www.apac.com. **Description:** APAC provides materials, services, and technology to the construction industry.

APAC INC.
4375 McCoy Drive, Pensacola FL 32503. 850/433-3001. **Contact:** Human Resources. **World Wide Web address:**

http://www.apac.com. **Description:** A contractor specializing in road construction.

APAC INC.
P.O. Box 2579, Sarasota FL 34230. 941/355-7178. **Contact:** Human Resources Department. **World Wide Web address:** http://www.apac.com. **Description:** A manufacturer of asphalt.

ASHLEY ALUMINUM, LLC
dba CAMERON ASHLEY BUILDING PRODUCTS
P.O. Drawer 15398, Tampa FL 33684. 813/884-0444. **Toll-free phone:** 800/749-4067. **Contact:** Human Resources. **World Wide Web address:** http://www.cabp.com. **Description:** A manufacturer and distributor of aluminum and vinyl building products. Founded in 1967. **Common positions include:** Accountant; Administrative Assistant; Auditor; Blue-Collar Worker Supervisor; Branch Manager; Chief Financial Officer; Clerical Supervisor; Computer Programmer; Controller; Customer Service Representative; General Manager; Human Resources Manager; Management Trainee; Operations Manager; Purchasing Agent/Manager; Sales Representative; Systems Analyst; Systems Manager. **Office hours:** Monday - Friday, 8:00 a.m. - 5:00 p.m. **Corporate headquarters location:** This location. **Other U.S. locations:** AL; GA; KY; LA; TX. **Listed on:** New York Stock Exchange. **Stock exchange symbol:** CAB. **President:** Steve Gaffney. **Annual sales/revenues:** More than $100 million. **Number of employees at this location:** 100. **Number of employees nationwide:** 500.

ATLANTIC MARINE, INC.
ATLANTIC DRY DOCK CORPORATION
8500 Heckscher Drive, Jacksonville FL 32226. 904/251-3164. **Contact:** Human Resources Department. **World Wide Web address:** http://www.atlanticmarine.com. **Description:** Builds, repairs, and converts ships for government, commercial, and consumer markets.

BERTRAM YACHT, INC.
P.O. Box 520774 GMF, Miami FL 33152. 305/633-8011. **Contact:** Manager of Human Resources. **Description:** A manufacturer of yachts. **Common positions include:** Buyer; Computer Programmer; Draftsperson; Electrical/Electronics Engineer; Electrician; Financial Analyst; Human Resources Manager; Mechanical Engineer; Operations/Production Manager; Quality Control Supervisor; Structural Engineer; Systems Analyst. **Corporate headquarters location:** This

location. **Parent company:** Bertram, Inc. **Operations at this facility include:** Manufacturing. **Number of employees at this location:** 240.

CATALINA YACHTS
7200 Bryan Dairy Road, Largo FL 33777. 727/544-6681. **Fax:** 727/546-7303. **Contact:** Georgia B. Law, Human Resources. **World Wide Web address:** http://www.catalinayachts.com. **Description:** A yacht manufacturer. Founded in 1984. **Corporate headquarters location:** Woodland Hills CA. **Number of employees at this location:** 170.

CENTEX ROONEY
7901 SW 6th Court, Plantation FL 33324. 954/585-4000. **Contact:** Human Resources. **World Wide Web address:** http://www.centex.com. **Description:** A construction and general contracting company. **Listed on:** New York Stock Exchange. **Stock exchange symbol:** CTX.

J.W. CONNER & SONS, INC.
P.O. Box 2522, Tampa FL 33601-2522. 813/247-4441. **Contact:** Michelle Williams, Human Resources. **Description:** A road and highway contractor.

DEVCON INTERNATIONAL CORPORATION
1350 East Newport Center Drive, Suite 201, Deerfield Beach FL 33442. 954/429-1500. **Contact:** Human Resources. **World Wide Web address:** http://www.devc.com. **Description:** Provides heavy construction services focusing on industrial projects in the Caribbean. **Number of employees at this location:** 640.

EXPONENT, INC.
4101 SW 71st Avenue, Miami FL 33155. 305/661-7726. **Toll-free phone:** 888/656-3976. **Contact:** Human Resources Department. **E-mail address:** hr@exponent.com. **World Wide Web address:** http://www.exponent.com. **Description:** Engaged in accident reconstruction, biomechanics, construction/structural engineering, aviation and marine investigations, environmental assessment, materials and product testing, warnings and labeling issues, accident statistic data analysis, and risk prevention/mitigation. Founded in 1967. **NOTE:** All hiring is conducted through the main offices of Exponent, Inc. Please send resumes to: Human Resources, 149 Commonwealth Drive, Menlo Park CA 94025. **Corporate headquarters location:** Menlo Park CA. **Listed on:** NASDAQ.

Stock exchange symbol: EXPO. **Number of employees nationwide:** 675.

FLORIDA CRUSHED STONE COMPANY
P.O. Box 490180, Leesburg FL 34749-0300. 352/787-0608.
Contact: Human Resources Department. **World Wide Web address:** http://www.fcsco.com. **Description:** Manufactures construction materials including cement, aggregates, and pavement components.

FLORIDA ENGINEERED CONSTRUCTION PRODUCTS
P.O. Box 24567, Tampa FL 33623. 813/621-4641. **Fax:** 813/630-5476. **Contact:** Larry Toll, Human Resources. **Description:** Manufactures building materials including precast lintels and sills, prestressed concrete beams and joints, roof trusses, and architectural precast slabs. **Common positions include:** Accountant/Auditor; Civil Engineer; Draftsperson; Management Trainee; Manufacturer's/Wholesaler's Sales Rep.; Operations/Production Manager; Quality Control Supervisor. **Corporate headquarters location:** This location. **Other area locations:** Kissimmee FL; Odessa FL; Sarasota FL; West Palm Beach FL; Winter Springs FL. **Operations at this facility include:** Administration; Divisional Headquarters; Manufacturing; Regional Headquarters; Sales; Service. **Listed on:** Privately held. **Number of employees at this location:** 250. **Number of employees nationwide:** 350.

THE HASKELL COMPANY
111 Riverside Avenue, Jacksonville FL 32202. 904/791-4500.
Contact: Coleman Walker, Director of Human Resources. **World Wide Web address:** http://www.thehaskellco.com. **Description:** The design-build company that provides architectural, construction, engineering, and real estate services. **Common positions include:** Accountant/Auditor; Administrator; Architect; Civil Engineer; Computer Programmer; Draftsperson; Electrical/Electronics Engineer; Human Resources Manager; Management Trainee; Mechanical Engineer; Operations/Production Manager; Quality Control Supervisor; Systems Analyst. **Corporate headquarters location:** This location. **Operations at this facility include:** Regional Headquarters.

HUBBARD CONSTRUCTION COMPANY
P.O. Box 547217, Orlando FL 32854-7217. 407/645-5500.
Contact: Margaret Collins, Director of Personnel. **World Wide Web address:** http://www.hubbard.com. **Description:** A general construction contractor that specializes in paving,

bridge-building, and highway construction. **Common positions include:** Blue-Collar Worker Supervisor; Civil Engineer; Estimator. **Corporate headquarters location:** This location. **Operations at this facility include:** Administration. **Number of employees at this location:** 750. **Number of employees nationwide:** 1,000.

MISENER MARINE CONSTRUCTION INC.
5440 West Tyson Avenue, Tampa FL 33611. 813/839-8441. **Contact:** Cindy Pierce, Human Resources. **World Wide Web address:** http://www.misenermarine.com. **Description:** Engaged in the heavy marine construction of bridges, docks, piers, underwater pipeline and cable, and foundation piling. **Common positions include:** Accountant/Auditor; Civil Engineer; Draftsperson; Geologist/Geophysicist; Purchasing Agent/Manager. **Corporate headquarters location:** This location.

NOBILITY HOMES, INC.
P. O. Box 1659, Ocala FL 34478. 352/732-5157. **Contact:** Human Resources Department. **World Wide Web address:** http://www.nobilityhomes.com. **Description:** Designs and manufactures factory-constructed homes. The company also operates real estate sales centers. **Corporate headquarters location:** This location.

ORIOLE HOMES CORPORATION
1690 South Congress Avenue, Suite 200, Delray Beach FL 33445. 561/274-2000. **Contact:** Steve Mahon, Director of Human Resources Department. **World Wide Web address:** http://www.oriolehomes.com. **Description:** Builds and sells houses and condominiums.

PALMER ELECTRIC COMPANY
SHOWCASE LIGHTING
875 Jackson Avenue, Winter Park FL 32789. 407/646-8700. **Contact:** Human Resources Department. **World Wide Web address:** http://www.palmer-electric.com. **Description:** Provides electrical services to commercial and residential customers.

POST, BUCKLEY, SCHUH AND JERNIGAN, INC.
2001 NW 107th Avenue, Miami FL 33172-2507. 305/592-7275. **Contact:** Human Resources. **World Wide Web address:** http://www.pbsj.com. **Description:** Offers architectural, engineering, and planning/design consulting services. **Common positions include:** Architect; Chemical Engineer;

Chemist; Civil Engineer; Draftsperson; Electrical/Electronics Engineer; Mechanical Engineer; Structural Engineer; Technical Writer/Editor; Transportation/Traffic Specialist. **Operations at this facility include:** Administration; Regional Headquarters; Sales; Service. **Number of employees nationwide:** 2,700.

REYNOLDS, SMITH AND HILLS, INC.
P.O. Box 4850, Jacksonville FL 32201-4850. 904/296-2000. **Contact:** Jack Higson, Human Resources Director. **World Wide Web address:** http://www.rsandh.com. **Description:** Offers architectural, engineering, and planning/design consulting services. **Common positions include:** Architect; Architectural Engineer; Civil Engineer; Electrical/Electronics Engineer; Energy Engineer; Environmental Engineer; Geologist/Geophysicist; Mechanical Engineer; Transit Engineer. **Other area locations:** Fort Meyers; Merritt Island; Orlando; Plantation; Tampa. **Other U.S. locations:** Chicago IL; Flint MI; Duluth MN; Austin TX; Houston TX. **Number of employees nationwide:** 375.

SCOTTY'S, INC.
5300 North Recker Highway, Winter Haven FL 33880. 863/299-1111. **Contact:** Human Resources. **World Wide Web address:** http://www.scottysinc.com. **Description:** A wholesale construction supply company. **Corporate headquarters location:** This location.

TRI-CITY ELECTRICAL CONTRACTORS
430 West Drive, Altamonte Springs FL 32714. 407/788-3500. **Contact:** Dori Silberman, Director of Human Resources. **Description:** Performs electrical contracting work for both commercial and residential clients.

WALT DISNEY IMAGINEERING
P.O. Box 10321, Lake Buena Vista FL 32830. 407/566-1900. **Physical address:** 200 Celebration Place, Celebration FL 34747. 407/566-1900. **Fax:** 407/566-4220. **Contact:** Human Resources. **World Wide Web address:** http://www.disney.com. **Description:** Responsible for the design, development, and construction of The Walt Disney Company's premiere attractions, resorts, and entertainment venues. **NOTE:** Entry-level positions are offered. **Company slogan:** We make the magic! **Common positions include:** Accountant; Administrative Assistant; Architect; Civil Engineer; Computer Engineer; Computer Programmer; Computer Support Technician; Computer Technician; Cost Estimator; Design Engineer; Electrical/Electronics Engineer; Financial Analyst; Mechanical

Engineer; MIS Specialist; Network/Systems Administrator; Secretary; Software Engineer; Systems Analyst. **Special programs:** Internships. **Corporate headquarters location:** Glendale CA. **Other U.S. locations:** Orlando FL. **Parent company:** The Walt Disney Company. **Operations at this facility include:** Regional Headquarters. **Listed on:** New York Stock Exchange. **Stock exchange symbol:** DIS. **Number of employees at this location:** 400. **Number of employees nationwide:** 50,000. **Number of employees worldwide:** 60,000.

WALTER INDUSTRIES
P.O. Box 31601, Tampa FL 33631. 813/871-4811. **Recorded jobline:** 813/871-4100. **Contact:** Employment Manager. **World Wide Web address:** http://www.walterind.com. **Description:** One of the nation's largest industrial companies, with leading interests in home building and financing, natural resources, and industrial manufacturing. **Listed on:** New York Stock Exchange. **Stock exchange symbol:** WLT.

WATKINS ENGINEERS & CONSTRUCTORS, INC.
P.O. Box 2194, Tallahassee FL 32316. 850/576-7181. **Contact:** Human Resources Department. **World Wide Web address:** http://www.watkinsec.com. **Description:** A contractor that specializes in industrial buildings and warehouses.

ARTS, ENTERTAINMENT, SPORTS, AND RECREATION

You can expect to find the following types of companies in this chapter:

Botanical and Zoological Gardens
Entertainment Groups
Motion Picture and Video Tape Production and Distribution
Museums and Art Galleries
Physical Fitness Facilities
Professional Sports Clubs
Public Golf Courses
Racing and Track Operations
Sporting and Recreational Camps
Theatrical Producers

ALLIANCE ENTERTAINMENT CORPORATION

4250 Coral Ridge Drive, Coral Springs FL 33065. 800/635-9082. **Fax:** 954/340-7641. **Contact:** Human Resources Department. **World Wide Web address:** http://www.aent.com. **Description:** Alliance Entertainment operates in two segments of the entertainment industry: the sale and distribution of prerecorded music and related products, and the acquisition and exploration of proprietary rights to recorded music, video, television, CD-ROMs, and books. **Corporate headquarters location:** This location.

ALLIED VAUGHN

4364 35th Street, Orlando FL 32811-6502. 407/649-0008. **Fax:** 407/649-9005. **Contact:** Human Resources. **World Wide Web address:** http://www.alliedvaughn.com. **Description:** One of the nation's leading independent multimedia manufacturing companies, offering CD-audio and CD-ROM mastering and replication; videocassette and audiocassette duplication; off-line and online video editing; motion picture film processing; film-to-tape and tape-to-film transfers; and complete finishing, packaging, warehousing, and fulfillment services. **NOTE:** When sending resumes, please specify the department to which you are applying.

BREVARD ZOO

8225 North Wickham Road, Melbourne FL 32940. 321/254-9453. **Fax:** 321/259-5966. **Contact:** Human Resources. **E-mail address:** info@brevardzoo.org. **World Wide Web address:** http://www.brevardzoo.org. **Description:** Features over 400 animals of Latin America, native Florida, and Australia in their natural habitat.

BUSCH GARDENS TAMPA BAY
ADVENTURE ISLAND

P.O. Box 9158, Tampa FL 33674. 813/987-5082. **Physical address:** 3605 East Bogainvillea Avenue, Tampa FL 33612 **Toll-free phone:** 888/800-5447. **Contact:** Human Resources. **World Wide Web address:** http://www.buschgardens.com. **Description:** A 300-acre theme park featuring shows, rides, attractions, and exotic animals. **NOTE:** All applications must be made in person at the Human Resources Office. A personal interview is required and all applicants must be a minimum of 18 years old. Please be aware that many technical and professional positions are filled by internal promotions.

CPAMERICA, INC.
2255 Glades Road, Suite 324 A, Boca Raton FL 33431.
561/988-2607. **Contact:** Human Resources. **E-mail address:**
cpamerica@worldnet.att.net. **World Wide Web address:**
http://www.cpamerica.com. **Description:** A consulting firm
organized to market celebrities, entertainers, and concert
performers to international corporations. **Corporate
headquarters location:** This location. **Other U.S. locations:** Las
Vegas NV. **Listed on:** Privately held. **President/CEO:** Jack
Wishna. **Number of employees at this location:** 10. **Number
of employees nationwide:** 20.

CARIBBEAN GARDENS
1590 Goodlette-Frank Road, Naples FL 34102-5260. 941/262-
5409. **Contact:** Human Resources Department. **E-mail address:**
info@caribbeangardens.com. **World Wide Web address:**
http://www.caribbeangardens.com. **Description:** A 52-acre
botanical and zoological preserve featuring exhibits of
endangered plant and animal species. Founded in 1919.

GATORLAND
14501 South Orange Blossom Trail, Orlando FL 32837.
407/855-5496. **Toll-free phone:** 800/393-JAWS. **Contact:**
Human Resources. **E-mail address:** info@gatorland.com.
World Wide Web address: http://www.gatorland.com.
Description: An attraction featuring a cypress swamp walk, a
children's water park, a children's petting zoo, and the 10-acre
Alligator Breeding Marsh.

GOLDEN BEAR GOLF INC.
11780 U.S. Highway 1, Suite 400, North Palm Beach FL
33408. 561/626-3900. **Contact:** Linda Clark, Personnel. **World
Wide Web address:** http://www.nicklaus.com. **Description:**
Franchises golf practice and instruction facilities, operates golf
schools, constructs golf courses through Weitz Golf
International (also at this location), and sells consumer golf
products and apparel. **Common positions include:**
Accountant/Auditor; Administrator; Architect; Civil Engineer;
Marketing Specialist. **Corporate headquarters location:** This
location. **Operations at this facility include:** Service. **Listed
on:** NASDAQ. **Stock exchange symbol:** JACK.

GULF BREEZE ZOO
5701 Gulf Breeze Parkway, Gulf Breeze FL 32561. 850/932-
2229. **Contact:** Human Resources. **World Wide Web address:**
http://www.cityshowcase.com/pensacola/attract/zoo.html.
Description: An attraction that offers botanical Japanese

gardens, a Safari Line train that drives through 30 acres of cageless animals, and a zoo that features more than 700 animals.

INTERNATIONAL SPEEDWAY CORPORATION
P.O. Box 2801, Daytona Beach FL 32120-2801. 386/254-2700. **Physical address:** 1801 West International Speedway Boulevard, Daytona Beach FL 32114. **Contact:** Director of Human Resources Department. **World Wide Web address:** http://www.daytonausa.com. **Description:** Organizes stock car, sports car, motorcycle, and go-cart racing events for spectators at six locations, including two in Daytona Beach. Among the major events conducted by the company are late-model stock car races sanctioned by the National Association for Stock Car Auto Racing, Inc. (NASCAR). The company also produces and syndicates race and race-related radio broadcasts through MRN Radio. **Other U.S. locations:** AL; AZ; NY; SC. **Subsidiaries include:** Amercrown Service Corporation conducts food, beverage, and souvenir operations. **Number of employees nationwide:** 4,620.

LION COUNTRY SAFARI
2003 Lion Country Safari Road, Loxahatchee FL 33470-3976. 561/793-1084. **Fax:** 561/793-9603. **Contact:** Human Resources Department. **World Wide Web address:** http://www.lioncountrysafari.com. **Description:** Features two parks including the Lion Country park, a 500-acre drive-through, cageless zoo; and Safari World, an amusement park with boat cruises, rides, and animals. Founded in 1967.

LOWRY PARK ZOO
1101 West Sligh Avenue, Tampa FL 33604. 813/935-8552. **Contact:** Human Resources Department. **World Wide Web address:** http://www.lowryparkzoo.com. **Description:** A zoo hosting approximately 600,000 visitors per year. The zoo features 1,500 animals and offers a wide variety of shows and exhibits.

M.E. PRODUCTIONS
2000 SW 30th Avenue, Pembroke Park FL 33009. 954/458-4000. **Fax:** 954/458-4003. **Contact:** Hal Etkin, President. **World Wide Web address:** http://www.meproductions.com. **Description:** A production corporation providing sets, lighting, staging, floral arrangements, decor, audio/visual, entertainment, and music services. **Common positions include:** Commercial Artist; Computer Programmer; Construction Contractor; Cost Estimator; Department Manager; Designer;

Draftsperson; Electrician; Manufacturer's/Wholesaler's Sales Rep.; Marketing Manager; Public Relations Specialist; Secretary; Sheet-Metal Worker; Travel Agent; Typist/Word Processor. **Special programs:** Internships. **Corporate headquarters location:** This location. **Operations at this facility include:** Administration; Manufacturing; Sales. **Number of employees at this location:** 60.

MANHATTAN TRANSFER MIAMI
1111 Lincoln Road, Suite 700, Miami Beach FL 33139. 305/674-0700. **Contact:** Human Resources Department. **World Wide Web address:** http://www.mtmiami.com. **Description:** Provides access to the Latin American and Spanish television markets. The company provides numerous production, post-production, and broadcast services to MTV Latino and The Discovery Channel Latin America/Iberia. Services include creative editing, film-to-tape transfer, electronic video editing, computer generated graphics, duplication, and audio services, as well as production and network facilities operations.

MIAMI METROZOO
12400 SW 152nd Street, Miami FL 33177. 305/251-0400. **Contact:** Human Resources Department. **World Wide Web address:** http://www.co.miami-dade.fl.us/parks/metrozoo.htm. **Description:** Features Asian River Life, the African Plains Exhibit, and more than 700 cageless, wild animals.

PARROT JUNGLE AND GARDENS
11000 SW 57th Avenue, Miami FL 33156. 305/666-7834. **Contact:** Human Resources Department. **E-mail address:** parrots@parrotjungle.com. **World Wide Web address:** http://www.parrotjungle.com. **Description:** An attraction dedicated to parrots and the Caribbean. It features a garden with more than 1200 varieties of exotic plants, a primate exhibit, and both free-flying and trained parrot exhibits.

SEA WORLD OF FLORIDA
7007 Sea World Drive, Orlando FL 32821. 407/351-3600. **Contact:** Professional Staffing Department. **World Wide Web address:** http://www.seaworld.com. **Description:** A marine-life park offering a variety of shows and exhibits. **Other U.S. locations:** CA; TX.

TALLAHASSEE MUSEUM OF HISTORY & NATURAL SCIENCE
3945 Museum Drive, Tallahassee FL 32310-6325. 850/575-8684. **Fax:** 850/574-8243. **Contact:** Department of Human

Resources. **World Wide Web address:**
http://www.tallahasseemuseum.org. **Description:** A museum
and zoo featuring historical buildings, an environmental
science center, and wild animals.

UNIVERSAL STUDIOS FLORIDA
1000 Universal Studios Plaza, Orlando FL 32819. 407/363-
8000. **Fax:** 407/363-8006. **Recorded jobline:** 407/363-8080.
Contact: Human Resources. **World Wide Web address:**
http://www.universalstudios.com. **Description:** A diversified
entertainment company and a worldwide leader in motion
pictures, television, music, and home and location-based
themed entertainment. The company's main operating
divisions include Universal Studios, Universal Studios
Recreation Group, Universal Studios Information Technology,
Universal Studios Operations Group, Universal Music Group,
Universal Pictures, Universal Networks & Worldwide
Television Distribution, Universal Studios Consumer Products
Group, Universal Studios Online, and Spencer Gifts. **NOTE:**
Entry-level positions are offered. **Company slogan:** It's a big
universe. Where do you fit in? **Special programs:** Co-ops;
Summer Jobs. **Corporate headquarters location:** Universal
City CA. **Other U.S. locations:** Nationwide. **International
locations:** Worldwide. **Parent company:** The Seagram Co. Ltd.
Listed on: New York Stock Exchange. **Stock exchange symbol:**
VOX. **Number of employees at this location:** 12,000.

WET 'N WILD
6200 International Drive, Orlando FL 32819. 407/351-1800.
Toll-free phone: 800/992-WILD. **Contact:** Human Resources.
E-mail address: getwet@wetnwild.com. **World Wide Web
address:** http://www.wetnwild.com. **Description:** A water park
offering a variety of activities for all ages.

WILDLIFE ON EASY STREET, INC.
12802 Easy Street, Tampa FL 33625. 813/920-4130. **Contact:**
Human Resources. **E-mail address:** savethecats@aol.com.
World Wide Web address: http://www.wildlifeeasyst.com.
Description: A nonprofit organization that serves as both a
wildlife sanctuary for large exotic cats and a home for over 200
unwanted animals.

AUTOMOTIVE

You can expect to find the following types of companies in this chapter:

Automotive Repair Shops
Automotive Stampings
Industrial Vehicles and Moving Equipment
Motor Vehicles and Equipment
Travel Trailers and Campers

AUTONATION INC.

P.O. Box 029030, Fort Lauderdale FL 33302. 954/769-6000. **Physical address:** 110 SE Sixth Street, Fort Lauderdale FL 33301. **Contact:** Human Resources Department. **World Wide Web address:** http://www.autonation.com. **Description:** Sells, finances, and services new and used vehicles. The company also provides aftermarket automotive products, collision repair services, parts and accessories, and extended warranties. **Corporate headquarters location:** This location. **Listed on:** New York Stock Exchange. **Stock exchange symbol:** AN.

BREED TECHNOLOGIES, INC.

P.O. Box 33050, Lakeland FL 33807. 863/668-6000. **Contact:** Human Resources Department. **World Wide Web address:** http://www.breedtech.com. **Description:** A designer, developer, manufacturer, and marketer of crash sensors and automotive airbag systems, used in the majority of airbag-equipped vehicles produced in the United States. The company's products are also used in Japan and Europe. Breed Technologies sells all-mechanical airbag systems (AMS systems) that are installed in the steering wheel. Breed Technologies has expanded its product line to include electronic sensing diagnostic modules and both driver- and passenger-side electrically initiated airbag inflation systems. **Common positions include:** Buyer; Chemical Engineer; Chemist; Designer; Draftsperson; Electrical/Electronics Engineer; Financial Analyst; Mechanical Engineer; Systems Analyst. **Corporate headquarters location:** This location. **Other U.S. locations:** St. Clair Shores MI; Sterling Heights MI; Boonton NJ; Dayton OH; Brownsville TX. **CEO:** John M. Reiss. **Number of employees at this location:** 600.

DISCOUNT AUTO PARTS, INC.

4900 South Frontage Road, Lakeland FL 33815. 863/687-9226. **Contact:** Human Resources. **World Wide Web address:** http://www.discountautoparts.net. **Description:** A specialty retailer of automotive replacement parts, maintenance items, and accessories for do-it-yourself customers. Founded in 1971. **Special programs:** Training. **Corporate headquarters location:** This location. **Other U.S. locations:** AL; GA; SC. **Listed on:** New York Stock Exchange. **Stock exchange symbol:** AAP. **Number of employees nationwide:** 3,000.

DURA AUTOMOTIVE SYSTEMS, INC.

9444 Florida Mining Boulevard, Jacksonville FL 32257-1178. 904/268-8300. **Fax:** 904/268-8350. **Contact:** Human Resources Department. **World Wide Web address:**

http://www.duraauto.com. **Description:** This location manufactures automobile windows. Overall, Dura Automotive Systems designs and manufactures driver control systems, engineered components, and cable-related products for the automotive industry worldwide. **Listed on:** NASDAQ. **Stock exchange symbol:** DRRA. **President/CEO:** Karl Storrie. **Annual sales/revenues:** More than $100 million.

EMERGENCY ONE INC.
P.O. Box 2710, Ocala FL 34478-2710. 352/237-1122. **Physical address:** 1601 SW 37th Street, Ocala FL 34474. **Fax:** 352/237-1151. **Contact:** Human Resources Department. **World Wide Web address:** http://www.e-one.com. **Description:** Manufactures fire rescue vehicles and equipment including aircraft rescue fire fighting vehicles, commercial pumpers, industrial tankers, rescue transport/ambulances, and aerial ladders and platforms. **Common positions include:** Accountant/Auditor; Administrative Manager; Automotive Mechanic; Blue-Collar Worker Supervisor; Budget Analyst; Buyer; Ceramics Engineer; Computer Programmer; Cost Estimator; Customer Service Representative; Designer; Draftsperson; Education Administrator; Electrical/Electronics Engineer; Electrician; Emergency Medical Technician; Financial Analyst; General Manager; Health Services Manager; Human Resources Manager; Industrial Engineer; Industrial Production Manager; Licensed Practical Nurse; Materials Engineer; Mechanical Engineer; Metallurgical Engineer; Operations/Production Manager; Purchasing Agent/Manager; Quality Control Supervisor; Registered Nurse; Services Sales Representative; Systems Analyst; Technical Writer/Editor; Transportation/Traffic Specialist. **Corporate headquarters location:** This location. **Parent company:** Federal Signal Corporation. **Operations at this facility include:** Administration; Manufacturing; Research and Development; Sales; Service. **Listed on:** New York Stock Exchange. **Stock exchange symbol:** FSS. **Number of employees nationwide:** 1,800.

HI-STAT MANUFACTURING COMPANY, INC.
7290 26th Court East, Sarasota FL 34243. 941/355-9761. **Fax:** 941/351-8342. **Contact:** Human Resources. **World Wide Web address:** http://www.histat.com. **Description:** Manufactures and distributes automotive sensors. The company's product line includes speed, temperature, ABS, and pressure sensors. **NOTE:** Entry-level positions and second and third shifts are offered. **Common positions include:** Blue-Collar Worker Supervisor; Computer Programmer; Electrician; Industrial

Engineer; Manufacturing Engineer; Project Manager; Quality Control Supervisor. **Corporate headquarters location:** This location. **Other U.S. locations:** Lexington OH. **Listed on:** Privately held. **Number of employees at this location:** 650. **Number of employees nationwide:** 1,500.

RECOTON CORPORATION
2950 Lake Emma Road, Lake Mary FL 32746. 407/333-0900. **Contact:** Human Resources. **World Wide Web address:** http://www.recoton.com. **Description:** Designs, manufactures, and markets consumer electronics, car stereo speakers, and loudspeakers. **Listed on:** NASDAQ. **Stock exchange symbol:** RCOT.

TI GROUP AUTOMOTIVE SYSTEMS
2660 Jewett Lane, Sanford FL 32771. 407/323-2780. **Contact:** Human Resources Department. **World Wide Web address:** http://www.tiauto.com. **Description:** Supplies fluid delivery and storage systems for brake, fuel, and powertrain applications to the automotive industry. **Parent company:** TI Group. **Other U.S. locations:** Nationwide. **International locations:** Worldwide. **CEO:** William J. Laule. **Number of employees worldwide:** 20,000.

WHEELED COACH INDUSTRIES, INC.
2737 North Forsyth Road, Winter Park FL 32792. 407/677-7777. **Toll-free phone:** 800/342-0720x272. **Fax:** 407/677-8948. **Contact:** Paul Holzapfel, Human Resources. **E-mail address:** paul.holzapfel@wheeledcoach.com. **World Wide Web address:** http://www.wheeledcoach.com. **Description:** One of the world's largest manufacturers of ambulances, buses, and other specialty vehicles. **Common positions include:** Accountant/Auditor; Automotive Mechanic; Blue-Collar Worker Supervisor; Buyer; Computer Programmer; Designer; Draftsperson; Electrical/Electronics Engineer; Emergency Medical Technician; Mechanical Engineer; Painter; Quality Control Supervisor; Systems Analyst; Welder. **Corporate headquarters location:** Hutchinson KS. **Other U.S. locations:** TX. **Parent company:** Collins Industries. **Operations at this facility include:** Administration; Divisional Headquarters; Manufacturing; Sales; Service.

BANKING/SAVINGS AND LOANS

You can expect to find the following types of companies in this chapter:

Banks
Bank Holding Companies and Associations
Lending Firms/Financial Services Institutions

AMSOUTH BANK
70 North Baylen Street, Pensacola FL 32501. 850/444-1000. **Contact:** Sharon Hensel, Human Resources. **World Wide Web address:** http://www.amsouth.com. **Description:** A commercial bank. **Corporate headquarters location:** Birmingham AL. **Other U.S. locations:** GA; TN.

BANK OF AMERICA
13099 U.S. 41 SE, 3rd Floor, Fort Myers FL 33907. 800/299-2265. **Recorded jobline:** 800/587-5627. **Contact:** Human Resources Department. **World Wide Web address:** http://www.bankofamerica.com. **Description:** This location is a bank. Overall, Bank of America is a full-service banking and financial institution. The company operates through four business segments: Global Corporate and Investment Banking, Principal Investing and Asset Management, Commercial Banking, and Consumer Banking. **Corporate headquarters location:** Charlotte NC. **Other U.S. locations:** Nationwide.

BANK OF AMERICA
50 North Laura Street, Jacksonville FL 32202. 904/791-7720. **Recorded jobline:** 800/587-5627. **Contact:** Human Resources. **World Wide Web address:** http://www.bankofamerica.com. **Description:** This location is a bank. Overall, Bank of America is a full-service banking and financial institution. The company operates through four business segments: Global Corporate and Investment Banking, Principal Investing and Asset Management, Commercial Banking, and Consumer Banking. **Corporate headquarters location:** Charlotte NC. **Other U.S. locations:** Nationwide.

BANKATLANTIC
1750 East Sunrise Boulevard, Fort Lauderdale FL 33304. 954/760-5480. **Fax:** 954/760-5489. **Recorded jobline:** 954/760-5550. **Contact:** Human Resources Department. **World Wide Web address:** http://www.bankatlantic.com. **Description:** A federal savings and loan bank. **Common positions include:** Accountant/Auditor; Branch Manager; Customer Service Representative; Securities Sales Representative. **Corporate headquarters location:** This location. **Parent company:** BankAtlantic Financial Corporation. **Listed on:** NASDAQ. **Stock exchange symbol:** BANCH. **Number of employees at this location:** 640.

CB RICHARD ELLIS
SUNTRUST
777 Brickell Avenue, Suite 1000, Miami FL 33131. 305/374-1000. **Fax:** 305/381-6462. **Contact:** Human Resources. **World Wide Web address:** http://www.cbre.com. **Description:** A real estate services company offering property sales and leasing, property and facility management, mortgage banking, and investment management services. **Corporate headquarters location:** Los Angeles CA. **Other U.S. locations:** Nationwide. **Listed on:** New York Stock Exchange. **Stock exchange symbol:** CBG. **Number of employees worldwide:** 9,000.

FIDELITY FEDERAL BANK & TRUST
205 Datura Street, West Palm Beach FL 33401. 561/659-9900. **Fax:** 561/659-9992. **Contact:** Human Resources. **World Wide Web address:** http://www.fidelityfederal.com. **Description:** A savings bank. Founded in 1952. **NOTE:** Entry-level positions and part-time jobs are offered. **Company slogan:** Count on us! **Common positions include:** Assistant Manager; Bank Teller; Branch Manager; Financial Services Sales Representative; Management Trainee; Sales Representative. **Corporate headquarters location:** This location. **Annual sales/revenues:** More than $100 million. **Number of employees at this location:** 410.

FIRST UNION NATIONAL BANK OF FLORIDA
1000 Tyrone Boulevard, Saint Petersburg FL 33710. 727/892-7441. **Contact:** Human Resources Department. **World Wide Web address:** http://www.firstunion.com. **Description:** A full-service commercial bank providing corporate and consumer services. First Union National Bank of Florida operates over 500 offices. **Parent company:** Wachovia First Union Corporation is one of the nation's largest bank holding companies with subsidiaries operating over 1,330 full-service bank branches in the south Atlantic states. These subsidiaries provide retail banking, retail investment, and commercial banking services. First Union Corporation provides other financial services including mortgage banking, home equity lending, leasing, insurance, and securities brokerage services from more than 220 branch locations. The company also operates one of the nation's largest ATM networks. **Listed on:** New York Stock Exchange. **Stock exchange symbol:** WB. **Number of employees nationwide:** 32,000.

FIRST UNION NATIONAL BANK OF FLORIDA
203 Avenue A NW, Winter Haven FL 33881. 863/291-6630. **Contact:** Human Resources Department. **World Wide Web**

address: http://www.firstunion.com. **Description:** A full-service commercial bank providing corporate and consumer services. First Union National Bank of Florida operates over 500 offices. **Parent company:** Wachovia First Union Corporation is one of the nation's largest bank holding companies with subsidiaries operating over 1,330 full-service bank branches in the south Atlantic states. These subsidiaries provide retail banking, retail investment, and commercial banking services. First Union Corporation provides other financial services including mortgage banking, home equity lending, leasing, insurance, and securities brokerage services from more than 220 branch locations. The company also operates one of the nation's largest ATM networks. **Listed on:** New York Stock Exchange. **Stock exchange symbol:** WB. **Number of employees at this location:** 400. **Number of employees nationwide:** 32,000.

FIRST UNION NATIONAL BANK OF FLORIDA
225 Water Street, Jacksonville FL 32202. 904/489-4000. **Contact:** Human Resources Department. **World Wide Web address:** http://www.firstunion.com. **Description:** A full-service commercial bank that operates over 500 offices. **Parent company:** Wachovia First Union Corporation is one of the nation's largest bank holding companies with subsidiaries operating over 1,330 full-service bank branches in the south Atlantic states. These subsidiaries provide retail banking, retail investment, and commercial banking services. First Union Corporation provides other financial services including mortgage banking, home equity lending, leasing, insurance, and securities brokerage services from more than 220 branch locations. The company also operates one of the nation's largest ATM networks. **Listed on:** New York Stock Exchange. **Stock exchange symbol:** WB. **Number of employees nationwide:** 32,000.

REGIONS BANK
P.O. Drawer 608, Milton FL 32572-0608. 850/623-3846. **Contact:** Human Resources Department. **World Wide Web address:** http://www.regionsbank.com. **Description:** A savings and loan bank. **Parent company:** Great Western Holding Company. **Listed on:** NASDAQ. **Stock exchange symbol:** RGBK.

SOUTHTRUST BANK
P.O. Box 7219, Jacksonville FL 32238-0219. 904/798-6300. **Contact:** Personnel. **E-mail address:** info@southtrust.com. **World Wide Web address:** http://www.southtrust.com. **Description:** This location is the main branch for the

Jacksonville area. Overall, SouthTrust Bank operates through 700 offices in the Southeast. **Corporate headquarters location:** Birmingham AL. **Other U.S. locations:** AL; GA; MS; NC; SC; TN; TX; VA. **Subsidiaries include:** South Trust Securities, Inc; SouthTrust Mortgage Corporation; SouthTrust Insurance, Inc. **Parent company:** SouthTrust Corporation. **Listed on:** NASDAQ. **Stock exchange symbol:** SOTR. **Annual sales/revenues:** More than $100 million. **Number of employees nationwide:** 13,000.

SUNTRUST BANK, GULF COAST, N.A.
P.O. Box 2138, Sarasota FL 34230. 941/951-3011. **Contact:** Human Resources Department. **World Wide Web address:** http://www.suntrust.com. **Description:** A full-service commercial bank. **Common positions include:** Accountant/Auditor; Advertising Clerk; Branch Manager; Department Manager; Human Resources Manager; Public Relations Specialist; Purchasing Agent/Manager; Services Sales Representative; Underwriter/Assistant Underwriter. **Corporate headquarters location:** Atlanta GA. **Other area locations:** Orlando FL; Miami FL; Tampa FL. **Other U.S. locations:** AL; DC; GA; MD; TN; VA. **Parent company:** SunTrust Banks, Inc. is a financial services company with three principal subsidiaries: SunTrust Banks of Florida, Inc.; SunTrust Banks of Georgia, Inc.; and SunTrust Banks of Tennessee, Inc. Together, these subsidiaries operate more than 1,100 full-service banking offices. The company's primary businesses include traditional deposit and credit services as well as trust and investment services. Additionally, SunTrust Banks, Inc. provides corporate finance, mortgage banking, factoring, credit card, discount brokerage, credit-related insurance, data processing, and information services. **Listed on:** New York Stock Exchange. **Stock exchange symbol:** STI. **President/CEO:** L. Phillip Humann.

SUNTRUST BANK, MIAMI, N.A.
777 Brickell Avenue, Miami FL 33131. 305/591-6000. **Fax:** 305/579-7217. **Contact:** Human Resources. **World Wide Web address:** http://www.suntrust.com. **Description:** A full-service commercial bank. **Corporate headquarters location:** Atlanta GA. **Other area locations:** Orlando FL; Sarasota FL; Tampa FL. **Other U.S. locations:** AL; DC; GA; MD; TN; VA. **Parent company:** SunTrust Banks, Inc. is a financial services company with three principal subsidiaries: SunTrust Banks of Florida, Inc.; SunTrust Banks of Georgia, Inc.; and SunTrust Banks of Tennessee, Inc. Together, these subsidiaries operate more than 1,100 full-service banking offices. The company's primary

businesses include traditional deposit and credit services as well as trust and investment services. Additionally, SunTrust Banks, Inc. provides corporate finance, mortgage banking, factoring, credit card, discount brokerage, credit-related insurance, data processing, and information services. **Listed on:** New York Stock Exchange. **Stock exchange symbol:** STI. **President/CEO:** L. Phillip Humann.

SUNTRUST BANK, TAMPA BAY, N.A.
401 East Jackson Street, 10th Floor, Tampa FL 33602. 813/224-2121. **Contact:** Human Resources Department. **World Wide Web address:** http://www.suntrust.com. **Description:** A full-service commercial bank. **Corporate headquarters location:** Atlanta GA. **Other area locations:** Orlando FL; Miami FL; Orlando FL; Sarasota FL. **Other U.S. locations:** AL; DC; GA; MD; TN; VA. **Parent company:** SunTrust Banks, Inc. is a financial services company with three principal subsidiaries: SunTrust Banks of Florida, Inc., SunTrust Banks of Georgia, Inc., and SunTrust Banks of Tennessee, Inc. Together, these subsidiaries operate more than 1,100 full-service banking offices. The company's primary businesses include traditional deposit and credit services as well as trust and investment services. Additionally, SunTrust Banks, Inc. provides corporate finance, mortgage banking, factoring, credit card, discount brokerage, credit-related insurance, data processing, and information services. **Listed on:** New York Stock Exchange. **Stock exchange symbol:** STI. **President/CEO:** L. Phillip Humann.

SUNTRUST BANK, CENTRAL FLORIDA, N.A.
P.O. Box 3833, Orlando FL 32802. 407/237-4216. **Contact:** Peggy Jackson, Human Resources Representative. **World Wide Web address:** http://www.suntrust.com. **Description:** A bank holding company. **Corporate headquarters location:** Atlanta GA. **Other area locations:** Orlando FL; Miami FL; Sarasota FL; Tampa FL. **Other U.S. locations:** AL; DC; GA; MD; TN; VA. **Parent company:** SunTrust Banks, Inc. is a financial services company with three principal subsidiaries: SunTrust Banks of Florida, Inc.; SunTrust Banks of Georgia, Inc.; and SunTrust Banks of Tennessee, Inc. Together, these subsidiaries operate more than 1,100 full-service banking offices. The company's primary businesses include traditional deposit and credit services as well as trust and investment services. Additionally, SunTrust Banks, Inc. provides corporate finance, mortgage banking, factoring, credit card, discount brokerage, credit-related insurance, data processing, and information services

Listed on: New York Stock Exchange. **Stock exchange symbol:** STI. **President/CEO:** L. Phillip Humann.

U.S. FEDERAL RESERVE BANK OF FLORIDA
P.O. Box 520847, Miami FL 33152. 305/471-6434. **Physical address:** 9100 NW 36th Street, Miami FL 33178. **Contact:** Amy Ginsberg, Human Resources. **World Wide Web address:** http://www.frbatlanta.org. **Description:** One of 12 regional Federal Reserve banks that, along with the Federal Reserve Board of Governors (Washington DC) and the Federal Open Market Committee (FOMC), form the Federal Reserve System, the central bank of the U.S. federal government. As the nation's central bank, the Federal Reserve is charged with three major responsibilities: monetary policy, banking supervision and regulation, and processing payments.

WACHOVIA BANK
450 South Australian Avenue, West Palm Beach FL 33401. 561/802-5704. **Recorded jobline:** 800/732-4754. **Contact:** Human Resources Department. **World Wide Web address:** http://www.wachovia.com. **Description:** This branch is a savings and mortgage bank. **Listed on:** NASDAQ. **Stock exchange symbol:** WB. **Annual sales/revenues:** More than $100 million.

BIOTECHNOLOGY, PHARMACEUTICALS, AND SCIENTIFIC R&D

You can expect to find the following types of companies in this chapter:

Clinical Labs
Lab Equipment Manufacturers
Pharmaceutical Manufacturers and Distributors

ABC RESEARCH CORPORATION
3437 SW 24th Avenue, Gainesville FL 32607. 352/372-0436.
Contact: Human Resources Department. **World Wide Web
address:** http://www.abcr.com. **Description:** A laboratory
specializing in food and water analysis.

BECKMAN COULTER, INC.
P.O. Box 169015, Miami FL 33116-9015. 305/380-3800. **Fax:**
305/380-3689. **Contact:** Human Resources. **World Wide Web
address:** http://www.beckmancoulter.com. **Description:** Sells
and services a diverse range of scientific instruments, reagents,
and related equipment. Products include DNA synthesizers,
robotic workstations, centrifuges, electrophoresis systems,
detection and measurement equipment, data processing
software, and specialty chemical and automated general
chemical systems. Many of the company's products are used in
research and development and diagnostic analysis. **Common
positions include:** Accountant/Auditor; Biological Scientist;
Computer Programmer; Designer; Electrical/Electronics
Engineer; Financial Analyst; Software Engineer; Systems
Analyst; Technical Writer/Editor. **Corporate headquarters
location:** Fullerton CA.

IVAX CORPORATION
4400 Biscayne Boulevard, Miami FL 33137. 305/575-6000.
Contact: Human Resources. **World Wide Web address:**
http://www.ivax.com. **Description:** IVAX Corporation is a
holding company with subsidiaries involved in specialty
chemicals, pharmaceuticals, personal care products, and
medical diagnostics. The company's principal business is the
research, development, manufacture, marketing, and
distribution of health care products. Brand name products,
marketed under the Baker Norton trade name, include the
urological medications Bicitra, Polycitra, Polycitra-K, Polycitra-
LC, Neutra-Phos, Neutra-Phos-K, Prohim, Urotrol, Lubraseptic
Jelly, and Pro-Banthine; and cardiovascular medicines
Cordilox, Triam-Co, Amil-Co, Spiro-Co, and Fru-Co. Other
drugs include Proglycem, used to treat hyperinsulinism;
Serenance, a neuroleptic used for psychiatric disorders; the
respiratory medications Cromogen, Salamol, and Beclazone
metered dose inhalers; the Steri-Nebs line of nebulization
products; and Eye-Crom and Glaucol. IVAX also markets
generic drugs. Through DVM Pharmaceuticals, Inc., IVAX
formulates, packages, and distributes veterinary products
including DermCaps, a daily dietary supplement; a line of
topical therapeutics including ChlorhexiDerm Flush and
shampoo, OxyDex shampoo and gel, HyLyt shampoo and

rinse, and Relief shampoo, rinse, and spray; two groups of optic products known as Clear and OtiCalm; the DuraKyl and SynerKyl line of ectoparasiticidals; and the wound dressing BioDres. **Corporate headquarters location:** This location. **Listed on:** American Stock Exchange. **Stock exchange symbol:** IVX. **Number of employees nationwide:** 2,910.

IVAX PHARMACEUTICALS
4400 Biscayne Boulevard, Miami FL 33137. 305/575-6000. **Toll-free phone:** 800/327-4114. **Contact:** Personnel. **World Wide Web address:** http://www.ivaxpharmaceuticals.com. **Description:** IVAX Pharmaceuticals manufactures generic pharmaceuticals. **Parent company:** IVAX Corporation. **Listed on:** American Stock Exchange. **Stock exchange symbol:** IVX.

THE MONTICELLO COMPANY
1604 Stockton Street, Jacksonville FL 32204. 904/384-3666. **Contact:** Human Resources. **World Wide Web address:** http://www.monticellocompanies.com. **Description:** This location provides administrative services. Overall, The Monticello Company manufactures and sells over-the-counter pharmaceuticals produced at the company's plant in Mexico. **Corporate headquarters location:** This location. **Parent company:** Monticello Companies.

NORTH AMERICAN BIOLOGICALS, INC.
5800 Park of Commerce Boulevard NW, Boca Raton FL 33487. 561/989-5800x5511. **Fax:** 561/989-5874. **Contact:** Darron Davis, Human Resources Manager. **Description:** Provides plasma and plasma-based products that aid in the prevention and treatment of diseases and disorders. **Corporate headquarters location:** This location. **Listed on:** NASDAQ. **Stock exchange symbol:** NBIO.

NOVEN PHARMACEUTICALS, INC.
11960 SW 144th Street, Miami FL 33186. 305/253-5099. **Fax:** 305/251-1887. **Contact:** Sandra Miller, Human Resources. **World Wide Web address:** http://www.noven.com. **Description:** Develops and manufactures transdermal and transmucosal drug delivery systems. **Listed on:** NASDAQ. **Stock exchange symbol:** NOVN.

PHARMERICA
PHARMACY MANAGEMENT SERVICES, INC. (PMSI)
175 Kelsey Lane, Tampa FL 33619. 813/626-7788. **Contact:** Human Resources Department. **World Wide Web address:** http://www.pharmerica.com. **Description:** A supplier of pharmaceuticals and related products to long-term care facilities, hospitals, and assisted living communities. PharMerica also provides nurse consultant services, infusion therapy and training, medical records consulting, and educational programs. PMSI (also at this location) offers medical equipment and supplies through mail-order delivery. **Corporate headquarters location:** This location. **Listed on:** New York Stock Exchange. **Stock exchange symbol:** ABC.

QUEST DIAGNOSTICS INCORPORATED
4225 East Fowler Avenue, Tampa FL 33617. 813/972-7100. **Toll-free phone:** 800/282-6613. **Fax:** 813/972-3986. **Contact:** Human Resources Department. **World Wide Web address:** http://www.questdiagnostics.com. **Description:** One of the largest clinical laboratories in North America, providing a broad range of clinical laboratory services to health care clients that include physicians, hospitals, clinics, dialysis centers, pharmaceutical companies, and corporations. The company offers and performs tests on blood, urine, and other bodily fluids and tissues to provide information for health and well-being. Founded in 1969. **Other U.S. locations:** Nationwide. **Listed on:** New York Stock Exchange. **Stock exchange symbol:** DGX. **Annual revenues:** More than $100 million.

QUEST DIAGNOSTICS INCORPORATED
1605 East Plaza Drive, Tallahassee FL 32308. **Contact:** Human Resources Department. **World Wide Web address:** http://www.questdiagnostics.com. **Description:** This location is a patient service center. Overall Quest Diagnostics is one of the largest clinical laboratories in North America, providing a broad range of clinical laboratory services to health care clients that include physicians, hospitals, clinics, dialysis centers, pharmaceutical companies, and corporations. The company offers and performs tests on blood, urine, and other bodily fluids and tissues to provide information for health and well-being. **Other U.S. locations:** Nationwide. **Listed on:** New York Stock Exchange. **Stock exchange symbol:** DGX. **Annual revenues:** More than $100 million.

RESEARCH TRIANGLE INSTITUTE (RTI)
3000 North Atlantic Avenue, Suite 108, Cocoa Beach FL 32931. 321/799-1607. **Contact:** Human Resources. **World**

Wide Web address: http://www.rti.org. **Description:** A nonprofit, independent research organization involved in many scientific fields. Clients include federal, state, and local governments, industrial associations, and public service agencies. The institute was created as a separately operated entity by the joint action of North Carolina State University, Duke University, and the University of North Carolina at Chapel Hill. RTI responds to national priorities in health, the environment, advanced technology, and social policy with contract research for the U.S. government including applications in statistics, social sciences, chemistry, life sciences, environmental sciences, engineering, and electronics. The institute operates a 180-acre campus in the center of Research Triangle Park NC, which includes laboratory and office facilities for all technical programs. **Corporate headquarters location:** Research Triangle Park NC. **Other U.S. locations:** Nationwide. **International locations:** England; Indonesia; South Africa. **Number of employees nationwide:** 1,950.

REXALL SHOWCASE INTERNATIONAL
853 Broken Sound Parkway NW, Boca Raton FL 33487. 801/226-2224. **Contact:** Human Resources. **World Wide Web address:** http://www.rexallshowcase.com. **Description:** Manufactures and distributes vitamins in both retail and wholesale markets. **Parent Company:** Unicity Network.

SCHERING-PLOUGH
13900 NW 57th Court, Miami FL 33014. 305/698-4600. **Contact:** Human Resources. **World Wide Web address:** http://www.schering-plough.com. **Description:** Schering-Plough Corporation is engaged in the discovery, development, manufacture, marketing, and testing of pharmaceutical and consumer products. Pharmaceutical products include prescription drugs, over-the-counter medicines, eye care products, and animal health products promoted to the medical and allied health professions. The consumer products group consists of proprietary medicines, toiletries, cosmetics, foot care, and sun care products marketed directly to the public. Products include Coricidin cough and cold medicines and Maybelline beauty products. **Common positions include:** Blue-Collar Worker Supervisor; Chemist; Operations/Production Manager; Quality Control Supervisor. **Listed on:** New York Stock Exchange. **Stock exchange symbol:** SGP.

SCIENTIFIC INSTRUMENTS, INC.
4400 West Tiffany Drive, West Palm Beach FL 33407.
561/881-8500. **Contact:** Leigh Ann Capers, Personnel. **World Wide Web address:** http://www.scientificinstruments.com.
Description: Manufactures temperature-sensing and controlling instruments as well as other laboratory instruments.

BUSINESS SERVICES AND NON-SCIENTIFIC RESEARCH

You can expect to find the following types of companies in this chapter:

Adjustment and Collection Services
Cleaning, Maintenance, and Pest Control Services
Credit Reporting
Detective, Guard, and Armored Car Services
Miscellaneous Equipment Rental and Leasing
Secretarial and Court Reporting Services

ADP TOTAL SOURCE
10200 Sunset Drive, Miami FL 33173. 561/615-7478. **Toll-free phone:** 800/447-3237. **Contact:** Human Resources. **World Wide Web address:** http://www.adptotalsource.com. **Description:** Provides benefits, payroll, and related human resources services.

ARAMARK CORPORATION
1301 Riverplace Boulevard, Suite C-20, Jacksonville FL 32207. 904/396-5037. **Contact:** Human Resources. **World Wide Web address:** http://www.aramark.com. **Description:** This location is a cafeteria. Overall, ARAMARK is one of the world's leading providers of managed services. The company operates in all 50 states and 10 foreign countries, offering a broad range of services to businesses of all sizes including many *Fortune* 500 companies and thousands of universities, hospitals, and municipal, state, and federal government facilities. ARAMARK's businesses include Food, Leisure, and Support Services including Campus Dining Services, School Nutrition Services, Leisure Services, Business Dining Services, International Services, Healthcare Support Services, Conference Center Management, and Refreshment Services; Facility Services; Correctional Services; Industrial Services; Uniform Services, which includes Wearguard, a direct marketer of work clothing; Health and Education Services including Spectrum Healthcare Services and Children's World Learning Centers; and Book and Magazine Services. **Corporate headquarters location:** Philadelphia PA. **Number of employees nationwide:** 150,000. **Listed on:** New York Stock Exchange. **Stock exchange symbol:** RMG.

ARMOR HOLDINGS, INC.
13386 International Parkway, Jacksonville FL 32218. 904/741-5400. **Contact:** Human Resources Department. **World Wide Web address:** http://www.armorholdings.com. **Description:** Develops, manufactures, and markets security products including body armor to corporate and government clients worldwide. Armor Holdings, Inc. also provides security solutions such as risk analysis and electronic surveillance. **Corporate headquarters location:** This location. **Other U.S. locations:** Nationwide. **International locations:** Worldwide. **Listed on:** New York Stock Exchange. **Stock exchange symbol:** AH. **Annual sales/revenues:** More than $100 million.

FIRST AMERICAN REAL ESTATE SOLUTIONS
1800 NW 66th Avenue, Fort Lauderdale FL 33313. 954/792-2000. **Contact:** Human Resources. **World Wide Web address:**

http://www.firstamres.com. **Description:** Maintains credit reports and provides information services for the real estate industry. **NOTE:** Please send resumes to: Human Resources, 5601 East La Palma Avenue, Anaheim CA 92802. **Common positions include:** Accountant/Auditor; Adjuster; Assistant Manager; Bindery Worker; Blue-Collar Worker Supervisor; Computer Operator; Computer Programmer; Construction and Building Inspector; Construction Trade Worker; Customer Service Representative; Department Manager; Draftsperson; Electrical/Electronics Engineer; Electrician; General Manager; Graphic Artist; Human Resources Manager; Industrial Engineer; Machinist; Market Research Analyst; Marketing Manager; Marketing Specialist; Mechanical Engineer; Operations/Production Manager; Printing Press Operator; Receptionist; Services Sales Representative; Software Engineer; Stock Clerk; Surveyor; Systems Analyst; Truck Driver; Typist/Word Processor. **Operations at this facility include:** Administration; Manufacturing; Regional Headquarters; Research and Development; Sales; Service. **Number of employees at this location:** 320. **Number of employees nationwide:** 1,200.

G&K SERVICES, INC.
14720 NW 24th Court, Opa Locka FL 33054. **Fax:** 305/688-1179. **Contact:** Human Resources. **World Wide Web address:** http://www.gkservices.com. **Description:** Provides uniform services to more than 85,000 businesses including those in the automotive, high-tech, maintenance/repair, and manufacturing industries. G&K's services include designing uniform programs that fit customers' needs; helping customers select a company logo, garment style, and colors; and introducing the uniform program to customers' employees. Products include executive wear, industrial wear, flame-resistant garments, clean room uniforms, treated dust mops, linens, and wiping towels. G&K also provides delivery of clean garments on a weekly basis. **Common positions include:** Administrative Assistant; Administrative Manager; Clerical Supervisor; Clerk; Engineering Technician; Office Manager; Plant Manager; Production Technician; Sales Manager; Sales Representative; Service Manager. **Other U.S. locations:** Nationwide. **International locations:** Canada. **Listed on:** NASDAQ. **Stock exchange symbol:** GKSRA. **Number of employees nationwide:** 8,000.

OSI COLLECTION SERVICES
5022 Gate Parkway North, Suite 204, Jacksonville FL 32256. 904/380-2600. **Contact:** Human Resources. **Description:** A

collection agency. **Corporate headquarters location:** This location.

PALM COAST DATA LTD.
11 Commerce Boulevard, Palm Coast FL 32164. 386/445-4662. **Contact:** Lynn Lawson, Director of Human Resources. **World Wide Web address:** http://www.palmcoastd.com. **Description:** Manages subscription lists for publishing companies. Founded in 1984. **Parent company:** DIMAC Direct.

SPHERION
2050 Spectrum Boulevard, Fort Lauderdale FL 33309. 954/938-7600. **Contact:** Human Resources. **World Wide Web address:** http://www.spherion.com. **Description:** This location houses administrative offices only. Overall, Spherion is an executive search firm that offers professional recruiting, testing, and assessment services. **Corporate headquarters location:** This location. **Other U.S. locations:** Nationwide. **International locations:** Worldwide. **Listed on:** New York Stock Exchange. **Stock exchange symbol:** SFN. **Number of employees worldwide:** 500,000.

TEAM STAFF RX
1901 Ulmerton Road, Suite 450, Clearwater FL 33762. 727/461-9642. **Toll-free phone:** 800/345-9642. **Fax:** 727/299-9065. **Contact:** Human Resources. **World Wide Web address:** http://www.teamstaffrx.com. **Description:** Team Staff Rx offers a full line of employer services including payroll processing, permanent and temporary placement of personnel, in-house hardware and software systems, outsourcing, facility management, employee leasing, and insurance services. **Listed on:** NASDAQ. **Stock exchange symbol:** TSTF. **Number of employees nationwide:** 20,000.

THE WACKENHUT CORPORATION
3974 Woodcock Drive, Suite 100, Jacksonville FL 32207. 904/398-1640. **Toll-free phone:** 800/254-4411. **Fax:** 904/396-6716. **Contact:** Human Resources. **World Wide Web address:** http://www.wackenhut.com. **Description:** Provides physical security services, correction services, and related products to businesses, governments, and individuals from more than 150 domestic and foreign offices. Specific services include security guard services; corrections staffing; private investigative services; the assembly and sale of electronic security equipment and systems; the training of security guards and fire and crash rescue personnel; providing fire protection and

emergency ambulance service to municipalities; security consulting; planning, designing, and implementing integrated security systems; and providing specialized services to the nuclear power industry. Wackenhut has 90 offices located in most major United States cities. **Common positions include:** Security Officer. **Office hours:** Monday - Friday, 8:30 a.m. - 5:00 p.m. **Corporate headquarters location:** Palm Beach Gardens FL. **International locations:** Worldwide. **Subsidiaries include:** Wackenhut Corrections, Inc.; Wackenhut International. **Listed on:** New York Stock Exchange. **Stock exchange symbol:** WAK. **Number of employees nationwide:** 40,000.

THE WACKENHUT CORPORATION
4200 Wackenhut Drive, Building 100, Palm Beach Gardens FL 33410. 561/622-5656. **Contact:** Human Resources. **World Wide Web address:** http://www.wackenhut.com. **Description:** Provides physical security services, correction services, and related products to businesses, governments, and individuals from more than 150 domestic and foreign offices. Specific services include security guard services; corrections staffing; private investigative services; the assembly and sale of electronic security equipment and systems; the training of security guards and fire and crash rescue personnel; providing fire protection and emergency ambulance service to municipalities; security consulting; planning, designing, and implementing integrated security systems; and providing specialized services to the nuclear power industry. Wackenhut has 90 offices located in major cities throughout the United States. **Common positions include:** Accountant/Auditor; Administrative Manager; Branch Manager; Clerical Supervisor; Computer Programmer; Customer Service Representative; General Manager; Human Resources Manager; Management Trainee; Services Sales Representative; Systems Analyst. **Corporate headquarters location:** This location. **Other U.S. locations:** Nationwide. **Subsidiaries include:** Wackenhut Corrections, Inc.; Wackenhut International. **Operations at this facility include:** Administration; Service. **Listed on:** New York Stock Exchange. **Stock exchange symbol:** WAK. **Number of employees at this location:** 275. **Number of employees nationwide:** 40,000.

CHARITIES AND SOCIAL SERVICES

You can expect to find the following types of organizations in this chapter:

Social and Human Service Agencies
Job Training and Vocational Rehabilitation Services
Nonprofit Organizations

AMERICAN CANCER SOCIETY
3901 NW 79th Avenue, Suite 224, Miami FL 33166. 305/594-4363. **Contact:** Human Resources Department. **World Wide Web address:** http://www.cancer.org. **Description:** A nationwide, community-based, nonprofit, voluntary health organization dedicated to eliminating cancer as a major health problem by funding cancer research and public education. The society helps patients directly by offering services including transportation to treatment and rehabilitation services.

AMERICAN RED CROSS
745 D Beal Parkway NW, Suite 11, Fort Walton Beach FL 32547. 850/314-0316. **Contact:** Manager. **World Wide Web address:** http://www.redcross.org. **Description:** A humanitarian organization that aids disaster victims, gathers blood for crisis distribution, trains individuals to respond to emergencies, educates individuals on various diseases, and raises funds for other charitable establishments. **Corporate headquarters location:** Washington DC. **Other U.S. locations:** Nationwide.

BAYFRONT YMCA
750 West Retta Esplanade, Punta Gorda FL 33950. 941/637-0797. **Contact:** Human Resources Department. **Description:** Offers a variety of classes in aerobics, yoga, and tai chi and social events including dances and bridge. Overall, the YMCA is one of the nation's largest and most comprehensive service organizations. The YMCA provides health and fitness programs; promotes social and personal development; offers sports and recreation; implements education and career development programs; and organizes camps and conferences for individuals of all ages and backgrounds. **Corporate headquarters location:** Chicago IL. **Other U.S. locations:** Nationwide.

BRADENTON YMCA
3805 59th Street West, Bradenton FL 34209. 941/792-7484. **Contact:** Human Resources Department. **E-mail address:** manateeymca@aol.com. **Description:** Offers a variety of aerobics and workout classes. Bradenton YMCA's facilities include an indoor heated pool and a gym. **Corporate headquarters location:** Chicago IL. **Other U.S. locations:** Nationwide.

CATHEDRAL RESIDENCES
601 North Newnan Street, Jacksonville FL 32202. 904/798-5353. **Contact:** Human Resources. **Description:** A nonprofit organization that focuses on the needs of elderly citizens.

Cathedral Foundation operates independent living apartments and a nursing home, and provides various community services.

ST. AUGUSTINE FAMILY YMCA
500 Pope Road, St. Augustine FL 32084. 904/471-9622. **Contact:** Michelle Cooligan, Program Director. **World Wide Web address:** http://www.ymcaffc.org. **Description:** One of the nation's largest and most comprehensive service organizations. The YMCA provides health and fitness, social and personal development, sports and recreation, education and career development, and camps and conferences to children, youths, adults, the elderly, families, the disabled, refugees and foreign nationals, YMCA residents, and community residents through a broad range of specific programs. **Corporate headquarters location:** Chicago IL. **Other U.S. locations:** Nationwide.

ST. PETERSBURG YMCA
70 35th Street South Petersburg, FL 33711. 727/895-9622. **Contact:** Human Resources. **Description:** One of the nation's largest and most comprehensive service organizations. The YMCA provides health and fitness, social and personal development, sports and recreation, education and career development, and camps and conferences to children, youths, adults, the elderly, families, the disabled, refugees and foreign nationals, YMCA residents, and community residents through a broad range of specific programs. **Corporate headquarters location:** Chicago IL. **Other U.S. locations:** Nationwide.

CHEMICALS/RUBBER AND PLASTICS

You can expect to find the following types of companies in this chapter:

Adhesives, Detergents, Inks, Paints, Soaps, Varnishes
Agricultural Chemicals and Fertilizers
Carbon and Graphite Products
Chemical Engineering Firms
Industrial Gases

ARIZONA CHEMICAL
P.O. Box 947, 345 Kenney Mill Road, Port St. Joe FL 32456. 850/229-8271. **Contact:** Human Resources Department. **E-mail address:** info.arizona@paper.com. **World Wide Web address:** http://www.arizona-chemical.com. **Description:** Produces chemical products by upgrading raw materials purchased from paper manufacturing companies. Arizona Chemical's products are used by other companies to manufacture glue, gum, perfume, and coatings. **NOTE:** Interested jobseekers should send resumes to ArizonaChem, Human Resources Department, P.O. Box 59447, Panama City FL 32412-0447. **Corporate headquarters location:** Jacksonville FL.

CF INDUSTRIES, INC./PLANT CITY
P.O. Drawer L, Plant City FL 33564. 813/782-1591. **Contact:** Harry Crosby, Human Resources Department. **World Wide Web address:** http://www.cfindustries.com. **Description:** This location manufactures phosphates for use in fertilizers.

CF INDUSTRIES, INC./TAMPA
2520 Guy Verger Boulevard, Tampa FL 33605. 813/247-5531. **Contact:** Ron Bigelow, Human Resources Department. **World Wide Web address:** http://www.cfindustries.com. **Description:** This location provides administrative and warehousing Human Resources. services to other locations of the company. Overall, CF Industries manufactures phosphates for use in fertilizers.

CARGILL FERTILIZER
8813 U.S. Highway 41 South, Riverview FL 33569-4866. 813/677-9111. **Contact:** Personnel. **World Wide Web address:** http://www.cargill.com/aghorizons/products/fert. **Description:** A chemical company that specializes in the production of phosphates for use in fertilizer.

DAYCO PRODUCTS
3100 SE Maricamp Road, Ocala FL 34471. 352/732-6191. **Contact:** Human Resources. **World Wide Web address:** http://www.dayco.com. **Description:** This facility manufactures braided and woven molded rubber hose. Overall, Dayco Products is a worldwide manufacturer and distributor of a wide range of highly-engineered rubber and plastic products. The company's principal markets include the agricultural, automotive, construction, energy, printing, mining, textile, and transportation industries.

HERCULES, INC.
7510 Baymeadows Way, Jacksonville FL 32256. 904/733-7110. **Contact:** Human Resources. **World Wide Web address:** http://www.herc.com. **Description:** Develops, sells, and services specialty process chemicals for the pulp and paper industry. **Common positions include:** Chemical Engineer; Chemist; Computer Programmer; Manufacturer's/Wholesaler's Sales Rep. **Special programs:** Internships. **Operations at this facility include:** Administration; Divisional Headquarters; Research and Development; Sales; Service. **Listed on:** New York Stock Exchange. **Stock exchange symbol:** HPC.

INTERNATIONAL FLAVORS & FRAGRANCES (IFF)
2051 North Lane Avenue, Jacksonville FL 32254. 904/783-2180. **Contact:** Human Resources Department. **World Wide Web address:** http://www.iff.com. **Description:** A manufacturer and distributor of flavors, fragrances, and aroma chemicals. **Common positions include:** Accountant/Auditor; Blue-Collar Worker Supervisor; Buyer; Chemical Engineer; Chemist; Computer Programmer; Customer Service Representative; Electrical/Electronics Engineer; Human Resources Manager; Manufacturer's/Wholesaler's Sales Representative; Operations/Production Manager; Purchasing Agent/Manager. **Corporate headquarters location:** New York NY. **Operations at this facility include:** Administration; Manufacturing; Research and Development; Sales. **Listed on:** New York Stock Exchange. **Stock exchange symbol:** IFF.

McNEEL INTERNATIONAL CORPORATION
5401 West Kennedy Boulevard, Tampa FL 33609. 813/286-8680. **Contact:** Human Resources. **Description:** Manufactures rubber and plastic products. **Corporate headquarters location:** This location. **International locations:** Worldwide.

REICHHOLD CHEMICALS, INC.
P.O. Box 1433, Pensacola FL 32596-1433. 850/433-7621. **Contact:** Human Resources Department. **World Wide Web address:** http://www.reichhold.com. **Description:** A chemical plant that manufactures coating resins, epoxy, epoxy hardeners, acrylic, and copolymer resins. **Common positions include:** Accountant/Auditor; Blue-Collar Worker Supervisor; Buyer; Chemical Engineer; Chemist; Electrician; General Manager; Human Service Worker; Industrial Production Manager; Mechanical Engineer; Plant Manager; Purchasing Agent/Manager. **Corporate headquarters location:** Durham NC. **Operations at this facility include:** Manufacturing. **Listed on:** Privately held. **Number of employees at this location:** 85.

SECURITY PLASTICS INC.
14427 NW 60th Avenue, Miami Lakes FL 33014. 305/364-7700. **Contact:** Human Resources Department. **E-mail address:** hrmiami@securityplastics.com. **World Wide Web address:** http://www.securityplastics.com. **Description:** Manufactures plastic components for original equipment manufacturers. **Common positions include:** Accountant/Auditor; Administrator; Computer Programmer; Credit Manager; Customer Service Representative; Department Manager; Manufacturer's/Wholesaler's Sales Representative; Marketing Specialist; Mechanical Engineer; Operations/Production Manager; Plastics Engineer; Quality Control Supervisor. **Corporate headquarters location:** This location. **Other area locations:** St. Petersburg FL. **Other U.S. locations:** McAllen TX. **International locations:** Malaysia; Mexico. **Operations at this facility include:** Manufacturing.

U.S. AGRI-CHEMICALS CORPORATION
3225 State Road 630 West, Fort Meade FL 33841. 863/285-8121x231. **Fax:** 863/285-9654. **Contact:** Irene Dobson, Director of Human Resources. **Description:** Manufacturer and supplier of phosphate fertilizers for domestic and international wholesale markets. **Common positions include:** Accountant; Buyer; Chemist; Civil Engineer; Electrical/Electronics Engineer; Human Resources Manager; Mechanical Engineer; Operations/Production Manager; Public Relations Specialist; Purchasing Agent/Manager; Quality Control Supervisor; Systems Analyst; Transportation/Traffic Specialist. **Corporate headquarters location:** This location. **Parent company:** Sinochem. **Operations at this facility include:** Administration; Manufacturing; Regional Headquarters; Sales.

UNIROYAL TECHNOLOGY CORPORATION
2 North Tamiami Trail, Suite 900, Sarasota FL 34236. 941/361-2100. **Fax:** 813/612-4413. **Contact:** Robert Pyle. **E-mail address:** robert.pyle@uniroyalopto.com. **World Wide Web address:** http://www.uniroyaltech.com. **Description:** Manufactures naugahyde and a variety of plastic products including foam and molded plastics. **NOTE:** Send resumes to: Robert Pyle, Uniroyal Optoelectronics, 3401 Cragmont Drive, Sabel Industrial Park, Tampa FL 33619. **Listed on:** NASDAQ. **Stock exchange symbol:** UTCI. **CEO:** Howard Curd.

COMMUNICATIONS: TELECOMMUNICATIONS AND BROADCASTING

You can expect to find the following types of companies in this chapter:

Cable/Pay Television Services
Communications Equipment
Radio and Television Broadcasting Systems
Telephone, Telegraph, and other Message Communications

API MEDIA
100 Lakehart Drive, Suite 1500, Orlando FL 32832. 407/826-2350. **Fax:** 407/826-2367. **Contact:** Paul Read, Producer. **E-mail address:** api@ccci.org. **World Wide Web address:** http://www.ccci.org/api. **Description:** Produces videos for the different ministries of its parent company. API also edits two daily radio programs. Founded in 1951. **Common positions include:** Graphic Artist; Graphic Designer; Radio/TV Announcer/Broadcaster; Video Editor; Video Production Coordinator. **Parent company:** Campus Crusade for Christ International (CCCI). **President:** Dr. Bill Bright. **Number of employees at this location:** 10. **Number of employees nationwide:** 3,000. **Number of employees worldwide:** 14,000.

AEROTRON-REPCO SYSTEMS, INC.
4602 Parkway Commerce Boulevard, Orlando FL 32808. 407/856-1953. **Toll-free phone:** 800/950-5633. **Fax:** 407/856-1960. **Contact:** Ted McDonald, Human Resources Manager. **World Wide Web address:** http://www.aerotron-repco.com. **Description:** A manufacturer of communications equipment including wireless modems and hand-held radios. **Corporate headquarters location:** This location. **Listed on:** Privately held. **Number of employees at this location:** 55.

AMERICA II ELECTRONICS, INC.
2600 118th Avenue North, St. Petersburg FL 33716. 727/573-0900. **Contact:** Human Resources Department. **World Wide Web address:** http://www.americall.com. **Description:** A teleservice outsourcing communications provider that offers customer service and support, interoffice messaging, dispatching sales, and reception services. Founded in 1938.

DICTAPHONE CORPORATION
3984 Pepsi Cola Drive, Melbourne FL 32924. **Toll-free phone:** 888/483-6266. **Contact:** Human Resources Department. **World Wide Web address:** http://www.dictaphone.com. **Description:** A manufacturer of voice recording equipment. Founded in 1923. **NOTE:** Jobseekers should send resumes to: Dictaphone Corporation, 3191 Broadbridge Avenue, Stratford CT 06614-2559. **Common positions include:** Accountant; Buyer; Computer Programmer; Electrical/Electronics Engineer; Environmental Engineer; Human Resources Manager; Manufacturing Engineer; Production Manager; Purchasing Agent/Manager; Software Engineer; Technical Writer/Editor. **Corporate headquarters location:** Stratford CT. **Other U.S. locations:** Nationwide. **International locations:** Germany;

South America; Switzerland; United Kingdom. **Annual sales/revenues:** More than $100 million.

DYCOM INDUSTRIES, INC.
First Union Center, Suite 500, 4440 PGA Boulevard, Palm Beach Gardens FL 33410. 561/627-7171. **Contact:** Human Resources. **E-mail address:** info@dycomind.com. **World Wide Web address:** http://www.dycomind.com. **Description:** A holding company for subsidiaries that manufacture mobile phones and provide communication services. Founded in 1969. **Corporate headquarters location:** This location. **Other U.S. locations:** Nationwide. **Listed on:** New York Stock Exchange. **Stock exchange symbol:** DY. **Annual sales/revenues:** More than $100 million. **President/CEO:** Steven E. Nielsen. **Number of employees nationwide:** 6,000.

HARRIS CORPORATION
1025 West NASA Boulevard, Mail Stop 19, Melbourne FL 32919. 321/727-9207. **Toll-free phone:** 800/4HA-RRIS. **Contact:** Human Resources. **World Wide Web address:** http://www.harris.com. **Description:** A communications equipment company that provides broadcast, network, government, and wireless support products and systems. **NOTE:** Send resumes to: Harris Corporation, Resume Proccessing, P.O. Box 549238, Suite 107, Waltham MA 02454. **Common positions include:** Accountant/Auditor; Administrator; Attorney; Blue-Collar Worker Supervisor; Computer Programmer; Customer Service Representative; Department Manager; Editor; Electrical/Electronics Engineer; Financial Analyst; General Manager; Human Resources Manager; Industrial Engineer; Manufacturer's/Wholesaler's Sales Rep.; Marketing Specialist; Mechanical Engineer; Metallurgical Engineer; Operations/Production Manager; Public Relations Specialist; Purchasing Agent/Manager; Quality Control Supervisor; Reporter; Systems Analyst. **Corporate headquarters location:** This location. **International locations:** Worldwide. **Operations at this facility include:** Administration; Manufacturing; Research and Development; Sales; Service. **Listed on:** New York Stock Exchange. **Stock exchange symbol:** HRS. **President/CEO:** Phillip W. Farmer. **Number of employees worldwide:** 10,000.

HARRIS TECHNICAL SERVICES CORPORATION
1225 Evans Road, Melbourne FL 32904. 321/952-7550. **Toll-free phone:** 888/952-9468. **Fax:** 321/733-7570. **Contact:** Human Resources Department. **World Wide Web address:** http://www.harris.com. **Description:** Develops software

solutions for commercial and government applications. **NOTE:** Entry-level positions are offered. Send resumes to: Harris Corporation, Resume Proccessing, P.O. Box 549238, Suite 107, Waltham MA 02454. **Common positions include:** Accountant/Auditor; Attorney; Blue-Collar Worker Supervisor; Computer Programmer; Customer Service Representative; Department Manager; Editor; Electrical/Electronics Engineer; Financial Analyst; General Manager; Human Resources Manager; Industrial Engineer; Manufacturer's/Wholesaler's Sales Representative; Marketing Specialist; Mechanical Engineer; Metallurgical Engineer; Operations/Production Manager; Public Relations Specialist; Purchasing Agent/Manager; Quality Control Supervisor; Reporter; Systems Analyst. **Office hours:** Monday - Friday, 8:00 a.m. - 5:00 p.m. **International locations:** Worldwide. **Parent company:** Harris Corporation. **Listed on:** New York Stock Exchange. **Stock exchange symbol:** HRS. **President/CEO:** Phillip W. Farmer. **Number of employees worldwide:** 10,000.

MANHATTAN TRANSFER MIAMI

1111 Lincoln Road, Suite 700, Miami Beach FL 33139. 305/674-0700. **Contact:** Human Resources Department. **World Wide Web address:** http://www.mtmiami.com. **Description:** Provides access to the Latin American and Spanish television markets. The company provides numerous production, post-production, and broadcast services to MTV Latino and The Discovery Channel Latin America/Iberia. Services include creative editing, film-to-tape transfer, electronic video editing, computer generated graphics, duplication, and audio services, as well as production and network facilities operations.

MOTOROLA, INC.

1500 Gateway Boulevard, Boynton Beach FL 33426. 561/739-2000. **Contact:** Human Resources. **World Wide Web address:** http://www.mot.com. **Description:** This location develops and manufactures pagers. Overall, Motorola provides applied research, development, manufacturing, and marketing of high-tech electronic systems and components for industry and government in the fields of communications, automotive, controls, semiconductor, information systems, and office information. Motorola manufactures communications equipment and electronic products including car radios, cellular phones, semiconductors, computer systems, cellular infrastructure equipment, pagers, cordless phones, and LANs. **Corporate headquarters location:** Schaumburg IL. **Other U.S. locations:** Nationwide. **International locations:** Worldwide.

Listed on: New York Stock Exchange. **Stock exchange symbol:** MOT.

MOTOROLA, INC.
8000 West Sunrise Boulevard, Plantation FL 33322. 954/723-5700. **Fax:** 954/723-4490. **Contact:** Staffing Manager. **World Wide Web address:** http://www.mot.com. **Job page:** http://www.motorolacareers.com. **Description:** This location manufactures two-way radios. Overall, Motorola provides applied research, development, manufacturing, and marketing of high-tech electronic systems and components for industry and government markets in the fields of communications, automotive, controls, semiconductor, information systems, and office information. Motorola manufactures communications equipment and electronic products including car radios, cellular phones, semiconductors, computer systems, cellular infrastructure equipment, pagers, cordless phones, and LANs. **Common positions include:** Accountant/Auditor; Chemical Engineer; Computer Programmer; Electrical/Electronics Engineer; Financial Analyst; Human Resources Manager; Industrial Designer; Industrial Engineer; Marketing Specialist; Mechanical Engineer; Metallurgical Engineer; Purchasing Agent/Manager; Systems Analyst; Technical Writer/Editor. **Corporate headquarters location:** Schaumburg IL. **Other U.S. locations:** Nationwide. **International locations:** Worldwide. **Operations at this facility include:** Administration; Divisional Headquarters; Manufacturing; Research and Development. **Listed on:** New York Stock Exchange. **Stock exchange symbol:** MOT.

NBC 6 / WTVJ
316 North Miami Avenue, Miami FL 33128. 305/379-6666. **Contact:** Department of Human Resources. **E-mail address:** nbc6.jobs@nbc.com. **World Wide Web address:** http://www.wtvj.com. **Description:** A television station owned and operated by NBC. WTVJ serves the Miami and Ft. Lauderdale areas. **Common positions include:** Account Representative; Administrator; Editor; Engineer; Graphic Artist; Operations/Production Manager; Production Worker; Reporter; Television Systems Technician. **Parent company:** General Electric.

NEXTEL COMMUNICATIONS
6700 North Andrews Avenue, Suite 700, Fort Lauderdale FL 33309. 954/202-7500. **Contact:** Human Resources. **World Wide Web address:** http://www.nextel.com. **Description:** Nextel Communications is engaged in the specialized mobile

radio (SMR) wireless communications business. These services permit the company's customers to dispatch fleets of vehicles and place calls using their two-way mobile radios to or from any telephone in North America through interconnection with the public switched telephone network. Nextel Communications also sells and rents two-way mobile radio equipment and provides related installation, repair, and maintenance services.

NEXTIRAONE
1619 North Harrison Parkway, Sunrise FL 33323. 954/846-5200. **Contact:** Human Resources. **World Wide Web address:** http://www.nextiraone.com. **Description:** Engaged in the design, manufacture, sale, and servicing of communications networking systems and equipment. The company also produces and distributes high-performance T-1 and T-3 networking systems. **Corporate headquarters location:** This location. **Other U.S. locations:** Irvine CA; Acton MA; Hackensack NJ; Dallas TX.

NEXTIRAONE
1619 North Harrison Parkway, Building D, Sunrise FL 33323. 954/846-1601. **Fax:** 954/846-5025. **Contact:** Human Resources Department. **World Wide Web address:** http://www.nextiraone.com. **Description:** Manufactures data communications equipment including WANs, LANs, and access products. The company also offers related services including project management, installation, consultation, network integration, maintenance, disaster recovery, and training. **Other U.S. locations:** Irvine CA; Acton MA; Hackensack NJ; Dallas TX.

PAXSON COMMUNICATIONS CORPORATION
601 Clearwater Park Road, West Palm Beach FL 33401. 561/659-4122. **Contact:** Human Resources. **World Wide Web address:** http://www.paxtv.com. **Description:** Operates the PAX-TV network, with affiliates throughout the country.

PROTEL, INC.
4150 Kidron Road, Lakeland FL 33811. 863/644-5558. **Contact:** Human Resources Department. **World Wide Web address:** http://www.protelinc.com. **Description:** Manufactures and distributes pay telephones.

SIEMENS BUSINESS COMMUNICATION SYSTEMS, INC.
900 Broken Sound Parkway, Boca Raton FL 33487. 561/923-5000. **Contact:** Human Resources. **World Wide Web address:**

http://www.siemens.com. **Description:** A leading provider of communications and communications integration technology, including OfficePoint ISDN systems, a high-speed integration product enabling transmission and reception of voice, data, image, and video over a single phone line. **Corporate headquarters location:** Santa Clara CA. **Parent company:** Siemens AG (Berlin, Germany). **Listed on:** New York Stock Exchange. **Stock exchange symbol:** SI. **President/CEO:** Dr. Heinrich Pierer. **Number of employees worldwide:** 60,000.

SIEMENS STROMBERG-CARLSON
400 Rinehart Road, Lake Mary FL 32746. 407/942-5000. **Contact:** Garth Shoemaker, Human Resources Department. **World Wide Web address:** http://www.siemens.com. **Description:** Manufactures telecommunications equipment including broadband switching and digital central office switching equipment, Internet telephony products, and data/voice network products. **Parent company:** Siemens AG (Berlin, Germany). **Listed on:** New York Stock Exchange. **Stock exchange symbol:** SI. **President/CEO:** Dr. Heinrich Pierer. **Number of employees worldwide:** 60,000.

SYMETRICS INDUSTRIES
1615 West NASA Boulevard, Melbourne FL 32901. 321/254-1500. **Fax:** 321/259-4122. **Contact:** Human Resources Department. **E-mail address:** sberry@symetrics.com. **World Wide Web address:** http://www.symetrics.com. **Description:** Manufactures voicemail and telecommunications systems. **Corporate headquarters location:** This location. **Annual sales/revenues:** More than $100 million.

WCTV
P.O. Box 3048, Tallahassee FL 32315. 850/893-6666. **Contact:** Human Resources. **Description:** A television station affiliated with CBS.

COMPUTER HARDWARE, SOFTWARE, AND SERVICES

You can expect to find the following types of companies in this chapter:

Computer Components and Hardware Manufacturers
Consultants and Computer Training Companies
Internet and Online Service Providers
Networking and Systems Services
Repair Services/Rental and Leasing
Resellers, Wholesalers, and Distributors
Software Developers/Programming Services
Web Technologies

AGRA BAYMONT
1400 58th Street North, Clearwater FL 33760. 727/578-0100.
Fax: 727/539-1661. **Contact:** Human Resources. **World Wide Web address:** http://www.baymont.com. **Description:** Provides automated mapping, facility management, and geographic information system technologies to government and industries worldwide. **Other U.S. locations:** Nationwide. **International locations:** Worldwide.

ALLEN SYSTEMS GROUP INC.
1333 Third Avenue South, Naples FL 34102. 941/263-6700. **Contact:** Human Resources. **World Wide Web address:** http://www.allensysgroup.com. **Description:** Supplies *Fortune* 1000 companies with system management, file transfer, and help desk software. **Corporate headquarters location:** This location.

AMERICAN RIBBON & TONER COMPANY
2895 West Prospect Road, Fort Lauderdale FL 33309. 954/733-4552. **Fax:** 954/733-0319. **Contact:** Human Resources. **World Wide Web address:** http://www.ribbontoner.com. **Description:** Manufactures ribbons and toner cartridges for printers, fax machines, and copiers.

ANALYSTS INTERNATIONAL CORPORATION (AIC)
3835 NW Boca Raton Boulevard, Suite 300C, Boca Raton FL 33431. 561/750-8588. **Contact:** Human Resources. **E-mail address:** bocajobs@analysts.com. **World Wide Web address:** http://www.analysts.com. **Description:** AIC is an international computer consulting firm. The company uses different programming languages and software to assist clients in developing systems for a variety of industries. **Corporate headquarters location:** Minneapolis MN.

ANALYSTS INTERNATIONAL CORPORATION (AIC)
600 North Westshore Boulevard, Suite 304, Tampa FL 33609-1145. 813/281-0458. **Contact:** Human Resources Department. **E-mail address:** tampajobs@analysts.com **World Wide Web address:** http://www.analysts.com. **Description:** AIC is an international computer consulting firm. The company uses different programming languages and software to assist clients in developing systems for a variety of industries. **Corporate headquarters location:** Minneapolis MN.

ANSWERTHINK CONSULTING GROUP
1001 Brickell Bay Drive, Suite 3000, Miami FL 33131. 305/375-8005. **Fax:** 305/379-8810. **Contact:** Human

Resources. **E-mail address:** careers@answerthink.com. **World Wide Web address:** http://www.answerthink.com. **Description:** Provides computer consulting and IT services to *Fortune* 1000 companies. **Corporate headquarters location:** Atlanta GA. **Other U.S. locations:** Fremont CA; Chicago IL; Burlington MA; Iselin NJ; Marlton NJ; New York NY; Hudson OH; Conshohocken PA; Dallas TX. **Listed on:** NASDAQ. **Stock exchange symbol:** ANSR.

BELL MICROPRODUCTS LATIN AMERICA
7630 NW 25th Street, Miami FL 33122. 305/477-6406. **Contact:** Human Resources Department. **World Wide Web address:** http://www.fti-inc.com. **Description:** Distributes a full-line of computer products to Latin America. The company also provides training, service, and technical support.

BENEFIT TECHNOLOGY INC.
2701 South Bayshore Drive, Suite 401, Miami FL 33133. 305/285-6900. **Contact:** Human Resources. **World Wide Web address:** http://www.benefittechnology.com. **Description:** Develops Visual Basic software for life insurance companies.

BOCA RESEARCH
1601 Clint Moore Road, Boca Raton FL 33487. 561/241-8088. **Contact:** Human Resources. **World Wide Web address:** http://www.bocaresearch.com. **Description:** Manufactures computer components including network cards and video cards. **Corporate headquarters location:** This location.

CPA SOFTWARE
One Pensacola Plaza, Suite 500, Pensacola FL 32501. 850/434-2685. **Contact:** Administrative Manager. **World Wide Web address:** http://www.cpasoftware.com. **Description:** Develops software for certified public accountants. **Common positions include:** Computer Programmer; Customer Service Representative; Marketing Specialist; Public Relations Specialist; Purchasing Agent/Manager; Services Sales Representative; Systems Analyst; Technical Writer/Editor. **Corporate headquarters location:** This location. **Parent company:** Fenimore Software Group, Inc. **Number of employees at this location:** 100.

CTG (COMPUTER TASK GROUP, INC.)
1335 Gateway Drive, Suite 2013, Melbourne FL 32901. 321/725-1300. **Contact:** Human Resources Department. **World Wide Web address:** http://www.ctg.com. **Description:** A computer consulting firm that performs programming and

networking services for corporate clients. **Corporate headquarters location:** Buffalo NY. **Other U.S. locations:** Nationwide. **Listed on:** New York Stock Exchange. **Stock exchange symbol:** CTG.

CARECENTRIC
1180 SW 36th Avenue, Pompano Beach FL 33069. 954/974-0707. **Toll-free phone:** 800/441-2331. **Fax:** 770/801-0789. **Contact:** Human Resources Department. **World Wide Web address:** http://www.carecentric.com. **Description:** Develops and publishes software for the home health care industry. **NOTE:** Jobseekers should send a resume to CareCentric, 6600 Powers Ferry Road, Atlanta GA 30339. **Common positions include:** Computer Programmer; Controller; Customer Service Representative; Marketing/Public Relations Manager; MIS Specialist; Quality Control Supervisor; Sales Representative; Systems Analyst; Technical Writer/Editor. **Corporate headquarters location:** Atlanta GA. **Annual sales/revenues:** $11 - $20 million. **Number of employees at this location:** 100. **Number of employees nationwide:** 300.

CITEL AMERICA, INC.
1515 NW 167th Street, Park Center Boulevard, Suite 5 - 223, Miami FL 33169. 305/621-0022. **Contact:** Human Resources. **World Wide Web address:** http://www.citelprotection.com. **Description:** Manufactures surge protectors for computers.

CITRIX SYSTEMS, INC.
6400 NW 6th Way, Fort Lauderdale FL 33309. 954/267-3000. **Fax:** 954/267-3018. **Contact:** Human Resources Department. **E-mail address:** resume@citrix.com. **World Wide Web address:** http://www.citrix.com. **Description:** Develops application server software and services. Founded in 1989. **Corporate headquarters location:** This location. **Listed on:** NASDAQ. **Stock exchange symbol:** CTXS. **Annual sales/revenues:** More than $100 million.

COLAMCO INC.
975 Florida Central Parkway, Suite 1100, Longwood FL 32750. 407/331-3737. **Toll-free phone:** 800/327-2722. **Contact:** Human Resources Department. **World Wide Web address:** http://www.colamco.com. **Description:** Sells and distributes IT products to a customer base made up of primarily small businesses.

COMPUCOM SYSTEMS, INC.
430 Park Place Boulevard, Clearwater FL 33765. 727/669-5778. **Fax:** 727/669-9588. **Contact:** Dave Costel, Human Resources. **World Wide Web address:** http://www.compucom. **Description:** Provides systems integration consulting services. **Listed on:** NASDAQ. **Stock exchange symbol:** CMPC.

COMPUTER ASSOCIATES INTERNATIONAL, INC.
8014 Bayberry Road, Jacksonville FL 32256. 904/680-2674. **Contact:** Human Resources Department. **World Wide Web address:** http://www.cai.com. **Description:** Computer Associates International is one of the world's leading developers of client/server and distributed computing software. The company develops, markets, and supports enterprise management, database and applications development, business applications, and consumer software products for a broad range of mainframe, midrange, and desktop computers. Computer Associates International serves major business, government, research, and educational organizations. **Corporate headquarters location:** Islandia NY. **Other U.S. locations:** Nationwide. **Annual sales/revenues:** More than $100 million. **Listed on:** New York Stock Exchange. **Stock exchange symbol:** CA. **CEO:** Sanjay Kumar.

COMSYS INC.
2170 West State Road 434, Suite 220, Longwood FL 32779. 407/869-7734. **Fax:** 407/869-8346. **Contact:** Human Resources Department. **World Wide Web address:** http://www.comsys.com. **Description:** Offers contract computer consulting services. **Corporate headquarters location:** Houston TX. **Other U. S. locations:** Nationwide.

CONCURRENT COMPUTER CORPORATION
2881 Gateway Drive, Pompano Beach FL 33069. 954/973-5300. **Fax:** 954/974-1700. **Contact:** Human Resources. **E-mail address:** resumes@ccur.com. **World Wide Web address:** http://www.ccur.com. **Description:** Provides networking systems, servers, software, technical support, and other services to companies in academic, aerospace/defense, CAD engineering, and scientific industries. **Common positions include:** Software Engineer. **Special programs:** Internships. **Corporate headquarters:** Duluth GA. **Listed on:** NASDAQ. **Stock exchange symbol:** CCUR. **Number of employees at this location:** 300. **Number of employees nationwide:** 425.

CONVERGYS
285 International Parkway, Lake Mary FL 32746. 407/771-8000. **Contact:** Human Resources. **World Wide Web address:** http://www.convergys.com. **Description:** A computer software company specializing in the telecommunications industry. **Common positions include:** Computer Programmer; Systems Analyst. **Special programs:** Internships. **Corporate headquarters location:** Cincinnati OH. **Operations at this facility include:** Regional Headquarters; Research and Development; Sales; Service. **Listed on:** New York Stock Exchange. **Stock exchange symbol:** CVG.

DMR CONSULTING GROUP
5110 Eisenhower Boulevard, Suite 105, Tampa FL 33634. 813/888-7400. **Toll-free phone:** 800/338-7326. **Fax:** 813/888-5334. **Contact:** Human Resources. **World Wide Web address:** http://www.dmr.com. **Description:** A computer consulting firm. **NOTE:** Entry-level positions are offered. **Common positions include:** Computer Programmer; Database Manager; Software Engineer; Systems Analyst; Systems Manager. **Special programs:** Training. **Corporate headquarters location:** Edison NJ. **Other U.S. locations:** Nationwide. **International locations:** Australia; Canada. **Parent company:** Fujitsu Limited. **Annual sales/revenues:** More than $100 million. **Number of employees at this location:** 60. **Number of employees nationwide:** 2,000. **Number of employees worldwide:** 8,000.

DATACO DEREX INC.
2280 NW 33rd Court, Pompano Beach FL 33069. 954/977-6362. **Contact:** Human Resources. **World Wide Web address:** http://www.dataco.com. **Description:** Sells and services computer printers. Founded in 1979. **Corporate headquarters location:** Overland Park KS.

ECI TELECOM
1201 West Cypress Creek Road, Fort Lauderdale FL 33309. 954/351-4490. **Fax:** 954/351-4404. **Contact:** Personnel. **World Wide Web address:** http://www.ecitele.com. **Description:** Provides wide-area network systems for voice and data systems. **Common positions include:** Electrical/Electronics Engineer; Systems Analyst. **Corporate headquarters location:** This location. **Other U.S. locations:** Calabasas CA; Clearwater FL; Orlando FL; Herndon VA. **International locations:** Worldwide. **Operations at this facility include:** Administration; Manufacturing; Research and Development. **Listed on:** NASDAQ. **Stock exchange symbol:** ECIL. **Number of employees at this location:** 220.

ENCORE REAL TIME COMPUTING, INC.
1700 NW 66th Avenue, Suite 103, Fort Lauderdale FL 33313. 954/377-1100. **Fax:** 954/377-1145. **Contact:** Personnel. **World Wide Web address:** http://www.encore.com. **Description:** Encore specializes in the manufacture of minicomputers for aerospace, defense, simulation, energy, and information systems. **Common positions include:** Electrical/Electronics Engineer; Software Engineer; Systems Analyst; Technical Writer/Editor. **Special programs:** Internships. **Corporate headquarters location:** This location. **Operations at this facility include:** Administration; Research and Development; Service.

EQUIFAX PAYMENT SERVICES
11601 North Roosevelt Boulevard, St. Petersburg FL 33716. 727/556-9000. **Contact:** Manager of Employment. **World Wide Web address:** http://www.equifax.com. **Description:** Offers payment authorization services for financial institutions and retail establishments via national online computer systems that enable authorization of check and credit card transactions. **NOTE:** Equifax lists all job opportunities through Norrell Services. Call any local Norrell office for further information. **Common positions include:** Accountant/Auditor; Computer Programmer; Financial Analyst; Operations/Production Manager; Systems Analyst. **Corporate headquarters location:** Atlanta GA. **Operations at this facility include:** Administration; Divisional Headquarters; Regional Headquarters; Research and Development; Sales; Service. **Listed on:** New York Stock Exchange. **Stock exchange symbol:** EFX.

EXECUTRAIN OF FLORIDA
One Urban Center, 4830 West Kennedy Boulevard, Suite 700, Tampa FL 33609. 813/288-2000. **Contact:** Human Resources. **E-mail address:** info@executrain.com. **World Wide Web address:** http://www.executrain.com/tampa. **Description:** Trains businesses and employees in the use of computer software and offers IT certification programs. **Other U.S. locations:** Nationwide. **International locations:** Worldwide.

FDP CORPORATION
2000 South Dixie Highway, Miami FL 33133. 305/858-8200. **Contact:** Human Resources Department. **World Wide Web address:** http://www.fdpcorp.com. **Description:** Develops financial software for insurance agencies.

FISCHER INTERNATIONAL SYSTEMS CORPORATION

3584 Mercantile Avenue, Naples FL 34104. 941/643-1500. **Contact:** Human Resources. **World Wide Web address:** http://www.fisc.com. **Description:** Develops and sells software for electronic mailings, directories, and security.

FORTEL

1717 Diplomacy Row, Orlando FL 32809-5703. 407/251-3030. **Contact:** Human Resources. **World wide Web address:** http://www.fortel.com. **Description:** Designs, develops, and manufactures high-performance, high-speed color printers, high-resolution nonimpact printer/plotters, ruggedized computers and workstations, and keyboards. The company serves the U.S. Department of Defense, U.S. prime defense contractors, international defense companies, and industrial and commercial original equipment manufacturers. **Corporate headquarters location:** Fremont CA. **President/CEO:** Asa Lanum.

GRC INTERNATIONAL, INC.

1980 North Atlantic Avenue, Suite 1030, Cocoa Beach FL 32931. 321/784-4030. **Fax:** 321/784-2009. **Contact:** Human Resources Department. **World Wide Web address:** http://www.grci.com. **Description:** This location provides technical services and systems engineering. Overall, GRC International creates large-scale, decision-support systems and software engineering environments; applies operations research and mathematical modeling to business and management systems; and implements advanced database technology. GRC International also provides studies and analysis capabilities for policy development and planning; modeling and simulation of hardware and software used in real-time testing of sensor, weapon, and battlefield management command, control, and communication systems; and testing and evaluation. GRC International's services are offered primarily to government and commercial customers. **Corporate headquarters location:** Vienna VA. **Other U.S. locations:** Nationwide. **Parent company:** AT&T. **Number of employees worldwide:** 1,300.

GEAC AEC BUSINESS SOLUTIONS

3938 Premier North Drive, Tampa FL 33624. 813/269-7900. **Contact:** Human Resources Department. **World Wide Web address:** http://www.geac.com. **Description:** Develops accounts receivable and accounts payable software.

HTE INC.
1000 Business Center Drive, Lake Mary FL 32746. 407/304-3235. **Contact:** Human Resources. **World Wide Web address:** http://www.hteinc.com. **Description:** Develops software for the government, education, law enforcement, and public safety markets. **Listed on:** NASDAQ. **Stock exchange symbol:** HTEI. **Annual revenues:** $51 - $100 million. **Number of employees at this location:** 500.

HARRIS CORPORATION
1025 West NASA Boulevard, Mail Stop 19, Melbourne FL 32919. 321/727-9207. **Toll-free phone:** 800/4HA-RRIS. **Contact:** Human Resources. **World Wide Web address:** http://www.harris.com. **Description:** A communications equipment company that provides broadcast, network, government, and wireless support products and systems. **NOTE:** Send resumes to: Harris Corporation, Resume Proccessing, P.O. Box 549238, Suite 107, Waltham MA 02454. **Common positions include:** Accountant/Auditor; Administrator; Attorney; Blue-Collar Worker Supervisor; Computer Programmer; Customer Service Representative; Department Manager; Editor; Electrical/Electronics Engineer; Financial Analyst; General Manager; Human Resources Manager; Industrial Engineer; Manufacturer's/Wholesaler's Sales Representative; Marketing Specialist; Mechanical Engineer; Metallurgical Engineer; Operations/Production Manager; Public Relations Specialist; Purchasing Agent/Manager; Quality Control Supervisor; Reporter; Systems Analyst. **Corporate headquarters location:** This location. **International locations:** Worldwide. **Operations at this facility include:** Administration; Manufacturing; Research and Development; Sales; Service. **Listed on:** New York Stock Exchange. **Stock exchange symbol:** HRS. **President/CEO:** Phillip W. Farmer. **Number of employees worldwide:** 10,000.

HARRIS TECHNICAL SERVICES CORPORATION
1225 Evans Road, Melbourne FL 32904. 321/952-7550. **Toll-free phone:** 888/952-9468. **Fax:** 321/733-7570. **Contact:** Human Resources Department. **World Wide Web address:** http://www.harris.com. **Description:** Develops software solutions for commercial and government applications. **NOTE:** Entry-level positions are offered. Send resumes to: Harris Corporation, Resume Proccessing, P.O. Box 549238, Suite 107, Waltham MA 02454. **Common positions include:** Accountant/Auditor; Administrator; Attorney; Blue-Collar Worker Supervisor; Computer Programmer; Customer Service Representative; Editor; Electrical/Electronics Engineer;

Financial Analyst; General Manager; Human Resources Manager; Industrial Engineer; Manufacturer's/Wholesaler's Sales Representative; Marketing Specialist; Mechanical Engineer; Metallurgical Engineer; Operations/Production Manager; Public Relations Specialist; Purchasing Agent/Manager; Quality Control Supervisor; Reporter; Systems Analyst. **Office hours:** Monday - Friday, 8:00 a.m. - 5:00 p.m. **International locations:** Worldwide. **Parent company:** Harris Corporation. **Listed on:** New York Stock Exchange. **Stock exchange symbol:** HRS. **President/CEO:** Phillip W. Farmer. **Number of employees worldwide:** 10,000.

HUMMINGBIRD, INC.
124 Marriott Drive, Tallahassee FL 32301. 850/942-3627. **Contact:** Cyndi Utt, Human Resources. **World Wide Web address:** http://www.hummingbird.com. **Description:** Develops document management software. Hummingbird also provides education, consulting, and support services for its products. **Listed on:** NASDAQ. **Stock exchange symbol:** HUMC.

IBM CORPORATION
3109 West Dr. Martin Luther King Junior Boulevard, Tampa FL 33607. 813/872-2277. **Toll-free phone:** 800/426-4968. **Contact:** Human Resources. **World Wide Web address:** http://www.ibm.com. **Description:** This location operates as a regional sales office. Overall, IBM is the developer, manufacturer, and marketer of advanced information processing products including computers and microelectronic technology, software, networking systems, and information technology-related services. **NOTE:** Jobseekers should send a resume to IBM Staffing Services, 1DPA/051, 3808 Six Forks Road, Raleigh NC 27609. **Corporate headquarters location:** Armonk NY. **Subsidiaries include:** IBM Credit Corporation; IBM Instruments, Inc.; IBM World Trade Corporation.

IKON OFFICE SOLUTIONS TECHNOLOGY SERVICES
5445 West Cypress Street, Suite 100, Tampa FL 33607. 813/261-2000. **Fax:** 813/267-2500. **Contact:** Kim McDaniels, Human Resources Department. **World Wide Web address:** http://www.ikon.com. **Description:** Provides client/server and workflow consulting, network integration, product fulfillment, and technical training. Founded in 1988. **Common positions include:** Account Manager; Account Representative; Computer Programmer; Customer Service Representative; Marketing Specialist; MIS Specialist; Project Manager; Sales Executive; Systems Analyst; Systems Manager. **Other area locations:** Fort

Lauderdale FL; Jacksonville FL; Orlando FL; Tallahassee FL. **Other U.S. locations:** Pittsburgh PA. **Operations at this facility include:** Sales. **Listed on:** New York Stock Exchange. **Stock exchange symbol:** IKN. **Annual sales/revenues:** $51 - $100 million. **Number of employees at this location:** 100. **Number of employees nationwide:** 210.

ISYS/BIOVATION
6925 Lake Ellenor Drive, Suite 135, Orlando FL 32809. 407/859-2881. **Contact:** Human Resources. **World Wide Web address:** http://www.isysbiov.com. **Description:** Designs computer hardware and software to help manage laboratory information for hospitals, universities, and doctors' offices.

KHAMELEON SOFTWARE
13830 58th Street North, Suite 401, Clearwater FL 33760. 727/539-1077. **Toll-free phone:** 800/655-6598. **Fax:** 727/539-1070. **Contact:** Human Resources. **World Wide Web address:** http://www.khameleon.com. **Description:** Provides software design, consulting, and related services to e-focused, software, and system-integration businesses. **Common positions include:** Account Manager; Accountant; Administrative Assistant; Computer Programmer; Computer Support Technician; Controller; Customer Service Representative; Database Administrator; Financial Analyst; Marketing Specialist; MIS Specialist; Network/Systems Administrator; Sales Executive; Sales Representative; Software Engineer; SQL Programmer; Systems Analyst; Webmaster. **Special programs:** Internships. **Corporate headquarters location:** This location. **Other U.S. locations:** San Francisco CA; Atlanta GA; New York NY.

LOCKHEED MARTIN TACTICAL DEFENSE SYSTEMS
P.O. Box 6000, Clearwater FL 33758. 813/855-5711. **Fax:** 813/854-7225. **Contact:** Human Resources. **World Wide Web address:** http://www.lockheedmartin.com. **Description:** This location is a computer hardware manufacturing facility. Overall, Lockheed Martin Tactical Defense Systems designs and builds 16-bit and 32-bit technical computing systems used in mil-spec environments. Applications include electronic warfare, signal intelligence, radar, sonar, and imaging where digital signal processing or general purpose computing is required. The company is also involved in systems engineering, software development tools, computer systems, and integrated workstations of commercial architectures for proof-of-concept program phases. **NOTE:** Entry-level positions and second shifts are offered. **Common positions include:** Blue-Collar Worker Supervisor; Electrical/Electronics Engineer;

Industrial Engineer; Industrial Production Manager; Manufacturing Engineer; Production Manager. **Special programs:** Training. **Corporate headquarters location:** Bethesda MD. **Other U.S. locations:** Nationwide. **International locations:** Worldwide. **Parent company:** Lockheed Martin Corporation. **Listed on:** New York Stock Exchange. **Stock exchange symbol:** LMT. **Number of employees at this location:** 500.

MACACADEMY/WINDOWS ACADEMY
FLORIDA MARKETING INTERNATIONAL, INC.
102 East Granada Boulevard, Ormond Beach FL 32176-1712. 386/677-1918. **Toll-free phone:** 800/527-1914. **Fax:** 386/677-6717. **Contact:** Human Resources. **World Wide Web address:** http://www.macacademy.com. **Description:** Offers CD-ROM and video training for several PC and MacIntosh computer applications. The company also offers live seminars and on-site training in the United States, the United Kingdom, Australia, and Japan.

McKESSONHBOC
1025 Greenwood Boulevard, Suite 500, Lake Mary FL 32746. 407/804-5000. **Fax:** 407/804-5005. **Contact:** Human Resources. **World Wide Web address:** http://www.hboc.com. **Description:** Provides information systems and technology to health care enterprises including hospitals, integrated delivery networks, and managed care organizations. McKessonHBOC's primary products are Pathways 2000, a family of client/server-based applications that allow the integration and uniting of health care providers; STAR, Series, and HealthQuest transaction systems; TRENDSTAR decision support system; and QUANTUM enterprise information system. The company also offers outsourcing services that include strategic information systems planning, data center operations, receivables management, business office administration, and major system conversions. **Corporate headquarters location:** San Francisco CA. **Other U.S. locations:** San Diego CA; Chicago IL; Minneapolis MN; Bedminster NJ; Dallas TX. **Subsidiaries include:** HBO & Company (UK) Limited; HBO & Company Canada Ltd. **Number of employees nationwide:** 470.

MODCOMP INC.
1650 West McNab Road, Fort Lauderdale FL 33309. 954/974-1380. **Contact:** Julie Slovin, Human Resources Manager. **World Wide Web address:** http://www.modcomp.com. **Description:** Manufactures computers designed for industrial

automation, energy transportation, and communication applications. Founded in 1970.

MODIS
One Independent Drive, Jacksonville FL 32202. 904/360-2900. **Toll-free phone:** 877/MOD-ISIT. **Fax:** 904/360-2110. **Contact:** Human Resources. **World Wide Web address:** http://www.modisit.com. **Description:** Provides a wide range of computer consulting services. **Corporate headquarters location:** This location. **Other U.S. locations:** Nationwide. **International locations:** Canada; United Kingdom; Western Europe.

MODUS OPERANDI
122 4th Avenue, Indialantic FL 32903. 321/984-3370. **Contact:** Human Resources. **World Wide Web address:** http://www.modusoperandi.com. **Description:** Designs high-tech software for the U.S. government.

NETWORK INFOSERVE, INC.
8370 West Hillsborough Avenue, Suite 201, Tampa FL 33615. 813/888-9208. **Fax:** 813/888-9481. **Contact:** Personnel. **World Wide Web address:** http://www.niicorp.com. **Description:** Engaged in systems integration.

NEXTIRAONE
1619 North Harrison Parkway, Sunrise FL 33323. 954/846-5200. **Contact:** Human Resources Department. **World Wide Web address:** http://www.nextiraone.com. **Description:** Engaged in the design, manufacture, sale, and servicing of communications networking systems and equipment. The company also produces and distributes high-performance T-1 and T-3 networking systems. **Corporate headquarters location:** This location. **Other U.S. locations:** Irvine CA; Acton MA; Hackensack NJ; Dallas TX.

NEXTIRAONE
1619 North Harrison Parkway, Building D, Sunrise FL 33323. 954/846-1601. **Fax:** 954/846-5025. **Contact:** Department of Human Resources. **World Wide Web address:** http://www.nextiraone.com. **Description:** Manufactures data communications equipment including WANs, LANs, and access products. The company also offers related services including project management, installation, consultation, network integration, maintenance, disaster recovery, and training. **Other U.S. locations:** Irvine CA; Acton MA; Hackensack NJ; Dallas TX.

OCE PRINTING SYSTEMS USA
5600 Broken Sound Boulevard NW, Boca Raton FL 33487. 561/997-3100. **Contact:** Human Resources. **World Wide Web address:** http://www.oceusa.com. **Description:** Services computer printers and copiers.

PARADYNE CORPORATION
8545 126th Avenue North, Largo FL 33773. 727/530-2000. **Contact:** Department of Human Resources. **World Wide Web address:** http://www.paradyne.com. **Description:** Manufactures and distributes WAN solutions including DSL, T1, and service-level management products. **Common positions include:** Accountant; Computer Programmer; Electrical/Electronics Engineer; Software Engineer; Systems Analyst. **Special programs:** Internships. **Listed on:** NASDAQ. **Stock exchange symbol:** PDYN. **Number of employees at this location:** 2,150.

PARAVANT COMPUTER SYSTEMS INC.
3520 U.S. Highway 1, Palm Bay FL 32905. 321/727-3672. **Fax:** 321/725-0496. **Contact:** Human Resources Department. **World Wide Web address:** http://www.paravant.com. **Description:** Manufactures rugged hand-held computer systems and software for the military. **Listed on:** NASDAQ. **Stock exchange symbol:** PVAT.

PAYFORMANCE CORPORATION
10550 Deerwood Park Boulevard, Suite 300, Jacksonville FL 32256. 904/997-6777. **Fax:** 904/997-8017. **Contact:** Department of Human Resources. **World Wide Web address:** http://www.payformance.com. **Description:** Develops computer hardware and software designed for payment automation systems. Payformance Corporation provides services to over 3,000 corporate customers worldwide. **Corporate headquarters location:** This location.

PAYSYS INTERNATIONAL
900 Winderley Place, Suite 140, Maitland FL 32751. 407/660-0343. **Contact:** Human Resources. **World Wide Web address:** http://www.paysys.com. **Description:** Develops credit card processing software.

PREMIO COMPUTER
1616 NW 84th Avenue, Miami FL 33126. 305/471-0199. **Contact:** Human Resources. **World Wide Web address:** http://www.premiopc.com. **Description:** A reseller of computers.

PYGMY COMPUTER SYSTEMS INC.
12415 SW 136th Avenue, Suite 3, Miami FL 33186. 305/253-1212. **Fax:** 305/255-1876. **Contact:** Personnel. **World Wide Web address:** http://www.pygmy.com. **Description:** Resells pocket computers and associated software.

SOLUTION 6 HOLDINGS LIMITED
101 North Monroe Street, Suite 800, Tallahassee FL 32301. 850/224-2200. **Contact:** Human Resources Department. **World Wide Web address:** http://www.solution6.com. **Description:** Develops financial software. Established in 1981. **NOTE:** Entry-level positions and part-time jobs are offered. **Common positions include:** Account Manager; Accountant; Administrative Assistant; Administrative Manager; Applications Engineer; Budget Analyst; Computer Engineer; Computer Programmer; Computer Support Technician; Computer Technician; Controller; Customer Service Representative; Database Administrator; Human Resources Manager; Marketing Manager; Marketing Specialist; MIS Specialist; Network/Systems Administrator; Project Manager; Public Relations Specialist; Purchasing Agent/Manager; Sales Manager; Sales Representative; Software Engineer; SQL Programmer; Systems Analyst; Vice President; Webmaster. **Special programs:** Training; Co-ops; Summer Jobs. **Corporate headquarters location:** Sydney, Australia. **Other U.S. locations:** Nationwide. **International locations:** Worldwide. **CEO:** Neil H. Gamble. **Number of employees worldwide:** 1,600.

SUN MICROSYSTEMS, INC.
3501 Quadrangle Boulevard, Suite 150, Orlando FL 32817. 407/380-0058. **Contact:** Human Resources Department. **World Wide Web address:** http://www.sun.com. **Description:** This location manufactures mainframe computers. Overall, Sun Microsystems produces high-performance computer systems, workstations, servers, CPUs, peripherals, and operating system software. Products include a microprocessor called SPARC. Products are sold to engineering, scientific, technical, and commercial markets worldwide. **Corporate headquarters location:** Palo Alto CA. **Other U.S. locations:** Nationwide. **International locations:** Worldwide. **Subsidiaries include:** Forte Software Inc. manufactures enterprise application integration software. **Listed on:** NASDAQ. **Stock exchange symbol:** SUNW. **CEO:** Scott McNealy. **Annual sales/revenues:** More than $100 million. **Number of employees worldwide:** 40,000.

TECH DATA CORPORATION
5350 Tech Data Drive, Clearwater FL 33760. 727/539-7429.
Contact: Personnel. **E-mail address:** jobs@techdata.com.
World Wide Web address: http://www.techdata.com.
Description: Distributes microcomputer-related hardware and software products to value-added resellers and computer retailers throughout the United States, Canada, Europe, Latin America, and the Caribbean. Tech Data Corporation purchases its products in large quantities directly from manufacturers and publishers, maintains an inventory of more than 25,000 products, and sells to an active base of over 50,000 customers. Tech Data Corporation provides its customers with products in networking, mass storage, peripherals, software, and systems from more than 600 manufacturers and publishers. Founded in 1974. **NOTE:** Entry-level positions and second and third shifts are offered. **Common positions include:** Account Manager; Account Representative; Accountant; Administrative Assistant; Administrative Manager; Assistant Manager; Attorney; Auditor; Budget Analyst; Buyer; Chief Financial Officer; Clerical Supervisor; Computer Operator; Computer Programmer; Credit Manager; Customer Service Representative; Database Manager; Finance Director; Financial Analyst; Human Resources Manager; Management Trainee; Marketing Manager; Marketing Specialist; MIS Specialist; Multimedia Designer; Operations Manager; Paralegal; Project Manager; Purchasing Agent/Manager; Sales Executive; Sales Manager; Sales Representative; Secretary; Systems Analyst; Systems Manager; Technical Writer/Editor; Telecommunications Manager; Vice President. **Corporate headquarters location:** This location. **Other U.S. locations:** CA; GA; IN; NJ; TX. **International locations:** Canada; The Caribbean; Europe; Latin America; Middle East. **Subsidiaries include:** Computer 2000 AG (Germany); Tech Data Canada Inc. (Ontario, Canada); Tech Data Education, Inc. (Clearwater FL); Tech Data Finance, Inc. (Walnut Creek CA); Tech Data France, SNC (Bobigny, France); Tech Data Latin America (Miami FL); Tech Data Pacific, Inc. (Clearwater FL); Tech Data Product Management, Inc. (Clearwater FL). **Operations at this facility include:** Administration; Divisional Headquarters; Regional Headquarters; Sales; Service. **Listed on:** NASDAQ. **Stock exchange symbol:** TECD. **CEO:** Steven A. Raymund. **Annual sales/revenues:** More than $100 million.

TIGERDIRECT, INC.
7795 West Flagler Street, Suite 35, 2nd Floor, Miami FL 33144. 305/415-2200. **Contact:** Nadia Barreto, Manager of Human Resources Department. **World Wide Web address:**

http://www.tigerdirect.com. **Description:** A reseller of computer hardware and software. **Listed on:** New York Stock Exchange. **Stock exchange symbol:** SYX. **President:** Carl Fiorentino. **Number of employees at this location:** 435.

TINGLEY SYSTEMS
P.O. Box 700, San Antonio FL 33576. 352/588-2250. **Physical address:** 31722 State Road 52, San Antonio FL 33576. 352/588-2250. **Contact:** Human Resources. **World Wide Web address:** http://www.tingleysystems.com. **Description:** Develops software for the health care industry.

TYBRIN CORPORATION
1030 Titan Court, Fort Walton Beach FL 32547. 850/337-2500. **Toll-free phone:** 800/989-2746. **Contact:** Human Resources. **World Wide Web address:** http://www.tybrin.com. **Description:** Tybrin Corporation provides engineering and computer support services to government and commercial customers. Founded in 1972. **Common positions include:** Administrative Assistant; Advertising Clerk; Budget Analyst; Chief Financial Officer; Computer Operator; Computer Programmer; Controller; Cost Estimator; Database Manager; Design Engineer; Financial Analyst; General Manager; Graphic Artist; Human Resources Manager; Marketing Manager; MIS Specialist; Online Content Specialist; Project Manager; Secretary; Software Engineer; Systems Analyst; Technical Writer/Editor. **Corporate headquarters location:** This location. **Other U.S. locations:** Nationwide. **Listed on:** Privately held. **Number of employees nationwide:** 825.

UNISYS CORPORATION
7000 West Palmetto Park Road, Suite 201, Boca Raton FL 33433. 561/750-5800. **Contact:** Human Resources. **World Wide Web address:** http://www.unisys.com. **Description:** This location is a regional headquarters office. Overall, Unisys Corporation provides information services, technology, and software. Unisys specializes in developing critical business solutions based on open information networks. The company's Enabling Software Team creates a variety of software projects that facilitate the building of user applications and the management of distributed systems. The company's Platforms Group is responsible for UNIX Operating Systems running across a wide range of multiple processor server platforms including all peripheral and communication drivers. The Unisys Commercial Parallel Processing Team develops microkernel-based operating systems, I/O device drivers, ATM hardware, diagnostics, and system architectures. The System

Management Group is in charge of the overall management of development programs for UNIX desktop and entry-server products. **Corporate headquarters location:** Blue Bell PA. **Other U.S. locations:** Nationwide. **International locations:** Worldwide. **Listed on:** New York Stock Exchange. **Stock exchange symbol:** UIS. **Number of employees worldwide:** 39,000.

VERIDIAN INC.
960 John Sims Parkway West, Niceville FL 32578-1823. 850/678-2126. **Fax:** 850/678-3977. **Contact:** Human Resources. **E-mail address:** careers.info@veridian.com. **World Wide Web address:** http://www.veridian.com. **Description:** This location offers computer support to nearby Air Force bases. Overall, Veridian provides engineering systems integration and technical services to government agencies. **Other U.S. locations:** Nationwide. **President/CEO:** David H. Langstaff. **Number of employees nationwide:** Over 5,000.

VERITAS SOFTWARE
400 International Parkway, Heathrow FL 32746. 407/531-7500. **Contact:** Human Resources. **World Wide Web address:** http://www.veritas.com. **Description:** Develops and markets backup software. **Corporate headquarters:** Mount View, CA. **Other U.S. locations:** Nationwide. **International locations:** Worldwide. **Listed on:** NASDAQ. **Stock exchange symbol:** VRTS. **Number of employees worldwide:** Over 5,000.

VICORP.COM
3845 Gateway Center Boulevard, Suite 300, Pinelllas Park FL 33782. 727/572-9300. **Contact:** Human Resources. **E-mail address:** careers@vicorp.com. **World Wide Web address:** http://www.vicorp.com. **Description:** Founded in 1981. Develops software for voice enhancement services and voice dialing. **Corporate headquarters location:** This location. **International locations:** The Netherlands; Singapore; United Kingdom. **Number of employees worldwide:** 70.

EDUCATIONAL SERVICES

You can expect to find the following types of facilities in this chapter:

Business/Secretarial/Data Processing Schools
Colleges/Universities/Professional Schools
Community Colleges/Technical Schools/Vocational Schools
Elementary and Secondary Schools
Preschool and Child Daycare Services

EDISON COMMUNITY COLLEGE

P.O. Box 60210, Fort Myers FL 33906-6210. 941/489-9280. **Fax:** 941/489-9041. **Recorded jobline:** 941/489-9120. **Contact:** Leslie Rider, Human Resources Specialist. **World Wide Web address:** http://www.edison.edu. **Description:** A two-year college offering associate's degrees, certification programs, and noncredit continuing education courses. **NOTE:** Part-time jobs are offered. **Common positions include:** Accountant; Administrative Assistant; Chief Financial Officer; Computer Programmer; Computer Technician; Counselor; Education Administrator; Finance Director; Human Resources Manager; Librarian; Library Technician; Purchasing Agent/Manager; Secretary; Systems Analyst; Teacher/Professor; Vice President of Finance; Vice President of Operations. **Office hours:** Monday - Friday, 8:30 a.m. - 4:30 p.m. **Corporate headquarters location:** This location. **Other area locations:** Naples FL; Port Charlotte FL. **Operations at this facility include:** Administration. **President:** Kenneth P. Walker. **Facilities Manager:** Ronald White. **Purchasing Manager:** Jay Collier. **Number of employees at this location:** 300.

EMBRY-RIDDLE AERONAUTICAL UNIVERSITY

600 South Clyde Morris Boulevard, Daytona Beach FL 32114-3900. 386/226-6145. **Contact:** Human Resources. **World Wide Web address:** http://www.db.erau.edu. **Description:** A private, four-year, coeducational, undergraduate university offering studies in aviation, aerospace, and engineering. **Common positions include:** Accountant/Auditor; Administrator; Blue-Collar Worker Supervisor; Buyer; Computer Programmer; Counselor; Department Manager; Electrical/Electronics Engineer; Financial Analyst; General Manager; Human Resources Manager; Management Trainee; Marketing Specialist; Physicist; Purchasing Agent/Manager; Statistician; Systems Analyst; Technical Writer/Editor; Transportation/Traffic Specialist. **Special programs:** Internships. **Other U.S. locations:** Prescott AZ. **Number of employees nationwide:** 1,200.

FLORIDA ATLANTIC UNIVERSITY

777 Glades Road, P.O. Box 3091, Boca Raton FL 33431. 561/297-3000. **Contact:** Human Resources. **World Wide Web address:** http://www.fau.edu. **Description:** A four-year liberal arts university offering bachelor's, master's (including MBA), and doctoral degrees. Approximately 11,500 undergraduate and 3,000 graduate students attend Florida Atlantic University.

FLORIDA COMMUNITY COLLEGE AT JACKSONVILLE
501 West State Street, Jacksonville FL 32202. 904/632-3210.
Recorded jobline: 904/632-3161. **Contact:** Employment
Manager, Human Resources Department. **World Wide Web
address:** http://www.fccj.org. **Description:** An accredited
institution offering associate's degrees, corporate and technical
training, and special and continuing education programs. Total
enrollment is approximately 28,000. Founded in 1966. **NOTE:**
Entry-level positions and part-time jobs are offered. **Common
positions include:** Advisor; Computer Support Technician;
Network Administrator; Secretary; Systems Analyst;
Typist/Word Processor **President:** Dr. Steven Wallace. **Number
of employees at this location:** 2,700.

FLORIDA MEMORIAL COLLEGE
15800 NW 42nd Avenue, Miami FL 33054. 305/626-3622.
Fax: 305/626-3109. **Contact:** Human Resources. **World Wide
Web address:** http://www.fmc.edu. **Description:** A private,
four-year, liberal arts college with an enrollment of
approximately 1,500 students. **Common positions include:**
Accountant/Auditor; Budget Analyst; Buyer; Computer
Programmer; Counselor; Education Administrator; Financial
Analyst; Human Resources Manager; Librarian; Library
Technician; Mathematician; Physicist; Psychologist; Public
Relations Specialist; Purchasing Agent/Manager; Statistician;
Systems Analyst; Teacher/Professor. **Special programs:**
Internships. **Operations at this facility include:** Administration.
Listed on: Privately held. **Number of employees at this
location:** 220.

FLORIDA STATE UNIVERSITY
6200-A University Center, Tallahassee FL 32306-2410.
850/644-6035. **Contact:** Phaedra Harris, Human Resources.
World Wide Web address: http://www.fsu.edu. **Description:** A
four-year state university offering certificates, bachelor's,
master's (including MBA), and doctoral degrees.
Approximately 21,500 undergraduate and 5,500 graduate
students attend Florida State University. **Common positions
include:** Accountant/Auditor; Budget Analyst; Library
Technician; Radio/TV Announcer/Broadcaster; Registered
Nurse; Systems Analyst. **Operations at this facility include:**
Administration; Research and Development. **Number of
employees at this location:** 2,500.

HILLSBOROUGH COMMUNITY COLLEGE
P.O. Box 31127, Tampa FL 33631-3127. 813/253-7000.
Physical address: 4001 Tampa Bay Boulevard, Tampa FL

33614. **Fax:** 813/253-7034. **Recorded jobline:** 813/253-7185. **Contact:** Human Resources Department. **World Wide Web address:** http://www.hcc.cc.fl.us. **Description:** This location offers programs specializing in computer programming, business management, fire science, and criminal justice training. Overall, Hillsborough Community College is a multicampus, state-run community college accredited by the Southern Association of Colleges and Schools. **Common positions include:** Accountant/Auditor; Administrative Worker/Clerk; Administrator; Buyer; Cashier; Clinical Lab Technician; Computer Programmer; Education Administrator; Human Resources Manager; Instructor/Trainer; Library Technician; Security Officer; Teacher/Professor. **Corporate headquarters location:** This location. **Number of employees at this location:** 1,500.

LYNN UNIVERSITY
3601 North Military Trail, Boca Raton FL 33431-5598. 561/237-7000. **Contact:** Human Resources. **World Wide Web address:** http://www.lynn.edu. **Description:** An accredited, private university offering 38 associate's, bachelor's, master's, and doctoral degree programs. Program areas include Arts and Sciences, Business, and Education. Founded in 1962.

MIAMI-DADE COMMUNITY COLLEGE
KENDALL CAMPUS
11011 SW 104th Street, Miami FL 33176. 305/237-2051. **Toll-free phone:** 800/955-8771. **Fax:** 305/237-0961. **Recorded jobline:** 305/237-2050. **Contact:** Human Resources. **World Wide Web address:** http://www.mdcc.edu. **Description:** A two-year state college offering an Associate in Science degree, Associate in Arts degree, and Vocational Credit Certificates. **NOTE:** Entry-level positions and second and third shifts are offered. **Common positions include:** Account Representative; Administrative Assistant; Blue-Collar Worker Supervisor; Buyer; Clerical Supervisor; Computer Operator; Computer Programmer; Counselor; Electrical/Electronics Engineer; Electrician; Emergency Medical Technician; ESL Teacher; Licensed Practical Nurse; Physical Therapist; Registered Nurse; Secretary; Systems Analyst; Telecommunications Manager; Typist/Word Processor. **Corporate headquarters location:** This location. **Operations at this facility include:** Administration. **Number of employees at this location:** 2,300.

MIAMI-DADE COMMUNITY COLLEGE
MEDICAL CENTER CAMPUS
950 NW 20th Street, Miami FL 33127. 305/237-4247. **Contact:** Human Resources. **World Wide Web address:** http://www.mdcc.edu. **Description:** A two-year state college offering programs through the School of Allied Health, School of Nursing, Physical Assistant Program, and Continuing Education.

MIAMI-DADE COMMUNITY COLLEGE
MITCHELL WOLFSON CAMPUS
300 NE Second Avenue, Miami FL 33132. 305/237-3000. **Contact:** Human Resources. **World Wide Web address:** http://www.mdcc.edu. **Description:** A two-year state college offering programs through the School of Allied Health, School of Nursing, Physical Assistant Program, and Continuing Education.

MIAMI-DADE COMMUNITY COLLEGE
NORTH CAMPUS
11380 NW 27th Avenue, Miami FL 33167. 305/237-1000. **Contact:** Human Resources. **World Wide Web address:** http://www.mdcc.edu. **Description:** A two-year state college offering programs through the School of Allied Health, School of Nursing, Physical Assistant Program, and Continuing Education.

NOVA SOUTHEASTERN UNIVERSITY
3301 College Avenue, Fort Lauderdale FL 33314. 954/262-7870. **Contact:** Human Resources Department. **World Wide Web address:** http://www.nova.edu. **Description:** A university offering undergraduate and graduate programs to approximately 18,000 students.

PALM BEACH COMMUNITY COLLEGE
4200 Congress Avenue, Lake Worth FL 33461. 561/868-3114. **Fax:** 561/439-8202. **Contact:** Human Resources. **World Wide Web address:** http://www.pbcc.cc.fl.us. **Description:** A community college offering associate's degrees in the arts and sciences. **Common positions include:** Accountant/Auditor; Buyer; Computer Programmer; Counselor; Education Administrator; Human Resources Manager; Librarian; Library Technician; Occupational Therapist; Registered Nurse; Respiratory Therapist; Systems Analyst; Teacher/Professor.

ROLLINS COLLEGE
1000 Holt Avenue, Campus Box 2718, Winter Park FL 32789.
407/646-2320. **Contact:** Human Resources. **World Wide Web
address:** http://www.rollins.edu/hr/jobindex.htm. **Description:**
A private, liberal arts college offering bachelor's and master's
degrees to approximately 1,400 students. **NOTE:** Jobseekers
may apply in person at the Warren Administration Building,
Monday - Thursday, 9:00 a.m. - 4:00 p.m. **Operations at this
facility include:** Administration. **Listed on:** Privately held.
President: Rita Bornstein. **Number of employees at this
location:** 530.

ST. PETERSBURG JUNIOR COLLEGE
P.O. Box 13489, St. Petersburg FL 33711. 727/341-3600.
Contact: Human Resources Department. **World Wide Web
address:** http://www.spjc.cc.fl.us. **Description:** A junior college
serving Pinellas County. The school offers associate's degrees
in the arts and sciences and prepares students for transferring
to other institutions. **NOTE:** To apply for a position you must
complete the on-line application. **Common positions include:**
Accountant/Auditor; Buyer; Clerical Supervisor; Clinical Lab
Technician; Computer Programmer; Counselor; Education
Administrator; Electrician; Human Resources Manager;
Librarian; Library Technician; Public Relations Specialist;
Purchasing Agent/Manager; Teacher/Professor. **Operations at
this facility include:** Administration; Service. **Number of
employees at this location:** 940.

UNIVERSITY OF CENTRAL FLORIDA
12565 Research Parkway, Suite 360, Orlando FL 32826-2912.
407/823-2771. **Contact:** Mark Roberts, Human Resources
Director. **World Wide Web address:** http://www.ucf.edu.
Description: A university offering bachelor's, master's, and
doctoral degrees to approximately 31,000 students.

UNIVERSITY OF FLORIDA
4th Floor Stadium, P.O. Box 115002, Gainesville FL 32611.
352/392-4621. **Fax:** 352/392-7094. **Recorded jobline:**
352/392-4631. **Contact:** Greg Marwede, Assistant Director of
Personnel Services. **World Wide Web address:**
http://www.ufl.edu. **Description:** A state university offering
graduate, undergraduate, and professional programs to
approximately 43,000 students. **NOTE:** Entry-level positions
are offered. **Common positions include:** Accountant;
Administrative Assistant; Applications Engineer; Architect;
AS400 Programmer Analyst; Auditor; Biological Scientist;
Budget Analyst; Certified Occupational Therapy Assistant;

Chemist; Computer Engineer; Computer Operator; Computer Programmer; Computer Support Technician; Computer Technician; Counselor; Database Administrator; Database Manager; Desktop Publishing Specialist; Dietician/Nutritionist; Editor; Editorial Assistant; Education Administrator; Electrical/Electronics Engineer; Electrician; Graphic Artist; Industrial Engineer; Instructional Technologist; Internet Services Manager; Librarian; Licensed Practical Nurse; MIS Specialist; Multimedia Designer; Network/Systems Administrator; Purchasing Agent/Manager; Registered Nurse; Secretary; Software Engineer; Special Education Teacher; SQL Programmer; Systems Analyst; Systems Manager; Teacher/Professor; Typist/Word Processor; Webmaster. **Corporate headquarters location:** This location. **Number of employees at this location:** 11,500.

UNIVERSITY OF MIAMI
1507 Levante Avenue, Coral Gables FL 33124. 305/284-2211. **Contact:** Human Resources Department. **World Wide Web address:** http://www.miami.edu. **Description:** A university offering bachelor's, master's, doctoral, and professional degrees. **NOTE:** Jobseekers are advised to obtain a copy of the university's job bulletin through the Website for information about employment opportunities. **Number of employees at this location:** More than 9,000.

UNIVERSITY OF NORTH FLORIDA
4567 St. John's Bluff Road South, Jacksonville FL 32224. 904/620-2903. **Contact:** Human Resources Department. **World Wide Web address:** http://www.unf.edu. **Description:** A university offering graduate and undergraduate programs to approximately 12,000 students. **Common positions include:** Accountant/Auditor; Blue-Collar Worker Supervisor; Broadcast Technician; Clerical Supervisor; Computer Programmer; Human Resources Manager; Library Technician; Purchasing Agent/Manager; Systems Analyst. **Corporate headquarters location:** Tallahassee FL. **President:** Annie H. Hopkins.

UNIVERSITY OF SOUTH FLORIDA (USF)
4202 East Fowler Avenue, SVC 2172, Tampa FL 33620-6980. 813/974-2974. **Contact:** Human Resources. **World Wide Web address:** http://www.usf.edu. **Description:** A state university serving approximately 37,000 undergraduate, graduate, and doctoral students.

UNIVERSITY OF WEST FLORIDA

11000 University Parkway, Pensacola FL 32514-5750. 850/474-2694. **Recorded jobline:** 850/474-2842. **Contact:** Human Resources Department. **World Wide Web address:** http://www.uwf.edu. **Description:** A university offering associate's, bachelor's, master's, and doctoral degrees to approximately 8,000 students. **President:** Dr. Morris L. Marx.

ELECTRONIC/INDUSTRIAL ELECTRICAL EQUIPMENT

You can expect to find the following types of companies in this chapter:

Electronic Machines and Systems
Semiconductor Manufacturers

A-1 COMPONENTS, INC.
625 West 18th Street, Hialeah FL 33010. 305/885-1911. **Fax:** 305/884-1847. **Contact:** Human Resources Department. **World Wide Web address:** http://www.a-1components.com. **Description:** Develops, manufactures, and distributes a wide range of climate control products and related equipment. The company's products include electronics controls, timers, and start kits; mechanical valves, fittings, tubing, and driers; pressure switches and temperature control devices; cam-stat controls; chemicals; thermostat guards; capacitors; relays; transformers; and motors. **Common positions include:** Accountant/Auditor; Blue-Collar Worker Supervisor; Buyer; Computer Operator; Computer Programmer; Credit Clerk and Authorizer; Credit Manager; Customer Service Representative; Department Manager; Draftsperson; Electrical/Electronics Engineer; Electrician; Financial Manager; Heating/AC/Refrigeration Technician; Human Resources Manager; Inspector/Tester/Grader; Machinist; Marketing Manager; Mechanical Engineer; Millwright; Payroll Clerk; Precision Assembler; Production Manager; Purchasing Agent/Manager; Quality Control Supervisor; Receptionist; Secretary; Statistician; Stock Clerk; Systems Analyst; Tool and Die Maker; Truck Driver; Typist/Word Processor; Welder. **Corporate headquarters location:** This location. **Operations at this facility include:** Administration; Manufacturing; Regional Headquarters; Research and Development; Sales; Service. **Number of employees at this location:** 300.

ACR ELECTRONICS
5757 Ravenswood Road, Fort Lauderdale FL 33312. 954/981-3333. **Contact:** Human Resources Department. **World Wide Web address:** http://www.acrelectronics.com. **Description:** Manufactures survival and safety electronics equipment for the government, marine, and outdoor recreation markets.

ATK INTEGRATED DEFENSE COMPANY
P.O. Box 4648, Clearwater FL 33758-4648. 727/572-1900. **Fax:** 727/572-2453. **Contact:** Human Resources. **World Wide Web address:** http://www.atk.com. **Description:** An electronics testing center and manufacturing facility. **Common positions include:** Draftsperson; Electrical/Electronics Engineer; General Manager; Hardware Engineer; Mechanical Engineer; Software Engineer; Systems Analyst; Technical Writer/Editor. **Corporate headquarters location:** Minneapolis MN. **Other U.S. locations:** Patuxent River MD; Eatontown NJ; San Antonio TX. **Parent company:** Alliant Techsystems. **Listed on:** New York Stock Exchange. **Stock exchange symbol:** ATK.

A.W. INDUSTRIES
6788 NW 17th Avenue, Fort Lauderdale FL 33309. 954/979-5696. **Contact:** Human Resources. **World Wide Web address:** http://www.awiconnectors.com. **Description:** Designs and manufactures electronic circuits.

ARTESYN TECHNOLOGIES
7900 Glades Road, Suite 500, Boca Raton FL 33434. 561/451-1000. **Fax:** 561/451-1050. **Contact:** Personnel. **World Wide Web address:** http://www.artesyn.com. **Description:** A designer and producer of electronic products and subsystems. The company manufactures both standard and custom products used in an array of applications including powering communications networks, controlling the manufacture of fiber optics, enabling voice messaging, powering multimedia applications for global Internet servers, and operating traffic signals with real-time embedded computers. The company consists of three business segments: Power Conversion supplies power systems technology to the communications industry; RTP Corporation delivers input/output products and intelligent controllers; and Heurikon Corporation designs and provides real-time computers and subsystems tailored to the markets of voice messaging, graphics, video-on-demand, machine vision, and simulation. **Common positions include:** Aerospace Engineer; Computer Programmer; Electrical/Electronics Engineer. **Other U.S. locations:** Fremont CA; Pompano Beach FL; Boston MA; Madison WI. **Operations at this facility include:** Administration. **Listed on:** NASDAQ. **Stock exchange symbol:** ATSN. **Number of employees nationwide:** 1,600.

BAE SYSTEMS
P.O. Box 1500, Tampa 33684. 813/885-7481. **Contact:** Personnel. **E-mail address:** careers@baesystems.com. **World Wide Web address:** http://www.baesystems.com. **Description:** Designs, manufactures, and sells flight simulators, weapon systems, tactical air defense systems, small arms, and training devices for the U.S. government, as well as commercial and international customers. BAE SYSTEMS also develops simulation-based devices for the entertainment industry. The company also provides a variety of simulator-related training services at customer-owned facilities, its Tampa training center, and the British Aerospace-owned Dulles training facility. BAE SYSTEMS conducts business through its three primary operating segments: Training Devices, Training Services, and Systems Management. **Common positions include:** Accountant/Auditor; Administrator; Aerospace

Engineer; Buyer; Draftsperson; Electrical/Electronics Engineer; Industrial Designer; Mechanical Engineer; Purchasing Agent/Manager; Quality Control Supervisor. **Corporate headquarters location:** This location. **Subsidiaries include:** Reflectone UK Limited. **Number of employees at this location:** 400. **Number of employees nationwide:** 980.

CHROMALLOY FLORIDA
630 Anchors Street NW, Fort Walton Beach FL 32548. 850/244-7684. **Contact:** Human Resources. **Description:** Repairs turbine jet engine component parts. **Common positions include:** Mechanical Engineer; Metallurgical Engineer. **Operations at this facility include:** Administration; Manufacturing.

CONAX FLORIDA CORPORATION
2801 75th Street North, St. Petersburg FL 33710. 727/345-8000. **Fax:** 727/345-4217. **Contact:** Sandy Nitz, Human Resources Administrator. **World Wide Web address:** http://www.conaxfl.com. **Description:** Manufactures temperature sensing devices, explosive actuated devices, and electrical penetrators. **Common positions include:** Electrical/Electronics Engineer; Mechanical Engineer. **Corporate headquarters location:** This location. **Listed on:** Privately held. **Number of employees at this location:** 125.

CONCORD CAMERA CORPORATION
4000 Hollywood Boulevard, Suite 650N, Hollywood FL 33021. 954/331-4200. **Fax:** 954/981-3055. **Contact:** Human Resources Department. **World Wide Web address:** http://www.concordcam.com. **Description:** Designs, develops, manufactures, and markets a wide range of digital, traditional 35-mm, instant, and single-use cameras. **Corporate headquarters location:** This location. **Listed on:** NASDAQ. **Stock exchange symbol:** LENS. **Annual sales/revenues:** More than $100 million. **Number of employees worldwide:** 6,000.

CYPRESS ELECTRONICS
10901 Malcolm McKinley Drive, Tampa FL 33612. 813/972-6000. **Fax:** 813/972-6012. **Contact:** Janice Beal, Personnel Director. **Description:** Custom designs and manufactures electronics systems, subsystems, and circuit card assemblies for the U.S. government and avionics, communications, and medical industries. **Corporate headquarters location:** This location.

DANKA OFFICE IMAGING
11201 Danka Circle North, St. Petersburg FL 33716. 727/576-6003. **Contact:** Human Resources. **World Wide Web address:** http://www.danka.com. **Description:** A wholesale distributor of fax machines and photocopiers. **Corporate headquarters location:** This location. **Listed on:** NASDAQ. **Stock exchange symbol:** DANKY.

DYNALCO CONTROLS
3690 NW 53rd Street, Fort Lauderdale FL 33309. 954/739-4300. **Contact:** Craig Woetzel, Human Resources Manager. **E-mail address:** careers@dynalco.com. **World Wide Web address:** http:// www.dynalco.com. **Description:** Manufactures electronic monitors, controls, sensors, and displays, primarily for stationary engines. **Common positions include:** Accountant/Auditor; Buyer; Electrical/Electronics Engineer; Operations/Production Manager; Technical Writer/Editor. **Corporate headquarters location:** Skokie IL. **Other U.S. locations:** Long Beach CA; Billerica MA; Tulsa OK. **Parent company:** Crane Company. **Operations at this facility include:** Administration; Manufacturing; Research and Development; Sales; Service. **Number of employees at this location:** 80.

ELECTRO CORPORATION
1845 57th Street, Sarasota FL 34243. 941/355-8411. **Contact:** Beverly Morrell, Human Resources Manager. **World Wide Web address:** http://www.electrocorp.com. **Description:** A manufacturer of magnetic sensing devices, tachometers, proximity switches, and circuit and control systems. **Common positions include:** Accountant/Auditor; Blue-Collar Worker Supervisor; Buyer; Computer Programmer; Customer Service Representative; Draftsperson; Electrical/Electronics Engineer; Human Resources Manager; Industrial Engineer; Marketing Specialist; Mechanical Engineer; Operations/Production Manager; Purchasing Agent/Manager; Quality Control Supervisor; Services Sales Representative; Systems Analyst. **Corporate headquarters location:** This location. **Parent company:** Invensys Sensor Systems. **Operations at this facility include:** Manufacturing.

ELTEC INSTRUMENTS INC.
P.O. Box 9610, Daytona Beach FL 32120. 386/252-0411. **Contact:** Samuel D. Mollenkof, Human Resources Director. **Description:** Develops, manufactures, and markets infrared sensors, industrial control systems, and ohm resistors. Primary customers include alarm manufacturers; building automation systems, heating, air conditioning, and lighting control

marketers; and process control systems developers. **Common positions include:** Accountant/Auditor; Administrator; Buyer; Draftsperson; Electrical/Electronics Engineer; Human Resources Manager; Operations/Production Manager; Purchasing Agent/Manager; Sensors Engineer; Systems Engineer. **Corporate headquarters location:** This location. **Operations at this facility include:** Administration; Manufacturing; Research and Development; Sales; Service.

GE AUTOMATION SERVICES
P.O. Box 7126, Pensacola FL 32534. 850/968-2191. **Contact:** Human Resources Department. **World Wide Web address:** http://www.geindustrial.com. **Description:** A manufacturer of industrial control instruments. **Listed on:** New York Stock Exchange. **Stock exchange symbol:** GE.

HARRIS CORPORATION
1025 West NASA Boulevard, Mail Stop 19, Melbourne FL 32919. 321/727-9207. **Toll-free phone:** 800/4HA-RRIS. **Contact:** Human Resources. **World Wide Web address:** http://www.harris.com. **Description:** A communications equipment company that provides broadcast, network, government, and wireless support products and systems. **NOTE:** Send resumes to: Harris Corporation, Resume Proccessing, P.O. Box 549238, Suite 107, Waltham MA 02454. **Common positions include:** Accountant/Auditor; Administrator; Attorney; Blue-Collar Worker Supervisor; Computer Programmer; Customer Service Representative; Department Manager; Editor; Electrical/Electronics Engineer; Financial Analyst; General Manager; Human Resources Manager; Industrial Engineer; Manufacturer's/Wholesaler's Sales Rep.; Marketing Specialist; Mechanical Engineer; Metallurgical Engineer; Operations/Production Manager; Public Relations Specialist; Purchasing Agent/Manager; Quality Control Supervisor; Reporter; Systems Analyst. **Corporate headquarters location:** This location. **International locations:** Worldwide. **Operations at this facility include:** Administration; Manufacturing; Research and Development; Sales; Service. **Listed on:** New York Stock Exchange. **Stock exchange symbol:** HRS. **President/CEO:** Phillip W. Farmer. **Number of employees worldwide:** 10,000.

HI*TECH ELECTRONIC DISPLAYS
13900 U.S. Highway 19 North, Clearwater FL 33764. 727/531-4800. **Toll-free phone:** 800/723-9402. **Fax:** 727/524-6655. **Contact:** Laurie Danielson, Human Resources. **World Wide Web address:** http://www.hitechled.com. **Description:**

Manufactures LED displays. Products and services include indoor and outdoor LED signs; customized graphics, logos, and animations; and software and computer accessories to run the company's LED displays. **NOTE:** Entry-level positions are offered. **Common positions include:** Advertising Clerk; Computer Programmer; Electrical/Electronics Engineer; Graphic Artist; Production Manager; Project Manager; Quality Control Supervisor; Sales Representative; Software Engineer. **Corporate headquarters location:** This location. **Parent company:** Paonessa Holding Company. **Annual sales/revenues:** $21 - $50 million. **Number of employees at this location:** 95.

LAMBDA NOVATRONICS INC.
2855 West McNab Road, Pompano Beach FL 33069. 954/984-7000. **Contact:** Pauline Akonskey, Human Resources. **World Wide Web address:** http://www.lambdanovatronics.com. **Description:** Designs and manufactures power supplies, avionics, and precision equipment for the defense and electronics industries. **Common positions include:** Aerospace Engineer; Electrical/Electronics Engineer; Industrial Engineer; Mechanical Engineer. **Corporate headquarters location:** Melville NY. **Number of employees at this location:** 240.

LIGHTING COMPONENTS & DESIGN, INC.
692 South Military Trail, Deerfield Beach FL 33442. 954/425-0123. **Contact:** Department of Human Resources. **E-mail address:** lcd@lightingcomponents.com. **World Wide Web address:** http://www.lightingcomponents.com. **Description:** A manufacturer of prewired electrical devices, indicator lights, and lamp holders. **Corporate headquarters location:** This location.

LOCKHEED MARTIN ELECTRONICS & MISSILES
498 Oak Road, Ocala FL 34472-3099. 352/687-2163. **Contact:** Human Resources Department. **World Wide Web address:** http://www.lockheedmartin.com. **Description:** Develops, manufactures, and supports advanced combat systems, electro-optics, and air defense technology. **Corporate headquarters location:** Bethesda MD. **Listed on:** New York Stock Exchange. **Stock exchange symbol:** LMT.

LOCKHEED MARTIN MISSILES AND FIRE CONTROL
5600 Sand Lake Road, Mail Point 9, Orlando FL 32819. 407/356-5215. **Fax:** 407/356-3639. **Contact:** Bruce Czarniak, Manager of Staffing. **World Wide Web address:** http://www.lockheedmartin.com. **Description:** Develops,

manufactures, and supports advanced combat systems, electro-optics, and air defense technologies. **Common positions include:** Accountant/Auditor; Aerospace Engineer; Buyer; Computer Programmer; Design Engineer; Designer; Electrical/Electronics Engineer; Financial Analyst; Human Resources Manager; Industrial Engineer; Manufacturing Engineer; Mechanical Engineer; Software Engineer; Structural Engineer; Systems Analyst. **Corporate headquarters location:** Bethesda MD. **Operations at this facility include:** Administration; Manufacturing; Research and Development; Sales. **Listed on:** New York Stock Exchange. **Stock exchange symbol:** LMT. **Annual sales/revenues:** More than $100 million. **Number of employees at this location:** 3,750.

LOCKHEED MARTIN TACTICAL DEFENSE SYSTEMS
P.O. Box 6000, Clearwater FL 33758. 813/855-5711. **Fax:** 813/854-7225. **Contact:** Human Resources Department. **World Wide Web address:** http://www.lockheedmartin.com. **Description:** This location is a computer hardware manufacturing facility. Overall, Lockheed Martin Tactical Defense Systems designs and builds 16-bit and 32-bit technical computing systems used in mil-spec environments. Applications include electronic warfare, signal intelligence, radar, sonar, and imaging where digital signal processing or general purpose computing is required. The company is also involved in systems engineering, software development tools, computer systems, and integrated workstations of commercial architectures for proof-of-concept program phases. **NOTE:** Entry-level positions and second shifts are offered. **Common positions include:** Blue-Collar Worker Supervisor; Electrical/Electronics Engineer; Industrial Engineer; Industrial Production Manager; Manufacturing Engineer; Production Manager. **Special programs:** Training. **Corporate headquarters location:** Bethesda MD. **Other U.S. locations:** Nationwide. **International locations:** Worldwide. **Parent company:** Lockheed Martin Corporation. **Listed on:** New York Stock Exchange. **Stock exchange symbol:** LMT. **Number of employees at this location:** 500.

MICRO SYSTEMS, INC.
35 Hill Avenue, Fort Walton Beach FL 32548. 850/244-2332. **Fax:** 850/243-1378. **Contact:** Tami L. Manard, Director of Human Resources Department. **World Wide Web address:** http://www.gomicrosystems.com. **Description:** Designs and manufactures real-time, microprocessor-based control systems that create interfaces between targets and their controlling ground stations. The company's equipment is built under

contract for the U.S. Department of Defense. **NOTE:** Entry-level positions are offered. **Common positions include:** Design Engineer; Draftsperson; Electrical/Electronics Engineer; Production Manager; Software Engineer. **Special programs:** Internships. **Corporate headquarters location:** This location. **Listed on:** Privately held. **Annual sales/revenues:** $5 - $10 million. **Number of employees at this location:** 100.

NORTHROP GRUMMAN
P.O. Box 547300, Orlando, FL 32854. 407/295-4010. **Contact:** Department of Human Resources. **World Wide Web address:** http://www.northropgrumman.com. **Description:** Designs, develops, and manufactures military and commercial laser systems. **Common positions include:** Accountant/Auditor; Aerospace Engineer; Buyer; Cashier; Chef/Cook/Kitchen Worker; Draftsperson; Electrical/Electronics Engineer; Financial Manager; Food and Beverage Service Worker; Human Resources Manager; Inspector/Tester/Grader; Librarian; Machinist; Mechanical Engineer; Payroll Clerk; Purchasing Agent/Manager; Secretary; Stock Clerk; Typist/Word Processor. **Corporate headquarters location:** Los Angeles CA. **Operations at this facility include:** Administration; Divisional Headquarters; Manufacturing; Research and Development. **Listed on:** New York Stock Exchange. **Stock exchange symbol:** NOC. **Number of employees at this location:** 400.

NORTHROP GRUMMAN
950 North Orlando Avenue, Suite 200, Winter Park FL 32789. 407/629-6010. **Contact:** Human Resources. **World Wide Web address:** http://northropgrumman.com. **Description:** Develops software and information technology systems for the U.S. military and government. **Corporate headquarters location:** Los Angeles CA. **Listed on:** New York Stock Exchange. **Stock exchange symbol:** NOC.

PIEZO TECHNOLOGY, INC. (PTI)
P.O. Box 547859, Orlando FL 32854. 407/298-2000. **Contact:** Human Resources. **E-mail address:** resume@piezotech.com. **World Wide Web address:** http://www.piezotech.com. **Description:** Manufactures frequency control systems for defense industry communications systems.

SENSORMATIC ELECTRONICS CORPORATION
6600 Congress Avenue, Boca Raton FL 33487. 561/912-6000. **Contact:** Human Resources. **World Wide Web address:** http://www.sensormatic.com. **Description:** Manufactures and services electronic security systems to retail and commercial

businesses worldwide. The company's products include AC500 Access Control System, which integrates hands-free access control with video imaging; SpeedDome programmable dome camera; Alligator antishoplifting tags; AisleKeeper, SekurPost, and SuperTag antishoplifting systems; Electronic Asset Protection systems; and SekurNed systems, which monitor and track hospital patients. **Common positions include:** Accountant/Auditor; Computer Programmer; Customer Service Rep.; Draftsperson; Electrical/Electronics Engineer; Financial Analyst; Industrial Engineer; Marketing Specialist; Mechanical Engineer; Operations/Production Manager; Purchasing Agent/Manager; Quality Control Supervisor; Services Sales Representative; Systems Analyst. **Operations at this facility include:** Administration; Manufacturing; Research and Development. **Listed on:** New York Stock Exchange. **Stock exchange symbol:** SRM. **Number of employees nationwide:** 5,500.

SIGNAL TECHNOLOGY CORPORATION
84 Hill Avenue, Fort Walton Beach FL 32548. 850/244-0043. **Contact:** Human Resources Department. **World Wide Web address:** http://www.sigtech.com. **Description:** Designs and manufactures power conversion equipment. **Other U.S. locations:** AZ; CA; MA; TX. **Listed on:** NASDAQ. **Stock exchange symbol:** STCO.

SOLECTRON
1601 Hill Avenue, West Palm Beach FL 33407. 561/845-8455. **Fax:** 561/881-2342. **Contact:** Human Resources Department. **World Wide Web address:** http://www.solectron.com. **Description:** A manufacturer of microcircuits, multichip modules, complex backpanels, and card cage assemblies. **Common positions include:** Accountant/Auditor; Administrator; Blue-Collar Worker Supervisor; Buyer; Ceramics Engineer; Chemical Engineer; Computer Programmer; Cost Estimator; Customer Service Representative; Department Manager; Electrical/Electronics Engineer; Environmental Engineer; General Manager; Health Services Worker; Human Resources Manager; Industrial Engineer; Mechanical Engineer; Process Engineer; Quality Assurance Engineer; Quality Control Supervisor; Systems Analyst; Test Engineer. **Other U.S. locations:** Nationwide. **International locations:** Worldwide. **Listed on:** New York Stock Exchange. **Stock exchange symbol:** SLR. **President/CEO:** Koichi Nishimura.

SOLITRON DEVICES, INC.
3301 Electronics Way, West Palm Beach FL 33407. 561/848-4311. **Fax:** 561/881-5652. **Contact:** Human Resources. **World Wide Web address:** http://www.solitrondevices.com. **Description:** Designs and manufactures high-density power components and circuitry. The company's semiconductor and hybrid circuit products are sold to national and international aerospace and defense programs. **Common positions include:** Accountant/Auditor; Advertising Clerk; Budget Analyst; Buyer; Chemical Engineer; Clerical Supervisor; Cost Estimator; Credit Clerk and Authorizer; Credit Manager; Customer Service Representative; Department Manager; Designer; Draftsperson; Electrical/Electronics Engineer; Electrician; Financial Manager; General Manager; Human Resources Manager; Industrial Engineer; Machinist; Manufacturer's/Wholesaler's Sales Rep.; Marketing Manager; Mechanical Engineer; Order Clerk; Payroll Clerk; Precision Assembler; Purchasing Agent/Manager; Quality Control Supervisor; Receptionist; Secretary; Stock Clerk; Systems Analyst; Tool and Die Maker. **Corporate headquarters location:** This location. **Other U.S. locations:** Nationwide. **Listed on:** NASDAQ. **Stock exchange symbol:** SODI. **Number of employees at this location:** 100.

SPARTON ELECTRONICS
P.O. Box 788, DeLeon Springs FL 32130. 386/985-4631. **Physical address:** 5612 Johnson Lake Road, DeLeon Springs FL 32130. **Fax:** 386/985-5036. **Contact:** Human Resources. **World Wide Web address:** http://www.sparton.com. **Description:** Offers electronics engineering and manufacturing services including design engineering, development engineering, manufacturing, and test engineering. Capabilities include DFMA, box build, board layout, rapid prototyping, mechanical design, system integration, full environmentals, design from concept, board-level assembly, software development, and concurrent engineering. Sparton technical design skills include electronics (analog, digital, solid-state devices, hybrid circuits, VHF transmitters, UHF receivers, custom integrated circuits, and signal processing); mechanics (die casting, injection molding, stamping, extrusions, blow molding, and flotation systems); sensors (hydrophones, transducers, magnetics, acoustics, ultrasonics, and pressure); computers (programming, modeling, automatic test, design analysis, statistical analysis, finite element analysis, and algorithms); chemistry (electrochemistry, batteries, polymers, adhesives, and encapsulants); and environmental (hi-g shock, random vibration, humidity, temperature, altitude, high pressure, and shelf life). **Common positions include:**

Accountant/Auditor; Design Engineer; Electrical/Electronics Engineer; Industrial Engineer; Manufacturing Engineer; Mechanical Engineer; Software Engineer. **Corporate headquarters location:** Jackson MI. **Other area locations:** Brooksville FL. **Other U.S. locations:** NM; NC. **International locations:** Canada. **Operations at this facility include:** Administration; Divisional Headquarters; Manufacturing. **Listed on:** New York Stock Exchange. **Stock exchange symbol:** SPA.

SPARTON ELECTRONICS
30167 Power Line Road, Brooksville FL 34602. 352/799-6520. **Fax:** 352/799-4759. **Contact:** Human Resources Department. **World Wide Web address:** http://www.sparton.com. **Description:** Offers electronics engineering and manufacturing services including design engineering, development engineering, manufacturing, and test engineering. Capabilities include DFMA, box build, board layout, rapid prototyping, mechanical design, system integration, full environmentals, design from concept, board-level assembly, software development, and concurrent engineering. Sparton technical design skills include electronics (analog, digital, solid-state devices, hybrid circuits, VHF transmitters, UHF receivers, custom integrated circuits, and signal processing); mechanics (die casting, injection molding, stamping, extrusions, blow molding, and flotation systems); sensors (hydrophones, transducers, magnetics, acoustics, ultrasonics, and pressure); computers (programming, modeling, automatic test, design analysis, statistical analysis, finite element analysis, and algorithms); chemistry (electrochemistry, batteries, polymers, adhesives, and encapsulants); and environmental (hi-g shock, random vibration, humidity, temperature, altitude, high pressure, and shelf life). **Corporate headquarters location:** Jackson MI. **Other area locations:** De Leon Springs FL. **Other U.S. locations:** NC; NM. **International locations:** Canada. **Listed on:** New York Stock Exchange. **Stock exchange symbol:** SPA.

TITAN CORPORATION
P.O. Box 550, Melbourne FL 32902-0550. 321/727-0660. **Contact:** Linda Rauscher, Human Resources Director. **World Wide Web address:** http://www.titan.com. **Description:** Develops and manufactures advanced analytical software for use in remote sensing and orbital mechanics and electronics systems for video tracking and precision film scanning digitizer applications. The company also develops specialized electronic systems for the United States Defense Department.

Common positions include: Computer Programmer; Electrical/Electronics Engineer; Systems Analyst. **Corporate headquarters location:** San Diego CA. **Other U.S. locations:** Nationwide. **International locations:** Worldwide. **Listed on:** New York Stock Exchange. **Stock exchange symbol:** TTN. **Number of employees at this location:** 130. **Number of employees worldwide:** 10,000.

TITAN SYSTEMS CORPORATION
7104 Laird Street, Panama City Beach FL 32408-7666. 850/234-3940. **Fax:** 850/234-1168. **Contact:** Personnel. **World Wide Web address:** http://www.titansystemscorp.com. **Description:** Provides information technology services and electronics systems to government and commercial customers worldwide. The company works principally in the following areas: Antisubmarine/Undersea Warfare, Surface Warfare, Torpedo/Electronics Countermeasures, Amphibious Warfare, War Gaming, Tactical Air Warfare, Unmanned Aerial Vehicles, and Littoral Warfare. In addition to supporting the military in system design and development, Titan Systems designs and builds its own high-tech products. These product areas include test equipment and simulation systems for the Global Positioning System markets, navigation systems for shipboard application, and air data systems for helicopters and other vertical-take-off-and-landing aircraft. **Corporate headquarters location:** San Diego CA. **Listed on:** NYSE. **Stock exchange symbol:** TTN. **Number of employees worldwide:** 10,000.

TRAK MICROWAVE CORPORATION
4726 Eisenhower Boulevard, Tampa FL 33634. 813/884-1411. **Fax:** 813/901-7497. **Contact:** Linda Reynolds, Manager of Human Resources. **World Wide Web address:** http://www.trak.com. **Description:** A supplier of active and passive electronic microwave components, microwave subsystems, ferrite products, and precision timing equipment for use in communication systems and radar products. The microwave components include energy sources (oscillators and amplifiers), frequency multipliers, filters, ferrite isolators and circulators, and a broad range of passive components for modulation and control of microwave energy. The microwave subsystems consist of synthesizers, frequency converters, and microwave receiver assemblies. TRAK's microwave components and subsystems can be found in defense products such as electronic warfare equipment, defense radars, communications equipment, and missile guidance systems. Space applications include components for communication, television broadcast, meteorological, earth resource, and

intelligence gathering satellites. Commercial applications include Transponder Collision Avoidance Systems, Microwave Landing Systems, radar altimeters, distance measuring equipment, and airborne weather radar. TRAK also builds timing systems for use by government and commercial organizations. Timing products are used to provide signals to time or initiate events by extracting time information from the NAVSTAR satellites of the Global Positioning System (operated by the U.S. government), and in the synchronizing of communication carrier signals between sites. **Common positions include:** Accountant/Auditor; Buyer; Computer Programmer; Draftsperson; Electrical/Electronics Engineer; Mechanical Engineer; Registered Nurse. **Other U.S. locations:** MD. **International locations:** Scotland. **Operations at this facility include:** Administration; Manufacturing; Sales. **Listed on:** Privately held.

ENVIRONMENTAL AND WASTE MANAGEMENT SERVICES

You can expect to find the following types of companies in this chapter:

Environmental Engineering Firms
Sanitary Services

AJT & ASSOCIATES, INC.
8910 Astronaut Boulevard, Cape Canaveral FL 32920-4225. 321/783-7989. **Contact:** Department of Human Resources. **World Wide Web address:** http://www.ajt-assoc.com. **Description:** Provides environmental science and architectural engineering services. **Common positions include:** Architect; Civil Engineer; Electrical/Electronics Engineer; Environmental Engineer; Mechanical Engineer.

ATC ASSOCIATES
9955 NW 116 Way, Suite 1, Miami FL 33178. 305/882-8200. **Contact:** Human Resources Department. **World Wide Web address:** http://www.atc-enviro.com. **Description:** Performs comprehensive environmental consulting, engineering, and on-site remediation services. Services include assessment of environmental regulations, investigation of contaminated sites, and the design and engineering of methods to correct or prevent the contamination. The company also performs remedial actions, and emergency response actions in cases of spills and accidental releases of hazardous waste. ATC Associates addresses hazardous and nonhazardous contaminants in municipal and industrial water supplies; in wastewater and storm water from municipal, industrial, and military installations; and in groundwater, soils, and air space. Customers include federal, state, and local government agencies.

BROWNING-FERRIS INDUSTRIES, INC. (BFI)
1475 SW 4th Avenue, Delray Beach FL 33444. 561/278-1717. **Contact:** Human Resources Department. **Description:** Engaged in the collection and disposal of solid waste for commercial, industrial, and residential customers. Services provided by Browning-Ferris Industries include landfill services, waste-to-energy programs, hazardous waste removal, and liquid waste removal. The company has worldwide operations at more than 500 facilities. **Parent company:** Allied Waste Industries, Inc.

EVANS ENVIRONMENTAL CORPORATION
14505 Commerce Way, Suite 400, Miami Lakes FL 33016. 305/374-8300. **Contact:** Human Resources. **World Wide Web address:** http://www.eandg.com. **Description:** Engaged in environmental testing and consulting, and in the manufacture and distribution of remote control cable television units. **Subsidiaries include:** ABC Cable Products, Inc.; Enviropact Consultants, Inc.; Evans Environmental & Geological Sciences & Management, Inc.; Evans Management Co.; Geos Inc.

HARDING ESE
P.O. Box 1703, Gainesville FL 32602-1703. 352/333-7622.
Physical address: 404 South West 140th Terrace, Newberry FL
32669-3000. **Fax:** 352/333-2611. **Contact:** Melody Creek,
Human Resources Generalist. **Description:** Offers a full range
of consulting services in environmental and engineering
consulting, laboratory analysis, asbestos management,
industrial hygiene, engineering, and architecture for
governmental, industrial, and commercial clients. **Other U.S.
locations:** Nationwide. **Subsidiaries include:** Keck Instruments,
Inc. **Number of employees at this location:** 420.

MUNTERS CORPORATION
P.O. Box 6428, Fort Myers FL 33911. 941/936-1555. **Contact:**
Human Resources Department. **World Wide Web address:**
http://www.munters-fl.com. **Description:** An environmental
technology and pollution control company. **Common positions
include:** Accountant/Auditor; Blue-Collar Worker Supervisor;
Draftsperson; Electrician; Industrial Production Manager;
Mechanical Engineer; Purchasing Agent/Manager. **Operations
at this facility include:** Administration; Manufacturing;
Research and Development; Sales. **Number of employees at
this location:** 120. **Number of employees nationwide:** 420.

SEVERN TRENT LABORATORIES, INC.
3355 Meclemore Drive, Pensacola FL 32514. 850/474-1001.
Contact: Human Resources Department. **World Wide Web
address:** http://www.stl-inc.com. **Description:** Provides a
complete range of environmental testing services to private
industry, engineering consultants, and government agencies in
support of federal and state environmental regulations. The
company also possesses analytical capabilities in the fields of
air toxins, field analytical services, radiochemistry/mixed
waste, and advanced technology. **Other area locations:** Tampa
FL. **Other U.S. locations:** Nationwide. **Parent Company:**
Severn Trent plc. **Number of employees nationwide:** Over
2,000.

SEVERN TRENT LABORATORIES, INC.
6712 Benjamin Road Suite 100, Tampa FL 33634. 813/621-
0784. **Fax:** 813/885-7049. **Contact:** Human Resources. **World
Wide Web address:** http://www.stl-inc.com. **Description:**
Provides a complete range of environmental testing services to
private industry, engineering consultants, and government
agencies in support of federal and state environmental
regulations. The company also possesses analytical capabilities
in the fields of air toxins, field analytical services,

radiochemistry/mixed waste, and advanced technology **Other area locations:** Pensacola FL. **Other U.S. locations:** Nationwide. **Parent Company:** Severn Trent plc. **Number of employees nationwide:** Over 2,000.

FABRICATED/PRIMARY METALS AND PRODUCTS

You can expect to find the following types of companies in this chapter:

Aluminum and Copper Foundries
Die-Castings
Iron and Steel Foundries
Steel Works, Blast Furnaces, and Rolling Mills

ASHLEY ALUMINUM, LLC
dba CAMERON ASHLEY BUILDING PRODUCTS
P.O. Drawer 15398, Tampa FL 33684. 813/884-0444. **Toll-free phone:** 800/749-4067. **Contact:** Human Resources. **World Wide Web address:** http://www.cabp.com. **Description:** A manufacturer and distributor of aluminum and vinyl building products. Founded in 1967. **Common positions include:** Accountant; Administrative Assistant; Auditor; Blue-Collar Worker Supervisor; Branch Manager; Chief Financial Officer; Clerical Supervisor; Computer Programmer; Controller; Customer Service Representative; General Manager; Human Resources Manager; Management Trainee; Operations Manager; Purchasing Agent/Manager; Sales Representative; Systems Analyst; Systems Manager. **Office hours:** Monday - Friday, 8:00 a.m. - 5:00 p.m. **Corporate headquarters location:** This location. **Other U.S. locations:** AL; GA; KY; LA; TX. **Listed on:** New York Stock Exchange. **Stock exchange symbol:** CAB. **President:** Steve Gaffney. **Annual sales/revenues:** More than $100 million. **Number of employees at this location:** 100. **Number of employees nationwide:** 500.

SONOCO PRODUCTS
1854 Central Florida Parkway, Orlando FL 32837. 407/851-5800. **Contact:** Human Resources. **World Wide Web address:** http://www.sonoco.com. **Description:** Manufactures a variety of packaging materials for industrial and consumer markets. **Corporate headquarters location:** Hartsville SC. **Other U.S. locations:** Nationwide. **International locations:** Worldwide. **Listed on:** New York Stock Exchange. **Stock exchange symbol:** SON. **President/CEO:** Harris E. DeLoach, Jr. **Annual sales/revenues:** More than $100 million. **Number of employees worldwide:** 18,000.

VAW OF AMERICA INC.
101 East Town Place, Suite 800, St. Augustine FL 32092. 904/794-1500. **Fax:** 904/940-1535. **Contact:** David Black. **E-mail address:** dblack@vawusa.com. **World Wide Web address:** http://www.vawusa.com. **Description:** Manufactures aluminum billets, drawn tubes, extrusions, and fabricated and finished products in three plants in the United States. **Common positions include:** Blue-Collar Worker Supervisor; Designer; Draftsperson; Industrial Production Manager; Maintenance Supervisor; Manufacturer's/Wholesaler's Sales Rep.; Mechanical Engineer; Metallurgical Engineer; Quality Control Supervisor. **Corporate headquarters location:** This location. **Other U.S. locations:** Phoenix AZ; Ellenville NY; Fayetteville

TN. **International locations:** Mexico. **Operations at this facility include:** Administration; Manufacturing; Sales. **Listed on:** Privately held. **Number of employees at this location:** 525. **Number of employees nationwide:** 1,400.

FINANCIAL SERVICES

You can expect to find the following types of companies in this chapter:

Consumer Finance and Credit Agencies
Investment Specialists
Mortgage Bankers and Loan Brokers
Security and Commodity Brokers, Dealers, and Exchanges

ALLIANCE MORTGAGE COMPANY
8100 Nations Way, Jacksonville FL 32256. 904/281-6000. **Fax:** 904/281-6165. **Contact:** Human Resources Department. **World Wide Web address:** http://www.alliance-mortgage.com. **Description:** Engaged in the origination, purchase, sale, and servicing of residential first mortgages. Founded in 1962. **Common positions include:** Accountant/Auditor; Clerical Supervisor; Customer Service Representative; Loan Officer; Loan Processor. **Corporate headquarters location:** This location. **Operations at this facility include:** Administration; Production; Service. **Listed on:** Privately held. **Number of employees at this location:** 250. **Number of employees nationwide:** 350.

FIRST UNION SECURITIES FINANCIAL NETWORK
980 North Federal Highway, Boca Raton FL 33432. 561/338-2600. **Contact:** Human Resources Department. **World Wide Web address:** http://www.firstunionsec.com. **Description:** Provides a wide range of financial services including equity research, investment banking and advisory, trading, insurance annuities, and mutual funds. **Corporate headquarters location:** Richmond VA.

FISERV INC.
1250 Grumman Place, Suite A, Titusville FL 32780. 321/268-2622. **Contact:** Human Resources Department. **World Wide Web address:** http://www.fiserv.com. **Description:** Conducts online data processing for credit unions. **Listed on:** NASDAQ. **Stock exchange symbol:** FISV.

RAYMOND JAMES AND ASSOCIATES
P.O. Box 12749, St. Petersburg FL 33733-2749. 727/573-3800. **Physical address:** 880 Carillon Parkway, St. Petersburg FL 33716. **Fax:** 727/573-8420. **Recorded jobline:** 727/573-8490. **Contact:** Human Resources Department. **E-mail address:** employment@hr.rjf.com. **World Wide Web address:** http://www.rjf.com. **Description:** An investment brokerage firm. Founded in 1962. **Common positions include:** Accountant/Auditor; Administrator; Advertising Clerk; Customer Service Representative; Financial Analyst; Technical Writer/Editor. **Parent company:** Raymond James Financial, Inc. **Operations at this facility include:** Administration; Divisional Headquarters; Regional Headquarters; Research and Development; Sales; Service. **Listed on:** New York Stock Exchange. **Stock exchange symbol:** RJF.

J.I. KISLAK MORTGAGE CORPORATION
7900 Miami Lakes Drive West, Miami Lakes FL 33016. 305/364-4116. **Contact:** Department of Human Resources. **Description:** A mortgage banking and real estate firm. **Common positions include:** Accountant/Auditor; Bank Officer/Manager; Branch Manager; Claim Representative; Computer Programmer; Customer Service Representative; Department Manager; Financial Analyst; Human Resources Manager; Industrial Agent/Broker; Loan Officer; Marketing Specialist; Systems Analyst; Underwriter/Assistant Underwriter. **Corporate headquarters location:** This location.

LBS CAPITAL MANAGEMENT, INC.
311 Park Place Boulevard, Suite 330, Clearwater FL 33759. 727/726-5656. **Toll-free phone:** 800/477-1296. **Contact:** Human Resources Department. **World Wide Web address:** http://www.lbs.com. **Description:** A financial consulting firm.

MBNA MARKETING SYSTEMS, INC.
1501 Yamato Road, Boca Raton FL 33431. 561/988-5602. **Toll-free phone:** 888/786-6262. **Contact:** Jeff Woodin, Human Resources Department. **World Wide Web address:** http://www.mbnainternational.com. **Description:** MBNA Marketing Systems cross-sells individual loan, deposit, and insurance products. **Corporate headquarters location:** Wilmington DE. **International locations:** United Kingdom. **Parent company:** MBNA Corporation (Newark DE). **Listed on:** New York Stock Exchange. **Stock exchange symbol:** KRB.

MARSHALL & ILSLEY TRUST COMPANY OF FLORIDA
800 Laurel Oak Drive, Suite 101, Naples FL 34108. 941/597-2933. **Contact:** William Wade, President. **World Wide Web address:** http://www.mitrust.com. **Description:** Provides trust and custodial services for corporate, institutional, and individual clients in the Southeast. **Parent company:** Marshall & Ilsley Corporation (Milwaukee WI) is a diversified, interstate bank holding company. Other subsidiaries of Marshall & Ilsley include M&I Data Services, Inc. (supplies data processing services and software for financial institutions throughout the United States and in foreign countries); M&I Investment Management Corp. (manages investment portfolios for corporations, nonprofit organizations, and individuals throughout the United States and acts as an investment advisor to the Marshall Funds); M&I Marshall & Ilsley Trust Company of Arizona (provides trust and custodial services to clients in the Southwest); M&I First National Leasing Corp. (leases equipment and machinery to businesses throughout the United

States, primarily to middle-market corporations); M&I Capital Markets Group, Inc. (invests in small and medium-sized companies to help establish new businesses or recapitalize existing companies); M&I Brokerage Services, Inc. (a brokerage company providing a full range of investment products including stocks, bonds, and mutual funds for individual investors and small businesses); M&I Mortgage Corp. (originates and services a wide variety of home mortgages for M&I banks and other financial institutions); Richter-Schroeder Company, Inc. (provides construction loans and arranges permanent financing on income properties); and M&I Insurance Services, Inc. (acts as an independent insurance agency providing a full range of insurance products including annuities).

MERRILL LYNCH
50 P.O. Box 1918, Jacksonville FL 32201. 904/634-6000. **Physical address:** 50 North Laura Street, Suite 3700, Jacksonville FL 32202. **Contact:** Human Resources Department. **World Wide Web address:** http://www.ml.com. **Description:** A diversified financial service organization. Merrill Lynch is a major broker in securities, option contracts, commodities and financial futures contracts, and insurance. The company also deals with corporate and municipal securities and investment banking. **NOTE:** Call for specific information on where to mail a resume. **Corporate headquarters location:** New York NY. **Listed on:** New York Stock Exchange. **Stock exchange symbol:** MER.

MERRILL LYNCH
1401 Manatee Avenue West, 7th Floor, Bradenton FL 34205. 941/746-1123. **Contact:** Conni Gallagher, Administrative Secretary. **World Wide Web address:** http://www.ml.com. **Description:** A diversified financial service organization. Merrill Lynch is a major broker in securities, option contracts, commodities and financial futures contracts, and insurance. The company also deals with corporate and municipal securities and investment banking. **NOTE:** Call for specific information on where to mail a resume. **Common positions include:** Financial Consultant. **Corporate headquarters location:** New York NY. **Listed on:** New York Stock Exchange. **Stock exchange symbol:** MER. **Number of employees at this location:** 30.

MERRILL LYNCH
601 Cleveland Street, Suite 900, Clearwater FL 33755. 727/462-2300. **Contact:** Human Resources. **World Wide Web**

address: http://www.ml.com. **Description:** A diversified financial service organization. Merrill Lynch is a major broker in securities, option contracts, commodities and financial futures contracts, and insurance. The company also deals with corporate and municipal securities and investment banking. **NOTE:** Call for specific information on where to mail a resume. **Corporate headquarters location:** New York NY. **Listed on:** New York Stock Exchange. **Stock exchange symbol:** MER.

PRUDENTIAL SECURITIES, INC.
P.O. Box 45049, Jacksonville FL 32232-5049. 904/391-3400. **Physical address:** 701 San Marcos Boulevard, 19th Floor, Jacksonville FL 32207. **Contact:** Branch Manager. **World Wide Web address:** http://www.prufn.com. **Description:** An international securities brokerage and investment firm. The company offers clients more than 70 investment products including stocks, options, bonds, commodities, tax-favored investments, and insurance. Prudential Securities also offers specialized financial services. **Corporate headquarters location:** New York NY.

QUICK AND REILLY, INC.
230 South County Road, Palm Beach FL 33480. 561/655-8000. **Contact:** Human Resources. **World Wide Web address:** http://www.quick-reilly.com. **Description:** Quick and Reilly is a holding company that, through its subsidiaries, provides discount brokerage services primarily to retail customers throughout the United States. The company also clears securities transactions for its own customers and for other brokerage firms and banks and acts as a specialist on the floor of the New York Stock Exchange. **Number of employees nationwide:** 850.

SALOMON SMITH BARNEY
1301 Riverplace Boulevard, Suite 600, Jacksonville FL 32207. 904/858-2350. **Contact:** Human Resources. **World Wide Web address:** http://www.salomonsmithbarney.com. **Description:** An international investment banking, market making, and research firm serving corporations, governments, and other financial institutions. **Common positions include:** Brokerage Clerk; Customer Service Representative; Securities Sales Representative. **Corporate headquarters location:** New York NY. **Parent company:** Citigroup. **Operations at this facility include:** Sales. **Listed on:** New York Stock Exchange. **Stock exchange symbol:** C.

UBS PAINEWEBBER INC.
One Independent Drive, 2nd Floor, Jacksonville FL 32202. 904/354-6000. **Contact:** Human Resources Department. **World Wide Web address:** http://www.ubspainewebber.com. **Description:** A full-service securities firm with over 300 offices nationwide. Services include investment banking, asset management, merger and acquisition consulting, municipal securities underwriting, estate planning, retirement programs, and transaction management. UBS PaineWebber offers its services to corporations, governments, institutions, and individuals. Founded in 1879. **Common positions include:** Services Sales Representative. **Special programs:** Internships. **Corporate headquarters location:** New York NY. **Other U.S. locations:** Nationwide. **Operations at this facility include:** Sales; Service. **Listed on:** New York Stock Exchange. **Stock exchange symbol:** UBS. **Annual sales/revenues:** More than $100 million.

FOOD AND BEVERAGES/ AGRICULTURE

You can expect to find the following types of companies in this chapter:

Crop Services and Farm Supplies
Dairy Farms
Food Manufacturers/Processors and Agricultural Producers
Tobacco Products

ABC FINE WINE & SPIRITS

P.O. Box 593688, Orlando FL 32859. 407/851-0000. **Physical address:** 8989 South Orange Avenue, Orlando FL 32824. **Contact:** Human Resources Department. **World Wide Web address:** http://www.abcfinewineandspirits.com. **Description:** A privately-owned retailer of cigars, fine wine, gourmet food, and liquor. ABC Fine Wine & Spirits operates over 150 stores throughout Florida. Founded in 1936.

CF INDUSTRIES, INC./PLANT CITY

P.O. Drawer L, Plant City FL 33564. 813/782-1591. **Contact:** Harry Crosby, Human Resources. **World Wide Web address:** http://www.cfindustries.com. **Description:** This location manufactures phosphates for use in fertilizers.

CF INDUSTRIES, INC./TAMPA

2520 Guy Verger Boulevard, Tampa FL 33605. 813/247-5531. **Contact:** Ron Bigelow, Human Resources Department. **World Wide Web address:** http://www.cfindustries.com. **Description:** This location provides administrative and warehousing Human Resources. services to other locations of the company. Overall, CF Industries manufactures phosphates for use in fertilizers.

CARGILL FERTILIZER

8813 U.S. Highway 41 South, Riverview FL 33569-4866. 813/677-9111. **Contact:** Personnel. **World Wide Web address:** http://www.cargill.com/aghorizons/products/fert. **Description:** A chemical company that specializes in the production of phosphates for use in fertilizer.

COCA-COLA BOTTLING COMPANY

3350 Pembroke Road, Hollywood FL 33021. 954/985-5000. **Contact:** Lori Welch, Director of Human Resources. **World Wide Web address:** http://www.cocacola.com. **Description:** A bottler of soft drink brands including Barq's, Dr. Pepper, and Coca-Cola. **NOTE:** Interested jobseekers should send resumes to 12333 SW 112th Avenue, Miami FL 33177. **Parent company:** Coca-Cola Enterprises, Inc. is a producer of soft drinks and nonalcoholic beverages, including spring and sparkling waters, juices, isotonics, and teas. The company operates in 38 states, the District of Columbia, the U.S. Virgin Islands, the Islands of Tortola and Grand Cayman, and the Netherlands. The company's franchises market its products to over 154 million people. Coca-Cola Enterprises operates 268 facilities; approximately 24,000 vehicles; and over 860,000 vending machines, beverage dispensers, and coolers. **Listed on:** New York Stock Exchange. **Stock exchange symbol:** KO.

COCA-COLA BOTTLING COMPANY
16569 SW 117th Avenue, Miami FL 33177. 305/378-1073.
Contact: Human Resources. **World Wide Web address:**
http://www.cocacola.com. **Description:** A bottler of soft drink
brands including Barq's, Dr. Pepper, and Coca-Cola. **NOTE:**
Interested jobseekers should send resumes to 12333 SW 112th
Avenue, Miami FL 33177. **Parent company:** Coca-Cola
Enterprises, Inc. is a producer of soft drinks and nonalcoholic
beverages, including spring and sparkling waters, juices,
isotonics, and teas. The company operates in 38 states, the
District of Columbia, the U.S. Virgin Islands, the Islands of
Tortola and Grand Cayman, and the Netherlands. The
company's franchises market its products to over 154 million
people. Coca-Cola Enterprises operates 268 facilities;
approximately 24,000 vehicles; and over 860,000 vending
machines, beverage dispensers, and coolers. **Listed on:** New
York Stock Exchange. **Stock exchange symbol:** KO.

FLORIDA GLOBAL CITRUS LIMITED
P.O. Box 37, Auburndale FL 33823. 863/967-4431. **Fax:**
863/965-2480. **Contact:** Human Resources Department.
Description: Processes citrus fruits and citrus fruit by-products
for bulk concentrate sales. The company is also engaged in
warehousing. **Common positions include:** Accountant/Auditor;
Blue-Collar Worker Supervisor; Clerical Supervisor; Computer
Programmer; Human Resources Manager; Payroll Clerk;
Production Manager; Purchasing Agent/Manager; Quality
Control Supervisor; Receptionist; Secretary; Truck Driver;
Typist/Word Processor; Welder. **Corporate headquarters
location:** This location. **Operations at this facility include:**
Administration; Manufacturing; Sales. **Number of employees
at this location:** 200.

FLORIDA'S NATURAL GROWERS
P.O. Box 1111, Lake Wales FL 33859-1111. 863/676-1411.
Physical address: 650 Highway 27 North, Lake Wales FL
33859. **Recorded jobline:** 877/842-9891. **Contact:** Human
Resources Department. **World Wide Web address:**
http://www.floridasnatural.com. **Description:** Processes and
packages citrus juice. Brand names include Florida's Natural,
Donald Duck, Bluebird, Texsun, and Vintage. **Common
positions include:** Accountant/Auditor; Blue-Collar Worker
Supervisor; Buyer; Chemical Engineer; Chemist; Clerical
Supervisor; Computer Programmer; Customer Service Rep.;
Draftsperson; Electrical/Electronics Engineer; Electrician; Food
Scientist/Technologist; General Manager; Industrial Engineer;
Industrial Production Manager; Mechanical Engineer; MIS

Specialist; Operations/Production Manager; Purchasing Agent/Manager; Quality Control Supervisor; Stationary Engineer; Systems Analyst; Typist/Word Processor. **Corporate headquarters location:** This location. **Listed on:** Privately held. **Annual sales/revenues:** More than $100 million. **Number of employees at this location:** 900. **Number of employees nationwide:** 1,000.

FORT MYERS COCA-COLA BOTTLING COMPANY
10051 Alico Road, Fort Myers FL 33913. 941/590-2653. **Contact:** Human Resources. **Description:** A bottler of soft drink brands including Barq's, Dr. Pepper, and Coca-Cola. **Parent company:** Coca-Cola Enterprises, Inc. is a producer of soft drinks and nonalcoholic beverages including spring and sparkling waters, juices, isotonics, and teas. The company operates in 38 states, the District of Columbia, the U.S. Virgin Islands, the Islands of Tortola and Grand Cayman, and the Netherlands. The company's franchises market its products to over 154 million people. Coca-Cola Enterprises operates 268 facilities; approximately 24,000 vehicles; and over 860,000 vending machines, beverage dispensers, and coolers.

GOLD KIST POULTRY
P.O. Box 1000, Live Oak FL 32064. 386/362-2544. **Contact:** David Mullis, Division Human Resources Manager. **World Wide Web address:** http://www.goldkist.com. **Description:** A poultry grow-out and processing complex. **Common positions include:** Food Service Manager; Management Trainee. **Corporate headquarters location:** Atlanta GA. **Operations at this facility include:** Divisional Headquarters. **Number of employees at this location:** 1,200. **Number of employees nationwide:** 18,000.

GOLDEN GEM GROWERS, INC.
P.O. Drawer 9, Umatilla FL 32784-0009. 352/669-2101. **Contact:** Jim Sears, Personnel Manager. **World Wide Web address:** http://www.goldengemgrowers.com. **Description:** Processors of fresh and frozen citrus fruits. **Corporate headquarters location:** This location. **Operations at this facility include:** Administration; Manufacturing.

JUICE BOWL PRODUCTS
P.O. Box 1048, Lakeland FL 33802-1048. 863/665-5515. **Fax:** 863/667-7137. **Contact:** Samantha Hayes, Director of Human Resources. **Description:** Cans and processes fruit. **Common positions include:** Accountant/Auditor; Buyer; Clinical Lab Technician; Computer Programmer; Credit Manager; Customer

Service Rep.; Electrician; Human Resources Manager; Mechanical Engineer; Operations/Production Manager; Public Relations Specialist; Purchasing Agent/Manager. **Operations at this facility include:** Administration; Manufacturing; Research and Development; Sales; Service. **Listed on:** Privately held. **Number of employees at this location:** 175.

KENDALL FOODS CORPORATION
P.O. Box 8, Goulds FL 33170. 305/258-1631. **Contact:** Human Resources Department. **Description:** Grows, markets, and processes tropical fruits including avocados, limes, mangos, and papayas. **Common positions include:** Accountant/Auditor; Administrator; Agricultural Engineer; Blue-Collar Worker Supervisor; Buyer; Chemist; Credit Manager; Food Scientist/Technologist; Industrial Engineer; Marketing Specialist; Operations/Production Manager; Purchasing Agent/Manager; Quality Control Supervisor; Sales Executive. **Corporate headquarters location:** This location. **Operations at this facility include:** Administration; Manufacturing; Research and Development; Sales; Service.

McARTHUR DAIRY
2451 NW 7th Avenue, Miami FL 33127. 305/576-2880. **Contact:** Human Resources Department. **Description:** Produces dairy products. **NOTE:** Interested jobseekers should address inquiries to: Human Resources, 500 Sawgrass Corporate Parkway, Sunrise FL 33325.

NATIONAL BEVERAGE CORPORATION
One North University Drive, Building A, 4th Floor, Plantation FL 33324. 954/581-0922. **Contact:** Personnel. **World Wide Web address:** http://www.nbcfiz.com. **Description:** National Beverage Corporation is an integrated producer and distributor of multiflavored soft drink products. Brand names include Shasta, Faygo, Big Shot, Everfresh, VooDoo Rain, and LaCroix. **Other U.S. locations:** Nationwide. **Listed on:** American Stock Exchange. **Stock exchange symbol:** FIZ.

OKEELANTA CORPORATION
P.O. Box 86, South Bay FL 33493. 561/996-9072. **Fax:** 561/992-7326. **Contact:** Human Resources. **Description:** Mills, refines, packages, and distributes sugar. **Listed on:** Privately held. **Number of employees at this location:** 1,250.

PEPSI-COLA BOTTLING COMPANY
1700 Directors Row, Orlando FL 32809. 407/826-5900. **Fax:** 407/826-5999. **Recorded jobline:** 407/826-5900x330.

Contact: Human Resources Department. **World Wide Web address:** http://www.pepsico.com. **Description:** A regional bottling plant. **Common positions include:** Computer Operator; Department Manager; Human Resources Manager; Industrial Production Manager; Manufacturer's/Wholesaler's Sales Rep.; Payroll Clerk; Quality Control Supervisor; Secretary; Truck Driver. **Special programs:** Internships. **Parent company:** PepsiCo, Inc. (Purchase NY) consists of Frito-Lay Company, Pepsi-Cola Company, Quaker Oats Company, and Tropicana Products Inc. **Operations at this facility include:** Manufacturing; Regional Headquarters; Sales; Service. **Listed on:** New York Stock Exchange. **Stock exchange symbol:** PEP. **Annual revenues:** More than $100 million. **Number of employees at this location:** 400. **Number of employees nationwide:** 26,000.

PEPSI-COLA COMPANY
7777 NW 41st Street, Miami FL 33166. 305/592-1980. **Contact:** Human Resources Department. **World Wide Web address:** http://www.pepsico.com. **Description:** Manufactures, sells, and distributes Pepsi-Cola products including 7-Up and Sunkist. **Special programs:** Internships. **Parent company:** PepsiCo, Inc. (Purchase NY) consists of Frito-Lay Company, Pepsi-Cola Company, Quaker Oats Company, and Tropicana Products Inc. **Listed on:** New York Stock Exchange. **Stock exchange symbol:** PEP. **Annual revenues:** More than $100 million. **Number of employees nationwide:** 26,000.

PEPSI-COLA COMPANY
3625 Dr. Martin Luther King Jr. Boulevard, Fort Myers FL 33916. 941/337-2011. **Contact:** Human Resources. **World Wide Web address:** http://www.pepsico.com. **Description:** Distributes various beverages including the brand names Pepsi-Cola, Mountain Dew, Mug Root Beer, and Slice. **Parent company:** PepsiCo, Inc. (Purchase NY) consists of Frito-Lay Company, Pepsi-Cola Company, Quaker Oats Company, and Tropicana Products Inc. **Listed on:** New York Stock Exchange. **Stock exchange symbol:** PEP. **Annual revenues:** More than $100 million. **Number of employees nationwide:** 26,000.

SWISHER INTERNATIONAL
P.O. Box 2230, Jacksonville FL 32203. 904/353-4311. **Contact:** Human Resources Department. **World Wide Web address:** http://www.swisher.com. **Description:** One of the world's largest manufacturers of cigars and smokeless tobacco. Brand names include King Edward, Bering, Redwood, and Silver Creek.

TROPICANA NORTH AMERICA

P.O. Box 338, Bradenton FL 34206. 941/747-4461. **Contact:** Human Resources Department. **World Wide Web address:** http://www.tropicana.com. **Description:** A leading producer and marketer of orange juice. **Common positions include:** Accountant/Auditor; Biological Scientist; Blue-Collar Worker Supervisor; Buyer; Chemical Engineer; Chemist; Computer Programmer; Draftsperson. **Corporate headquarters location:** This location. **Parent company:** PepsiCo, Inc. (Purchase NY) consists of Frito-Lay Company, Quaker Oats, Pepsi-Cola Company, and Tropicana Products, Inc. **Operations at this facility include:** Administration; Manufacturing; Research and Development; Sales; Service.

TYSON FOODS, INC.

5421 West Beaver Street, Jacksonville FL 32254. 904/693-5600. **Contact:** Susan Tellez, Human Resources Director. **World Wide Web address:** http://www.tyson.com. **Description:** This location is a poultry processing plant. Overall, Tyson Foods, Inc. is one of the world's largest fully-integrated producers, processors, and marketers of poultry-based food products. Tyson products include Tyson Holly Farms Fresh Chicken, Weaver, Louis Kemp Crab, Lobster Delights, Healthy Portion, Beef Stir Fry, Crab Delights Stir Fry, Chicken Fried Rice Kits, Pork Chops with Cinnamon Apples, Salmon Grill Kits, Fish 'n Chips Kits, and Rotisserie Chicken. **Corporate headquarters location:** Springdale AR. **Other U.S. locations:** Nationwide. **International locations:** Worldwide. **Listed on:** New York Stock Exchange. **Stock exchange symbol:** TSN. **CEO:** John Tyson. **Annual sales/revenues:** More than $100 million. **Number of employees worldwide:** 120,000.

U. S. BEVERAGE

P.O. Box 3628, Lakeland FL 33802-2004. 863/686-1173. **Contact:** Human Resources. **Description:** Processes a wide variety of juices. **Corporate headquarters location:** This location.

U.S. FOODSERVICE

P.O. Box 2246, Daytona Beach FL 32145. 386/677-2240. **Fax:** 386/672-5476. **Contact:** Human Resources Department. **World Wide Web address:** http://www.usfoodservice.com. **Description:** An institutional food production and distribution company serving clients in the restaurant and health care industries. **Corporate headquarters location:** Columbia MD. **Other U.S. locations:** Nationwide. **Parent company:** Royal Ahold. **Listed on:** American Stock Exchange. **Stock exchange**

symbol: AHLN. **Annual revenues:** Over $100 million. **Number of employees nationwide:** 34,000.

UNITED STATES SUGAR CORPORATION

111 Ponce de Leon Avenue, P.O. Box Drawer 1207, Clewiston FL 33440. 863/902-2885. **Fax:** 863/902-2889. **Contact:** Human Resources Department. **E-mail address:** mmaturana@ussugar.com. **World Wide Web address:** http://www.ussugar.com. **Description:** One of the nation's largest agricultural cooperatives, with primary interests in sugar and citrus. Founded in 1931. **NOTE:** Be sure to include the job vacancy number on your application. **Common positions include:** Accountant/Auditor; Agricultural Engineer; Biological Scientist; Blue-Collar Worker Supervisor; Buyer; Chemical Engineer; Chemist; Claim Rep.; Computer Programmer; Department Manager; Electrical/Electronics Engineer; General Manager; Human Resources Manager; Industrial Engineer; Mechanical Engineer; Operations/Production Manager; Systems Analyst. **Corporate headquarters location:** This location. **Operations at this facility include:** Administration; Manufacturing; Research and Development; Sales; Service. **Number of employees at this location:** More than 3,000.

GEORGE WESTON BAKERIES INC.

3325 NW 62nd Street, Miami FL 33147. 305/836-4900. **Fax:** 305/835-1349. **Contact:** Human Resources. **World Wide Web address:** http://www.weston.ca/en/gwb.html. **Description:** This location is the headquarters for the Southeast Region. Overall, George Weston Bakeries Inc. bakes cakes, cookies, pies, and doughnuts. **Corporate headquarters location:** Bayshore NY. **Operations at this facility include:** Regional Headquarters.

GOVERNMENT

You can expect to find the following types of agencies in this chapter:

Courts
Executive, Legislative, and General Government
Public Agencies (Firefighters, Military, Police) United States Postal Service

CHARLOTTE COUNTY RECORDING DEPARTMENT
P.O. Box 511687, Punta Gorda FL 33951. 941/637-2245. **Contact:** Human Resources. **Description:** Records all county records including land and court documents.

FLORIDA DEPARTMENT OF TRANSPORTATION
605 Suwannee Street, Mail Stop #50, Tallahassee FL 32399-0450. 850/414-5300. **Contact:** Walter R. Mitchell, Personnel. **World Wide Web address:** http://www11.myflorida.com. **Description:** A state agency responsible for developing and maintaining Florida's transportation systems. **Common positions include:** Accountant/Auditor; Administrative Manager; Attorney; Budget Analyst; Civil Engineer; Clerical Supervisor; Computer Programmer; Draftsperson; Electrician; Environmental Engineer; Human Resources Manager; Landscape Architect; Management Analyst/Consultant; Management Trainee; Materials Engineer; Paralegal; Property and Real Estate Manager; Public Relations Specialist; Purchasing Agent/Manager; Structural Engineer; Surveyor; Systems Analyst; Transportation/Traffic Specialist. **Corporate headquarters location:** This location. **Operations at this facility include:** Administration. **Number of employees at this location:** 2,000. **Number of employees nationwide:** 10,000.

HILLSBOROUGH, COUNTY OF
P.O. Box 1110, Tampa FL 33601. 813/272-6400. **Physical address:** 601 East Kennedy Boulevard, Tampa FL 33601. **Contact:** Human Resources. **World Wide Web address:** http://www.hillsborough.org. **Description:** The administrative offices for the Hillsborough county government.

JACKSONVILLE, CITY OF
117 West Duval Street, Suite 100, Jacksonville FL 32202. 904/630-1114. **Contact:** Human Resources. **World Wide Web address:** http://www.coj.net. **Description:** This location houses the human resources division and is responsible for the hiring of all municipal employees for the city of Jacksonville.

JACKSONVILLE PORT AUTHORITY
P.O. Box 3005, Jacksonville FL 32206. 904/630-3069. **Fax:** 904/630-3076. **Contact:** Karen Hebert, Human Resources Manager. **World Wide Web address:** http://www.jaxport.com. **Description:** Oversees the daily activities of the port of Jacksonville including the operation of the Blount Island and Talleyrand Docks Marine Terminals, as well as the Jacksonville International Airport and two general aviation airports. **Common positions include:** Accountant/Auditor; Automotive

Mechanic; Cargo Handler. **Corporate headquarters location:** This location. **Operations at this facility include:** Administration; Sales; Service. **Number of employees at this location:** 350.

LANTANA, TOWN OF
500 Greynolds Circle, Lantana FL 33462. 561/540-5000. **Contact:** Human Resources. **World Wide Web address:** http://www.lantana.org. **Description:** Municipal offices for the town of Lantana.

LEON, COUNTY OF
BOARD OF COUNTY COMMISSIONERS
301 South Monroe Street, Suite 201, Tallahassee FL 32301. 850/487-2220. **Fax:** 850/488-6293. **Contact:** Department of Human Resources. **World Wide Web address:** http://www.co.leon.fl.us. **Description:** Government and administrative offices of Leon County. **Special programs:** Internships. **Operations at this facility include:** Administration. **Number of employees at this location:** 600.

NAVAL SURFACE WARFARE CENTER
Human Resources PC, Code XPP, 6703 West Highway 98, Panama City FL 32407-7001. 850/235-5554. **Contact:** Human Resources. **Description:** The U.S. Navy's principal research and development laboratory.

NORTH LAUDERDALE, CITY OF
701 SW 71st Avenue, North Lauderdale FL 33068. 954/724-7068. **Fax:** 954/720-2064. **Recorded jobline:** 954/724-7067. **Contact:** Human Resources. **World Wide Web address:** http://www.nlauderdale.org. **Description:** Municipal offices for the city of North Lauderdale.

U.S. POSTAL SERVICE
5201 West Spruce Street, Tampa FL 33630-5000. **Toll-free phone:** 800/275-8777. **Contact:** Human Resources. **World Wide Web address:** http://www.usps.com. **Description:** A 24-hour airmail postal facility. **Other U.S. locations:** Nationwide.

HEALTH CARE: SERVICES, EQUIPMENT, AND PRODUCTS

You can expect to find the following types of companies in this chapter:

Dental Labs and Equipment
Home Health Care Agencies
Hospitals and Medical Centers
Medical Equipment Manufacturers and Wholesalers
Offices and Clinics of Health Practitioners
Residential Treatment Centers/Nursing Homes
Veterinary Services

ALIMED HOME INFUSION
1028 NE 45th Street, Fort Lauderdale FL 33334. **Contact:** Manager. **Description:** Provides a wide range of home health care services to patients recently released from the hospital.

APRIA HEALTHCARE GROUP INC.
5414 Beaumont Center Boulevard, Suite 206, Tampa FL 33634. 813/622-7285. **Contact:** Human Resources. **World Wide Web address:** http://www.apria.com. **Description:** One of the largest national providers of home health care products and services including a broad range of respiratory therapy services, home medical equipment, and infusion therapy services. Apria has over 400 branches throughout the United States and two respiratory therapy branches in the United Kingdom. In conjunction with medical professionals, Apria personnel deliver, install, and service medical equipment, as well as provide appropriate therapies and coordinate plans of care for their patients. Apria personnel also instruct patients and caregivers in the correct use of equipment and monitor the equipment's effectiveness. **Corporate headquarters location:** Costa Mesa CA. **Listed on:** New York Stock Exchange. **Stock exchange symbol:** AHG.

ASO CORPORATION
300 Sarasota Center Boulevard, Sarasota FL 34240. 941/379-0300. **Fax:** 941/378-9040. **Contact:** Human Resources. **E-mail address:** careers@asocorp.com. **World Wide Web address:** http://www.asocorp.com. **Description:** A manufacturer and distributor of wound care products. **NOTE:** Second and third shifts are offered. **Common positions include:** Account Manager; Accountant; Administrative Assistant; Blue-Collar Worker Supervisor; Buyer; Chief Financial Officer; Computer Programmer; Controller; Credit Manager; Customer Service Representative; Human Resources Manager; Marketing Manager; MIS Specialist; Purchasing Agent/Manager; Quality Control Supervisor; Sales Executive; Sales Manager; Secretary; Systems Analyst; Technical Writer/Editor; Typist/Word Processor. **Corporate headquarters location:** This location. **Subsidiaries include:** Aso Pharmaceutical Co., Ltd. (Kumamoto, Japan); Aso Seiyaku Philippines, Inc. (Cebu, Philippines); Texas Aso Corporation (El Paso TX). **Parent company:** Aso International. **Listed on:** Privately held. **Facilities Manager:** R. Van Ostenbridge. **Number of employees at this location:** 100.

BAPTIST ST. VINCENT'S HEALTH SYSTEMS
BAPTIST ST. VINCENT MEDICAL CENTER

1800 Barrs Street, Jacksonville FL 32204. 904/308-7307. **Fax:** 904/308-2951. **Contact:** Human Resources. **Description:** Operates the Baptist St. Vincent Medical Center (also at this location) and the St. Catherine Laboure Manor nursing home in Jacksonville. Baptist St. Vincent Medical Center is a 711-bed hospital that provides the following services and facilities: acute care, AIDS treatment, behavioral medicine, a cancer center, cardiology, chemical dependency treatment, emergency services, geriatrics, gastroenterology, laser surgery, neonatology, neurosurgery, OB/GYN, occupational health, orthopedics, otolaryngology, otology, pediatrics, plastic surgery, psychiatric, substance abuse, and women's/children's services. Baptist St. Vincent's Health Systems is a member of the Daughters of Charity national health system, which also includes Mercy Hospital (Miami FL), Sacred Heart Hospital (Pensacola FL), and the Haven of Our Lady of Peace nursing home (Pensacola FL). **Common positions include:** EKG Technician; Emergency Medical Technician; Licensed Practical Nurse; Medical Records Technician; Occupational Therapist; Pharmacist; Physical Therapist; Registered Nurse; Respiratory Therapist; Speech-Language Pathologist; Surgical Technician. **Corporate headquarters location:** St. Louis MO. **Number of employees at this location:** 4,000.

BAPTIST ST. VINCENT'S VISITING NURSES

3563 Phillips Highway, Suite 202, Jacksonville FL 32207. 904/202-4300. **Contact:** Human Resources. **Description:** Provides home health care services as part of the greater Baptist St. Vincent's medical organization.

BAUSCH & LOMB PHARMACEUTICALS, INC.

8500 Hidden River Parkway, Tampa FL 33637. 813/975-7700. **Fax:** 813/975-7779. **Contact:** Human Resources. **World Wide Web address:** http://www.bausch.com. **Description:** This location manufactures contact lenses and related products, ophthalmic drugs, dental plaque removal devices, and optical items. Overall, Bausch & Lomb operates in selected segments of global health care and optical markets. The health care segment consists of three sectors: personal health, medical, and biomedical. The personal health sector is comprised of branded products purchased directly by consumers in health and beauty aid sections of pharmacies, food stores, and mass merchandise outlets. Products include contact lens care solutions, oral care, eye and skin care products, and nonprescription medications. The medical sector manufactures contact lenses, ophthalmic pharmaceuticals, hearing aids, dental implants, and other products sold to health care professionals or obtained by consumers through a prescription. The biomedical sector is engaged in the research and development of pharmaceuticals and the production of genetically-engineered materials. These include purpose-bred research animals, bioprocessing services, and products derived from specific pathogen-free eggs. The optics segment consists primarily of premium-priced sunglasses sold under such brand names as Ray-Ban and Revo. The company's manufacturing or marketing organizations have been established in 34 countries and the company's products are distributed in more than 70 other nations. **Listed on:** New York Stock Exchange. **Stock exchange symbol:** BOL. **Number of employees worldwide:** 14,400.

BAXTER HEALTHCARE CORPORATION
14600 NW 60th Avenue, Miami Lakes FL 33014-2811. 305/823-5240. **Contact:** Human Resources. **World Wide Web address:** http://www.baxter.com. **Description:** An international company that manufactures and markets critical therapies for conditions involving the blood and circulatory system. The company operates within three main areas. The BioScience division manufactures products that collect, separate, and store blood. The Renal products are designed to cleanse the blood. Intravenous products are designed to help infuse drugs and other solutions into the blood stream. **Common positions include:** Accountant/Auditor; Biomedical Engineer; Blue-Collar Worker Supervisor; Buyer; Chemical Engineer; Chemist; Computer Programmer; Credit Manager; Customer Service Rep.; Human Resources Manager; Marketing Specialist; Mechanical Engineer; Operations/Production Manager; Purchasing Agent/Manager; Quality Control Supervisor; Systems Analyst. **Corporate headquarters location:** Deerfield IL. **Operations at this facility include:** Administration; Manufacturing; Research and Development; Sales. **Listed on:** New York Stock Exchange. **Stock exchange symbol:** BAX.

BAYFRONT MEDICAL CENTER
701 Sixth Street South, St. Petersburg FL 33701. 727/823-1234. **Contact:** Human Resources. **World Wide Web address:** http://www.bsahealth.org. **Description:** A nonprofit, 502-bed hospital. **Parent company:** Bayfront-St. Anthony's Health Care.

BON SECOURS-ST. JOSEPH HOSPITAL
2500 Harbor Boulevard, Port Charlotte FL 33952. 941/766-4122. **Fax:** 941/766-4296. **Contact:** Human Resources. **World Wide Web address:** http://www.bonsecours.org. **Description:** A JCAHO-accredited, 212-bed, acute care facility with an affiliated 104-bed, long-term care facility located on the Gulf Coast of southwestern Florida. Bon Secours-St. Joseph Hospital is part of the Bon Secours Health System. **Common positions include:** Licensed Practical Nurse; Medical Records Technician; Nuclear Engineer; Nuclear Medicine Technologist; Pharmacist; Radiological Technologist; Registered Nurse; Respiratory Therapist; Surgical Technician; Systems Analyst. **Special programs:** Internships. **Corporate headquarters location:** Mariottsville MD. **Other area locations:** Miami FL; St. Petersburg FL. **Other U.S. locations:** St. Clair Shores MI; Charlotte NC; Richmond VA. **Operations at this facility include:** Administration; Service. **Number of employees at this location:** 1,000.

CALADESI ANIMAL HOSPITAL
903 Curlew Road, Dunedin FL 34698. 727/733-9395. **Contact:** Human Resources Department. **World Wide Web address:** http://www.caladesi.com. **Description:** Caladesi Animal Hospital offers general surgical and medical care, acupuncture, orthopedic surgery, boarding services, a pet taxi, and travel services.

CARE MEDICAL EQUIPMENT
102 Drennen Road, Suite B-1, Orlando FL 32806. 407/856-2273. **Contact:** Human Resources. **World Wide Web address:** http://www.caremedicalequipment.com. **Description:** Engaged in the short-term rental of wheelchairs, scooters, shower chairs, lifts, hospital beds, and IV stands to hotels, condos, and homes.

CHARLOTTE REGIONAL MEDICAL CENTER
809 East Marion Street, Punta Gorda FL 33950. 941/637-2552. **Toll-free phone:** 800/677-3132. **Fax:** 941/637-2469. **Recorded jobline:** 888/639-3166. **Contact:** Human Resources. **World Wide Web address:** http://www.charlotteregional.com. **Description:** A 208-bed, private, acute care hospital with specialized services including cardiac care; a sports medicine/wellness program (physical fitness, aerobics, aquatic programs, and rehabilitative services); a behavioral center (mental health and addictions treatment); sleep disorder programs; a pulmonary rehabilitation program (breathing disorder treatment); home health services; occupational

medicine (offered through an outpatient clinic in North Port); an emergency department; an ambulatory care center; a critical care recovery unit (recovery from open heart surgery); a diabetes center; and a lifeline emergency response system. **Common positions include:** Clerical Supervisor; Dietician/Nutritionist; EEG Technologist; EKG Technician; Electrician; Human Resources Manager; Licensed Practical Nurse; Medical Records Technician; Nuclear Medicine Technologist; Occupational Therapist; Pharmacist; Physical Therapist; Physician; Psychologist; Public Relations Specialist; Recreational Therapist; Registered Nurse; Respiratory Therapist; Social Worker; Speech-Language Pathologist. **Special programs:** Internships. **Office hours:** Monday - Friday, 8:00 a.m. - 5:00 p.m. **Corporate headquarters location:** Naples FL. **Parent company:** Health Management Associates, Inc. operates 29 hospitals in 11 states across the Southeast and Southwest, focusing on acquiring underachieving community health care facilities with solid potential. **Operations at this facility include:** Administration; Service. **Listed on:** New York Stock Exchange. **Stock exchange symbol:** HMA. **Number of employees at this location:** 830.

CLEVELAND CLINIC FLORIDA HOSPITAL
2950 Cleveland Clinic Boulevard, Weston FL 33331. 954/978-5000. **Fax:** 954/978-7487. **Contact:** Human Resources. **World Wide Web address:** http://www.ccf.org. **Description:** Operates an outpatient clinic and outpatient surgery center that specializes in the diagnosis and treatment of complex medical problems that have resisted previous forms of treatment. Founded in 1921. **NOTE:** Entry-level positions are offered. **Common positions include:** Accountant; Administrative Assistant; Auditor; Blue-Collar Worker Supervisor; Budget Analyst; Buyer; Certified Nurses Aide; Chief Financial Officer; Claim Representative; Clerical Supervisor; Clinical Lab Technician; Computer Operator; Computer Programmer; Finance Director; Financial Analyst; Fund Manager; Human Resources Manager; Librarian; Licensed Practical Nurse; Marketing Manager; Marketing Specialist; Medical Records Technician; MIS Specialist; Nuclear Medicine Technologist; Operations Manager; Pharmacist; Physical Therapist; Physician; Project Manager; Public Relations Specialist; Purchasing Agent/Manager; Radiological Technologist; Registered Nurse; Respiratory Therapist; Secretary; Social Worker; Surgical Technician; Systems Analyst; Systems Manager; Telecommunications Manager. **Special programs:** Internships. **Corporate headquarters location:** Cleveland OH. **Number of employees at this location:** 500.

CLEVELAND CLINIC FLORIDA HOSPITAL
3100 Weston Road, Weston FL 33331. 954/568-1000.
Contact: Human Resources. **World Wide Web address:**
http://www.ccf.org. **Description:** A 150-bed hospital offering a
wide variety of inpatient, outpatient, cardiac rehabilitation, and
radiologic services. Founded in 1921. **Corporate headquarters
location:** Cleveland OH. **Parent company:** Cleveland Clinic
Foundation.

COLUMBIA NEW PORT RICHEY HOSPITAL
5637 Marine Parkway, New Port Richey FL 34656. 727/845-
9117. **Fax:** 727/845-9167. **Recorded jobline:** 727/845-4379.
Contact: Mark Cohen, Director of Human Resources. **World
Wide Web address:** http://www.communityhospitalnpr.com.
Description: A 415-bed, JCAHO-accredited hospital. Services
offered to the community include medical/surgical nursing,
telemetry, psychiatry, ambulatory surgery, a catheterization
lab, an in-house pool, critical care nursing, emergency rooms,
and OR/RR. Columbia New Port Richey Hospital also has
laboratory, radiology, nuclear medicine, pharmacy, and
surgical suites. **NOTE:** Second and third shifts are offered.
Common positions include: Accountant; Certified Nurses
Aide; Clinical Lab Technician; Dietician/Nutritionist; EEG
Technologist; EKG Technician; Electrician; Emergency Medical
Technician; Licensed Practical Nurse; Medical Records
Technician; Nuclear Medicine Technologist; Pharmacist;
Radiological Technologist; Registered Nurse; Respiratory
Therapist; Social Worker; Surgical Technician; Systems
Analyst. **Corporate headquarters location:** Nashville TN. **CEO:**
Andrew Oravec, Jr.

CORAM HEALTHCARE CORPORATION
9143 Phillips Highway, Suite 300, Jacksonville FL 32256. **Toll-
free phone:** 800/365-6275. **Contact:** Human Resources. **World
Wide Web address:** http://www.coram-healthcare.com.
Description: One of the largest home health infusion therapy
companies in the United States. The company provides a wide
range of alternate site delivery services including ambulatory
and home infusion therapies, lithotripsy, and institutional
pharmacy services. Coram Healthcare Corporation has a
network of more than 85 locations nationwide. **NOTE:**
Jobseekers should send employment inquiries to Coram
Healthcare, Human Resources, 1125 17th Street, Suite 1500,
Denver CO 80202. **Corporate headquarters location:** Denver
CO. **Number of employees nationwide:** 4,000.

CORDIS CORPORATION

14201 NW 60th Avenue, Miami Lakes FL 33014. 305/824-2000. **Contact:** Human Resources. **World Wide Web address:** http://www.cordis.com. **Description:** Manufactures medical devices including angiographics and neurovascular products. The company also acts as a supplier for hospitals and physicians. **Common positions include:** Administrator; Biomedical Engineer; Blue-Collar Worker Supervisor; Buyer; Chemical Engineer; Customer Service Rep.; Financial Analyst; Industrial Engineer; Marketing Specialist; Mechanical Engineer; Operations/Production Manager; Production Manager; Quality Control Supervisor; Sales Rep.; Technical Writer/Editor. **Parent company:** Johnson & Johnson.

CYPRESS VILLAGE

4600 Middleton Park Circle East, Jacksonville FL 32224. 904/223-6100. **Toll-free phone:** 800/228-6163. **Fax:** 904/223-6186. **Contact:** Human Resources Department. **World Wide Web address:** http://www.cypressvillage.com. **Description:** A nonprofit, multilevel retirement community consisting of single-family homes, townhouses, and apartments for independent living. There are also 39 assisted living units, a 120-bed skilled nursing facility, and an Alzheimer's facility with 60 beds. Founded in 1991. **NOTE:** Second and third shifts are offered. **Common positions include:** Account Manager; Accountant; Administrative Assistant; Certified Nurses Aide; Dietician/Nutritionist; Human Resources Manager; Licensed Practical Nurse; Medical Records Technician; Registered Nurse; Secretary; Social Worker. **Office hours:** Monday - Friday, 8:00 a.m. - 5:00 p.m. **Parent company:** National Benevolent Association (St. Louis MO). **Annual sales/revenues:** $11 - $20 million. **Number of employees at this location:** 300.

DELRAY MEDICAL CENTER

5352 Linton Boulevard, Suite 210, Delray Beach FL 33484. 561/637-5350. **Toll-free phone:** 800/926-8282. **Fax:** 561/637-5357. **Recorded jobline:** 561/495-3459. **Contact:** Human Resources Department. **World Wide Web address:** http://www.delraymedicalctr.com. **Description:** A 343-bed hospital offering a variety of specialized services including rehabilitation and psychiatric services. Founded in 1982.

ESSILOR OF AMERICA

4900 Park Street North, St. Petersburg FL 33709. 727/541-5733. **Contact:** Clair Amrhein, Personnel Director. **World Wide Web address:** http://www.essilor.com. **Description:** A manufacturer of optical lenses for eyeglasses.

FLORIDA INFUSION SERVICES
1053 Progress Court, Palm Harbor FL 34683. 727/942-1829. **Fax:** 727/942-6165. **Contact:** Human Resources. **World Wide Web address:** http://www.floridainfusion.com. **Description:** A distributor of pharmaceutical and medical supplies. Florida Infusion Services also provides a variety of pharmacy services.

FLORIDA STATE HOSPITAL
P.O. Box 1000, Chattahoochee FL 32324-1000. 850/663-7258. **Contact:** Tom Carpenter, Recruitment Coordinator. **Description:** Florida State Hospital is a rehabilitative mental health institution for persons with mental/addictive illnesses. **Common positions include:** Accountant/Auditor; Computer Programmer; Counselor; Dental Assistant/Dental Hygienist; Dentist; Dietician/Nutritionist; Electrical/Electronics Engineer; Electrician; Food Scientist/Technologist; Human Service Worker; Landscape Architect; Librarian; Library Technician; Licensed Practical Nurse; Medical Records Technician; Occupational Therapist; Paralegal; Pharmacist; Physical Therapist; Physician; Psychologist; Quality Control Supervisor; Recreational Therapist; Registered Nurse; Respiratory Therapist; Restaurant/Food Service Manager; Social Worker; Teacher/Professor; Transportation/Traffic Specialist. **Special programs:** Internships. **Corporate headquarters location:** Tallahassee FL. **Operations at this facility include:** Administration. **Number of employees at this location:** 3,000.

FREEDOM SQUARE RETIREMENT CENTER
7800 Liberty Lane, Seminole FL 33772. 727/398-0166. **Contact:** Human Resources. **World Wide Web address:** http://www.arclp.com. **Description:** A retirement community providing all levels of nursing care to its clients. **Listed on:** New York Stock Exchange. **Stock exchange symbol:** ACR.

FREEDOM VILLAGE
6501 17th Avenue West, Bradenton FL 34209. 941/798-8200. **Employment hotline:** 941/798-8143. **Contact:** Sharon Peters, Human Resources Director. **World Wide Web address:** http://www.freedomvillage.com. **Description:** A continuing care retirement center offering skilled nursing, assisted living, and independent living options. **Common positions include:** Accountant; Certified Nurses Aide; Certified Occupational Therapy Assistant; Dietician/Nutritionist; Home Health Aide; Human Resources Manager; Licensed Practical Nurse; Marketing Specialist; Medical Records Technician; Occupational Therapist; Physical Therapist; Physical Therapy Assistant; Registered Nurse; Respiratory Therapist; Sales

Representative; Social Worker; Speech-Language Pathologist. **Office hours:** Monday - Friday, 8:30 a.m. - 5:00 p.m. **Corporate headquarters location:** This location. **Number of employees at this location:** 550.

GENTIVA HEALTH SERVICES
417-B NW Race Track Road, Suite C, Fort Walton Beach FL 32547. 850/862-3240. **Contact:** Personnel. **World Wide Web address:** http://www.gentiva.com. **Description:** This location is a home health care agency. Overall, Gentiva Health Services provides home health care services, pharmaceutical support, and supplemental staffing services.

GENTIVA HEALTH SERVICES
4500 North State Road 7, Building I, Suite 105, Fort Lauderdale FL 33319. 954/485-5500. **Contact:** Human Resources Department. **World Wide Web address:** http://www.gentiva.com. **Description:** This location is a home health care agency. Overall, Gentiva Health Services provides home health care services, pharmaceutical support, and supplemental staffing services.

GULF COAST CENTER
5820 Buckingham Road, Fort Myers FL 33905. 941/694-2151. **Contact:** Human Resources Department. **Description:** A state-run residential facility for people with mental disabilities.

HEALTH FIRST/HOLMES REGIONAL MEDICAL CENTER PALM BAY COMMUNITY HOSPITAL
1350 South Hickory Street, Melbourne FL 32901. 321/434-7110. **Fax:** 321/434-8587. **Contact:** Dennis Voglas, Director of Employment. **World Wide Web address:** http://www.health-first.org. **Description:** A medical center. **Common positions include:** Clinical Lab Technician; EKG Technician; Occupational Therapist; Physical Therapist; Registered Nurse; Respiratory Therapist; Social Worker; Surgical Technician. **Operations at this facility include:** Service. **Number of employees at this location:** 2,800.

HEALTH MANAGEMENT ASSOCIATES, INC.
5811 Pelican Bay Boulevard, Suite 500, Naples FL 34108. 941/598-3131. **Contact:** Human Resources. **World Wide Web address:** http://www.hma-corp.com. **Description:** Provides a broad range of general, acute care health services to rural communities through its ownership of several hospitals and medical centers. **Listed on:** New York Stock Exchange. **Stock**

exchange symbol: HMA. **Number of employees nationwide:** 5,300.

HEALTHSOUTH DOCTORS HOSPITAL
5000 University Drive, Coral Gables FL 33146. 305/666-2111. **Contact:** Director of Human Resources. **World Wide Web address:** http://www.healthsouth.com. **Description:** A 218-bed hospital offering a variety of specialized services including orthopedics, radiological imaging, neuroscience, and sports medicine. **Listed on:** New York Stock Exchange. **Stock exchange symbol:** HRC.

HEARTLAND REHABILITATION CENTER
5401 Sawyer Road, Sarasota FL 34233. 941/925-3427. **Contact:** Human Resources. **Description:** A physical therapy facility offering both inpatient and outpatient services.

HOSPICE BY THE SEA, INC.
1531 West Palmetto Park Road, Boca Raton FL 33486. 561/395-5031. **Fax:** 561/395-9897. **Contact:** Human Resources Department. **World Wide Web address:** http://www.hospicebytheseafl.org. **Description:** Provides nonprofit health care services to terminally ill patients and offers bereavement counseling and other services for the families of the patients. **NOTE:** Second and third shifts are offered. **Common positions include:** Account Manager; Account Representative; Administrative Assistant; Certified Nurses Aide; Chief Financial Officer; Counselor; Daycare Worker; Dietician/Nutritionist; Education Administrator; Human Resources Manager; Licensed Practical Nurse; Medical Records Technician; MIS Specialist; Occupational Therapist; Pharmacist; Physical Therapist; Physician; Preschool Worker; Public Relations Specialist; Purchasing Agent/Manager; Quality Control Supervisor; Registered Nurse; Secretary; Social Worker; Speech-Language Pathologist. **Special programs:** Internships; Summer Jobs. **Office hours:** Monday - Friday, 8:30 a.m. - 5:00 p.m. **CEO:** Trudi Webb. **Facilities Manager:** Glen Rogers. **Annual sales/revenues:** $11 - $20 million. **Number of employees at this location:** 350.

HOSPICE OF NORTHEAST FLORIDA
4266 Sunbeam Road, Jacksonville FL 32257. 904/268-5200. **Contact:** Human Resources. **Description:** Provides health care services for terminally ill patients in their homes or in nursing facilities.

INDIAN RIVER MEMORIAL HOSPITAL
1000 36th Street, Vero Beach FL 32960-6592. 561/567-4311. **Contact:** Human Resources. **World Wide Web address:** http://www.irmh.com. **Description:** A 335-bed community hospital. Founded in 1932.

INTERIM HEALTHCARE INC.
32644 Blossom Lane, Leesburg FL 34788. 352/326-0400. **Contact:** Human Resources Department. **World Wide Web address:** http://www.interimhealthcare.com. **Description:** A home health care agency.

JACKSON MEMORIAL HOSPITAL
1611 NW 12th Avenue, Park Plaza West L-301, Miami FL 33136. 305/585-6081. **Fax:** 305/326-9470. **Recorded jobline:** 305/585-7886. **Contact:** Ruth Francis, Employment Manager. **World Wide Web address:** http://www.um-jmh.org. **Description:** A 1,567-bed, tertiary, teaching hospital offering specialized services in neurology, pediatrics, dermatology, radiology, pathology, and obstetrics and gynecology. Founded in 1952. **Common positions include:** Accountant/Auditor; Adjuster; Budget Analyst; Buyer; Clinical Lab Technician; Computer Programmer; Construction and Building Inspector; Credit Manager; Customer Service Representative; Dental Assistant/Dental Hygienist; Dental Lab Technician; Dentist; Dietician/Nutritionist; EEG Technologist; EKG Technician; Electrician; Emergency Medical Technician; Environmental Engineer; Financial Analyst; Health Services Manager; Human Resources Manager; Industrial Engineer; Licensed Practical Nurse; Mechanical Engineer; Medical Records Technician; Nuclear Medicine Technologist; Occupational Therapist; Paralegal; Pharmacist; Physical Therapist; Physician; Property and Real Estate Manager; Psychologist; Radiological Technologist; Recreational Therapist; Registered Nurse; Respiratory Therapist; Social Worker; Software Engineer; Speech-Language Pathologist; Statistician; Surgical Technician; Systems Analyst; Technical Writer/Editor. **Operations at this facility include:** Administration.

JOHN KNOX VILLAGE OF CENTRAL FLORIDA
101 Northlake Drive, Orange City FL 32763. 386/775-3840. **Contact:** Human Resources. **World Wide Web address:** http://www.johnknoxvillage.com. **Description:** A continuing care retirement community offering skilled nursing, assisted living, and independent living.

JOHN KNOX VILLAGE OF FLORIDA
651 SW 6th Street, Pompano Beach FL 33060. 954/783-4000. **Contact:** Human Resources. **World Wide Web address:** http://www.johnknoxvillage.com. **Description:** A continuing care retirement community offering skilled nursing, assisted living, and independent living.

JOHN KNOX VILLAGE OF TAMPA BAY
4100 East Fletcher Avenue, Tampa FL 33613. 813/977-4950. **Contact:** Human Resources. **World Wide Web address:** http://www.johnknoxvillage.com. **Description:** A continuing care retirement community offering skilled nursing, assisted living, and independent living.

KELLY ASSISTED LIVING SERVICES
300 31st Street, Suite 330, St. Petersburg FL 33713. 727/327-5961. **Contact:** Human Resources Department. **Description:** Provides home health care services.

KENDALL MEDICAL CENTER
11750 SW 40th Street, Miami FL 33175. 305/223-3000. **Contact:** Human Resources Department. **World Wide Web address:** http://www.kendallmed.com. **Description:** A full-service hospital that features LDRP Maternity Suites, advanced diagnostic services, and a 24-hour emergency department.

KINDRED HEALTHCARE
1859 Van Buren Street, Hollywood FL 33020. 954/920-9000. **Contact:** Human Resources Department. **World Wide Web address:** http://www.kindredhealthcare.com. **Description:** A hospital that specializes in the long-term critical care of patients suffering from acute-level chronic diseases. Founded in 1985. **Corporate headquarters:** Louisville, KY. **Other U.S. locations:** Nationwide. **President/CEO:** Paul J. Diaz. **Number of employees nationwide:** 53,000.

KISSIMMEE GOOD SAMARITAN VILLAGE
1500 Southgate Drive, Kissimmee FL 34746. 407/846-7201. **Contact:** Human Resources. **World Wide Web address:** http://www.good-sam.com. **Description:** A nursing home licensed for 166 beds. **Other U.S. locations:** Nationwide.

LA AMISTAD BEHAVIORAL HEALTH SERVICES

1650 Park Avenue North, Maitland FL 32751. 407/647-0660. **Contact:** Ann Spariosu, Human Resources Director. **World Wide Web address:** http://www.lamistad.com. **Job page:** http://www.lamistad.com/jobs.htm. **Description:** Operates a 50-bed inpatient facility. La Amistad offers the following: Deaf and Hearing Impaired Program, Child Psychiatric Program, Adolescent Psychiatric Program, Conversion Treatment Programs, a Dual Diagnosis Psychiatric Treatment Program, an Adult Psychiatric Program, and Academic Programs. **Other U.S. locations:** Winter Park FL. **Parent company:** Universal Health Services.

LEE MEMORIAL HEALTH SYSTEM

P.O. Box 2218, Fort Myers FL 33902. 941/332-1111. **Physical address:** 2776 Cleveland Avenue, Fort Myers FL 33901. **Toll-free phone:** 800/642-5267. **Fax:** 941/332-4199. **Contact:** Human Resources Department. **World Wide Web address:** http://www.leememorial.org. **Description:** A leading provider of health care in southwest Florida. The nonprofit hospital is comprised of three acute care hospitals, a skilled nursing facility, home health services, and physician offices. Founded in 1916. **NOTE:** Entry-level positions and second and third shifts are offered. **Common positions include:** Attorney; Biomedical Engineer; Buyer; Certified Nurses Aide; Chief Financial Officer; Clinical Lab Technician; Computer Operator; Daycare Worker; Dietician/Nutritionist; EEG Technologist; EKG Technician; Emergency Medical Technician; Financial Analyst; Human Resources Manager; Licensed Practical Nurse; Marketing Specialist; Medical Records Technician; MIS Specialist; Nuclear Medicine Technologist; Nurse Practitioner; Occupational Therapist; Pharmacist; Physical Therapist; Physician; Public Relations Specialist; Radiological Technologist; Registered Nurse; Respiratory Therapist; Secretary; Social Worker; Speech-Language Pathologist; Surgical Technician; Telecommunications Manager. **Corporate headquarters location:** This location. **Operations at this facility include:** Administration; Service. **Number of employees at this location:** 5,200.

LIFE CARE SERVICES

800 NW 17th Avenue, Delray Beach FL 33445. 561/272-7779. **Contact:** Human Resources. **Description:** Provides home health care services and manages nursing staffs at various facilities.

LINVATEC CORPORATION
11311 Concept Boulevard, Largo FL 33773. 727/392-6464. **Fax:** 727/399-9900. **Contact:** Human Resources Department. **World Wide Web address:** http://www.linvatec.com. **Description:** Manufactures and markets medical instruments used in orthoscopy and endoscopy for minimally invasive surgery. **Common positions include:** Accountant/Auditor; Buyer; Compliance Analyst; Computer Programmer; Customer Service Representative; Designer; Draftsperson; Financial Analyst; Mechanical Engineer; Purchasing Agent/Manager; Quality Control Supervisor. **Corporate headquarters location:** New York NY. **Parent company:** Bristol-Myers Squibb.

MANATEE MEMORIAL HOSPITAL
206 Second Street East, Bradenton FL 34208. 941/745-7319. **Fax:** 941/745-7405. **Contact:** Personnel. **World Wide Web address:** http://www.manateememorial.com. **Description:** A 512-bed, acute care hospital whose departments include emergency, telemetry, ICU, CVSICU, CCU, and surgery. **Common positions include:** Nurse; Registered Nurse. **Parent company:** Universal Health Services. **CEO:** Brian Flynn.

MARTIN MEMORIAL HEALTH SYSTEMS, INC.
P.O. Box 9010, Stuart FL 34995. 561/287-5200. **Physical address:** 200 SE Hospital Avenue, Stuart FL 34994. **Contact:** Jennifer T. Slaugh, Employment Coordinator. **Description:** A nonprofit, 336-bed, multifacility health care organization. Martin Memorial Health Systems is comprised of Martin Memorial Medical Center and Martin Memorial Hospital South, both accredited facilities. The medical center is a 236-bed, acute care facility providing a range of inpatient and outpatient services including cancer and cardiac care, a 24-hour emergency department, maternity and pediatrics, and a wide variety of laser surgeries. Martin Memorial Hospital South is a 100-bed community hospital providing inpatient and outpatient services with 92 private rooms, an 8-bed intensive care unit, and a 24-hour emergency department. **Common positions include:** EEG Technologist; EKG Technician; Emergency Medical Technician; Medical Technologist; MIS Specialist; Occupational Therapist; Pharmacist; Physical Therapist; Physician; Radiological Technologist; Registered Nurse; Respiratory Therapist; Speech-Language Pathologist; Surgical Technician; Telecommunications Manager. **Corporate headquarters location:** This location. **Annual sales/revenues:** More than $100 million. **Number of employees at this location:** 2,000.

MAYO CLINIC
4500 San Pueblo Road, Jacksonville FL 32224. 904/953-2000. **Toll-free phone:** 800/336-2838. **Fax:** 904/296-4668. **Recorded jobline:** 904/296-5588. **Contact:** Human Resources. **E-mail address:** mcjhr@mayo.edu. **World Wide Web address:** http://www.mayo.edu. **Description:** An outpatient medical and surgical clinic offering a wide variety of specialty care services. Founded in 1986. **President/CEO:** Robert M. Walters. **Facilities Manager:** Gary Pezall. **Information Systems Manager:** Barbara Cummings. **Purchasing Manager:** David Johnson.

MEDICAL TECHNOLOGY SYSTEMS
12920 Automobile Boulevard, Clearwater FL 33762. 727/576-6311. **Fax:** 727/579-8067. **Contact:** Peter Benjamin, Vice President of Human Resources. **Description:** Manufactures and markets blister cards for drug packaging and pharmaceutical dispensing systems for use in nursing homes and hospitals. **Listed on:** NASDAQ. **Stock exchange symbol:** MSYS.

MEDTRONIC XOMED SURGICAL PRODUCTS, INC.
6743 Southpoint Drive North, Jacksonville FL 32216. 904/296-9600. **Contact:** Human Resources. **World Wide Web address:** http://www.xomed.com. **Description:** Manufactures medical devices and products for ear, nose, and throat surgery. **Common positions include:** Accountant/Auditor; Biomedical Engineer; Buyer; Customer Service Representative; Draftsperson; Electrical/Electronics Engineer; Electrician; Financial Manager; Machinist; Manufacturer's/Wholesaler's Sales Rep.; Market Research Analyst; Mechanical Engineer; Purchasing Agent/Manager; Quality Control Supervisor; Software Engineer; Tool and Die Maker; Typist/Word Processor. **Corporate headquarters location:** This location. **Operations at this facility include:** Divisional Headquarters; Manufacturing; Research and Development.

MEMORIAL HOSPITAL OF TAMPA
2901 Swann Avenue, Tampa FL 33609. 813/873-6400. **Fax:** 813/873-6494. **Contact:** Cathy Massessa, Director of Human Resources Department. **Description:** A hospital that provides inpatient and outpatient services. **Common positions include:** Accountant/Auditor; Biomedical Engineer; Clinical Lab Technician; EEG Technologist; EKG Technician; Emergency Medical Technician; Human Resources Manager; Licensed Practical Nurse; Medical Records Technician; Nuclear Medicine Technologist; Pharmacist; Physical Therapist; Physician; Radiological Technologist; Registered Nurse; Respiratory Therapist; Social Worker. **Corporate headquarters**

location: Dallas TX. **Parent company:** AMI. **Operations at this facility include:** Service. **Number of employees at this location:** 600.

MIAMI JEWISH HOME & HOSPITAL

5200 NE 2nd Avenue, Miami FL 33137. 305/751-8626. **Contact:** Larry McDonald, Director of Human Resources. **Description:** A hospital that also operates a nursing home for senior citizens.

MOORINGS PARK

111 Moorings Park Drive, Naples FL 34105. 941/261-1616. **Contact:** Human Resources. **Description:** A continuing care retirement community offering skilled nursing, assisted living, and independent living.

MORTON PLANT HOSPITAL

300 Pinelles Street, Clearwater FL 33756. 727/462-7000. **Contact:** Human Resources Department. **Description:** A 687-bed community hospital offering a full range of medical/surgical services.

MORTON PLANT MEASE HEALTH CARE

501 Main Street, Dunedin FL 34698. 727/734-6435. **Fax:** 727/734-6119. **Recorded jobline:** 727/734-6937. **Contact:** Department of Human Resources. **World Wide Web address:** http://www.mpmhealth.com. **Description:** A nonprofit, full-service hospital. Specialties include cancer treatment, cardiovascular medicine, neurosciences, orthopedics, rehabilitation, and surgery services. **Common positions include:** Accountant; Certified Nurses Aide; Claim Rep.; Clinical Lab Technician; Computer Operator; Computer Programmer; Customer Service Rep.; Dietician/Nutritionist; EEG Technologist; EKG Technician; Electrician; Emergency Medical Technician; Financial Analyst; Librarian; Licensed Practical Nurse; Medical Records Technician; Nuclear Medicine Technologist; Occupational Therapist; Pharmacist; Physical Therapist; Physician; Registered Nurse; Respiratory Therapist; Secretary; Social Worker; Software Engineer; Speech-Language Pathologist; Surgical Technician; Systems Analyst. **Corporate headquarters location:** This location. **Number of employees at this location:** 6,000.

NAPLES MEDICAL CENTER

400 8th Street North, Naples FL 34102. 941/649-3355. **Fax:** 941/649-3301. **Contact:** Kathleen Phelps, Personnel. **World Wide Web address:** http://www.naplesmedicalcenter.com.

Description: A multispecialty medical center with diagnostic and administrative departments. Founded in 1958. **NOTE:** Entry-level positions are offered. **Common positions include:** Account Manager; Accountant; Administrative Assistant; Administrative Manager; Certified Nurses Aide; Chief Financial Officer; Controller; Database Manager; EKG Technician; Human Resources Manager; Licensed Practical Nurse; Medical Records Technician; Physician; Registered Nurse; Secretary; Speech-Language Pathologist. **Parent company:** ProMedCo Management Corporation. **Listed on:** Privately held. **Number of employees at this location:** 230.

NUMED HOME HEALTH CARE, INC.
12900 DuPont Circle, Suite B, Tampa FL 33626. 813/925-3530. **Fax:** 813/925-3859. **Contact:** Human Resources. **World Wide Web address:** http://www.numed.com. **Description:** A holding company for home health care organizations. **Corporate headquarters location:** This location. **Listed on:** NASDAQ. **Stock exchange symbol:** NUMD.

ORLANDO REGIONAL HEALTHCARE
1414 South Kuhl Avenue, Orlando FL 32806-2008. 407/841-5111. **Fax:** 407/237-6374. **Contact:** Nancy Dinon, Vice-President. **World Wide Web address:** http://www.orhs.org. **Description:** A comprehensive medical system that operates several health care facilities throughout central Florida. **NOTE:** Entry-level positions, part-time jobs, and second and third shifts are offered. **Common positions include:** Accountant; Administrative Assistant; Assistant Manager; Budget Analyst; Certified Nurses Aide; Certified Occupational Therapy Assistant; Computer Programmer; Computer Technician; Customer Service Representative; Dietician/Nutritionist; EEG Technologist; EKG Technician; Electrical/Electronics Engineer; Electrician; Emergency Medical Technician; Financial Analyst; Geneticist; Help-Desk Technician; Home Health Aide; Human Resources Manager; Librarian; Licensed Practical Nurse; Market Research Analyst; Marketing Specialist; Medical Assistant; Medical Records Technician; Medical Secretary; Network/Systems Administrator; Nuclear Medicine Technologist; Nurse Practitioner; Occupational Therapist; Pharmacist; Physical Therapist; Physical Therapy Assistant; Physician Assistant; Radiological Technologist; Registered Nurse; Respiratory Therapist; Secretary; Social Worker; Speech-Language Pathologist; Surgical Technician; Systems Analyst; Webmaster. **Special programs:** Internships; Summer Jobs. **Number of employees nationwide:** 9,000.

ORLANDO REGIONAL LUCERNE HOSPITAL
818 Main Lane, Orlando FL 32806. 407/649-6111. **Contact:** Human Resources Department. **World Wide Web address:** http://www.orlandoregional.org. **Description:** A medical center serving Orlando and its surrounding cities.

OSCEOLA REGIONAL MEDICAL CENTER
700 West Oak Street, Kissimmee FL 34741. 407/846-2266. **Contact:** Silvia Loillis, Director of Personnel. **World Wide Web address:** http://www.osceolaregional.com. **Description:** A 171-bed hospital offering a full range of services including diagnostic testing, cardiac care, and rehabilitation.

PLANTATION GENERAL HOSPITAL
401 NW 42nd Avenue, Plantation FL 33317. 954/797-6450. **Fax:** 954/587-7869. **Recorded jobline:** 954/321-4068. **Contact:** Human Resources Department. **World Wide Web address:** http://www.plantationgeneral.com. **Description:** A hospital offering a full range of inpatient and outpatient services. **Common positions include:** Accountant/Auditor; Biomedical Engineer; Clinical Lab Technician; Customer Service Rep.; Dietician/Nutritionist; Electrician; Health Services Manager; Human Resources Manager; Licensed Practical Nurse; Medical Records Technician; MIS Specialist; Nuclear Medicine Technologist; Pharmacist; Physical Therapist; Purchasing Agent/Manager; Radiological Technologist; Registered Nurse; Respiratory Therapist; Surgical Technician; Typist/Word Processor. **Special programs:** Internships. **CEO:** Anthony M. Degina, Jr.

PRIME CARE HEALTH AGENCY INC.
8405 NW 53rd Street, Building 106, Miami FL 33166. 305/591-7774. **Toll-free phone:** 800/591-7747. **Fax:** 305/594-8951. **Recorded jobline:** 305/591-7774x815. **Contact:** Josie Melero, Human Resources Director. **Description:** Provides in-home nursing services. Founded in 1985. **Common positions include:** Certified Nurses Aide; Home Health Aide; Licensed Practical Nurse; Registered Nurse; Respiratory Therapist. **Office hours:** Monday - Friday, 8:00 a.m. - 5:00 p.m. **President:** Barry G. Shoor. **Number of employees at this location:** 250. **Number of employees nationwide:** 300.

RAMSAY YOUTH SERVICES, INC.

Columbus Center, One Alhambra Plaza, Suite 750, Coral Gables FL 33134. 305/569-6993. **Fax:** 305/569-4647. **Contact:** Human Resources Department. **World Wide Web address:** http://www.ramsay.com. **Description:** Ramsay Youth Services, Inc. is a provider and manager of juvenile justice and behavioral healthcare treatment programs and services. The programs and services are provided primarily to at-risk and troubled youth in residential and nonresidential settings. **Common positions include:** Accountant/Auditor; Computer Programmer; Counselor; Human Resources Manager; Human Service Worker; Licensed Practical Nurse; Medical Records Technician; Pharmacist; Physical Therapist; Psychologist; Recreational Therapist; Registered Nurse; Restaurant/Food Service Manager; Social Worker. **Other U.S. locations:** Nationwide. **Operations at this facility include:** Administration. **Listed on:** NASDAQ. **Stock exchange symbol:** RYOU.

ROTECH MEDICAL CORPORATION

4506 L.B. McLeod Road, Suite F, Orlando FL 32811. 407/841-2115. **Contact:** Human Resources. **Description:** RoTech Medical Corporation markets, provides, and delivers outpatient health care products and services to patients in physician offices and at their home. Services and products involve respiratory therapy equipment, convalescent medical equipment, prelabeled and prepackaged pharmaceuticals, and home infusion therapy products. **Other U.S. locations:** Nationwide. **Listed on:** NASDAQ. **Stock exchange symbol:** ROTC. **Number of employees at this location:** 350.

S.H. MEDICAL CORPORATION

3061 NW 82nd Avenue, Miami FL 33122. 305/406-2222. **Fax:** 305/406-2113. **Contact:** Hiring Manager. **World Wide Web address:** http://www.shmedical.com. **Description:** A medical equipment distribution and export company that sells new, refurbished, and preowned medical equipment. The company specializes in diagnostic equipment, endoscopy equipment and instruments, fetal monitors, parts, pulse oximeters, surgical instruments, and ultrasounds. **Corporate headquarters location:** This location.

SACRED HEART HEALTH SYSTEMS

5151 North Ninth Avenue, Pensacola FL 32513. 850/416-7175. **Fax:** 850/416-6740. **Contact:** Sue Byrd, Director of Human Resources Department. **World Wide Web address:** http://www.sacred-heart.org. **Description:** A member of the

Daughters of Charity national health system. Sacred Heart Health Systems is a 431-bed acute care facility. The hospital offers services in the following areas: cardiology, cardiovascular surgery, emergency, gastroenterology, laser surgery, neonatology, neurology, OB/GYN, oncology, orthopedics, otolaryngology, otology, pediatrics, and plastic surgery. Sacred Heart Health Systems also operates a skilled nursing facility, medical residence programs, and a wellness/health education center. **NOTE:** Job seekers may apply in person at the employment office from 8:00 a.m. to 3:00 p.m. The employment office is located at 5110 Bayou Boulevard, Pensacola FL 32513. **Common positions include:** Computer Programmer; EEG Technologist; EKG Technician; Emergency Medical Technician; Human Resources Manager; Licensed Practical Nurse; Medical Records Technician; Nuclear Medicine Technologist; Occupational Therapist; Pharmacist; Physical Therapist; Radiological Technologist; Registered Nurse; Respiratory Therapist. **Corporate headquarters location:** St. Louis MO. **Number of employees at this location:** 2,500. **CEO:** Patrick J. Madden.

SKYWAY ANIMAL HOSPITAL
3258 Fifth Avenue South, St. Petersburg FL 33712. 727/327-5141. **Fax:** 727/327-3405. **Contact:** Human Resources. **World Wide Web address:** http://www.skywayah.com. **Description:** Provides general medical, surgical, dental, and radiological services to small animals.

SMITH DENTAL LABS
2131 Art Museum Drive, Jacksonville FL 32207. 904/398-6844. **Contact:** Human Resources. **World Wide Web address:** http://www.smithdentallab.com. **Description:** Provides a full range of custom-made dental prosthetic appliances, divided into three main groups: restorative products (crowns and bridges); reconstructive products (partial and full dentures); and cosmetic products (porcelain veneers and ceramic crowns). **Corporate headquarters location:** Wayland MA. **Parent company:** National Dentex Corporation is one of the largest operators of dental laboratories in the United States. Each lab is operated as a stand-alone facility under the direction of a local manager. All sales and marketing is done through each lab's own direct sales force. **Other U.S. locations:** Nationwide. **Listed on:** NASDAQ. **Stock exchange symbol:** NADX. **Annual sales/revenues:** Less than $5 million.

STAR MULTICARE SERVICES INC.
2929 North Comerse Parkway, Miramar FL 33025. 954/435-1550. **Contact:** Human Resources. **World Wide Web address:** http://www.starmulticare.com. **Description:** A home health care agency that also provides temporary personnel to health care facilities. **Corporate headquarters location:** Huntington Station NY. **Other U.S. locations:** NJ; NY; OH; PA. **Listed on:** NASDAQ. **Stock exchange symbol:** SMCS.

SUNRISE COMMUNITY, INC.
22300 SW 162nd Avenue, Miami FL 33170. 305/245-6150. **Contact:** Human Resources. **World Wide Web address:** http://www.sunrisegroup.com. **Description:** A residential treatment facility for individuals with developmental disabilities. **Other area locations:** Cape Coral FL; Clewiston FL; Lakeland FL; Naples FL; Panama City FL; St. Petersburg FL; Tallahassee FL. **Other U.S. locations:** AL; CT; GA; TN; VA. **President/CEO:** Les Leech, Jr. **Number of employees nationwide:** 4,000.

SUNRISE COMMUNITY, INC.
9040 Sunset Drive, Suite A, Miami FL 33173. 305/596-9040. **Contact:** Human Resources Department. **World Wide Web address:** http://www.sunrisegroup.com. **Description:** A residential treatment center for individuals with developmental disabilities. **Other area locations:** Cape Coral FL; Clewiston FL; Lakeland FL; Naples FL; Panama City FL; St. Petersburg FL; Tallahassee FL. **Other U.S. locations:** AL; CT; GA; TN; VA. **President/CEO:** Les Leech, Jr. **Number of employees nationwide:** 4,000.

SWANHOLM NURSING AND REHABILITATION
6200 Central Avenue, St. Petersburg FL 33707. 727/347-5196. **Contact:** Human Resources. **Description:** A nursing home and rehabilitation center that also provides assisted-living services.

TALLAHASSEE COMMUNITY HOSPITAL
2626 Capital Medical Boulevard, Tallahassee FL 32308. 850/656-5000. **Contact:** Human Resources. **World Wide Web address:** http://www.tallahasseehospital.com. **World Wide Web address:** http://www.ctch.com. **Description:** A 180-bed, acute-care hospital. Founded in 1979.

TAMPA GENERAL HOSPITAL
P.O. Box 1289, Tampa FL 33601. 813/844-7551. **Fax:** 813/844-4345. **Recorded jobline:** 813/844-4100. **Contact:** Human Resources Department. **World Wide Web address:**

http://www.tgh.org. **Description:** A medical facility providing hospital and ambulatory services. **Common positions include:** Accountant/Auditor; Budget Analyst; Clinical Lab Technician; EEG Technologist; EKG Technician; Electrician; Financial Analyst; Food Scientist/Technologist; Human Resources Manager; Industrial Engineer; Licensed Practical Nurse; Occupational Therapist; Registered Nurse; Respiratory Therapist; Social Worker; Speech-Language Pathologist; Surgical Technician. **Special programs:** Internships. **CEO:** Ron Hytoff. **Operations at this facility include:** Administration. **Number of employees at this location:** 3,000.

TENDER LOVING CARE/STAFF BUILDERS
3075 West Oakland Park Boulevard, Suite 100, Fort Lauderdale FL 33311. 954/486-5506. **Fax:** 954/739-5129. **Contact:** Human Resources. **World Wide Web address:** http://www.tlcathome.com. **Description:** A home health care agency. **Common positions include:** Certified Nurses Aide; Licensed Practical Nurse; Occupational Therapist; Physical Therapist; Registered Nurse; Social Worker; Speech-Language Pathologist. **Corporate headquarters location:** Lake Success NY. **Other U.S. locations:** Nationwide. **CEO:** Stephen Savitsky. **Number of employees nationwide:** 20,000.

TENDER LOVING CARE/STAFF BUILDERS
1900 South Congress Avenue, Suite A, West Palm Beach FL 33406. 561/641-6667. **Contact:** Human Resources. **World Wide Web address:** http://www.tlcathome.com. **Description:** A home health care agency. **Corporate headquarters location:** Lake Success NY. **Other U.S. locations:** Nationwide. **CEO:** Stephen Savitsky. **Number of employees nationwide:** 20,000.

TENDER LOVING CARE/STAFF BUILDERS
9342 South U.S. Highway 1, Village Green Plaza, Port St. Lucie FL 34952. 561/878-8820. **Contact:** Human Resources. **World Wide Web address:** http://www.tlcathome.com. **Description:** A home health care agency. **Corporate headquarters location:** Lake Success NY. **Other U.S. locations:** Nationwide. **CEO:** Stephen Savitsky. **Number of employees nationwide:** 20,000.

TENDER LOVING CARE/STAFF BUILDERS
9143 Phillips Highway, Suite 533, Jacksonville FL 32256. 904/519-6699. **Contact:** Human Resources. **World Wide Web address:** http://www.tlcathome.com. **Description:** A home health care agency. **Common positions include:** Home Health Aide; Licensed Practical Nurse; Registered Nurse. **Corporate**

headquarters location: Lake Success NY. **Other U.S. locations:** Nationwide. **CEO:** Stephen Savitsky. **Number of employees nationwide:** 20,000.

3I (IMPLANT INNOVATIONS, INC.)
4555 Riverside Drive, Palm Beach Gardens FL 33410. 561/776-6700. **Fax:** 561/776-6825. **Contact:** Human Resources. **E-mail address:** mfischer@3implant.com. **World Wide Web address:** http://www.3Ionline.com. **Description:** A manufacturer and distributor of dental implants.

TRANSITIONS OPTICAL INC.
9251 Belcher Road, Pinellas Park FL 33782. 727/545-0400. **Contact:** Human Resources. **World Wide Web address:** http://www.transitions.com. **Description:** Manufactures plastic photochromatic ophthalmic lenses. Founded in 1990. **Listed on:** Privately held. **Annual sales/revenues:** More than $100 million.

TYCO HEALTHCARE/KENDALL
P.O. Box 62078, DeLand FL 32721-2078. 386/734-3685. **Contact:** J. Ralph Mills, Human Resources Manager. **World Wide Web address:** http://www.kendallhq.com. **Description:** Manufactures disposable hypodermic needles and syringes. Founded in 1903. **NOTE:** Second and third shifts are offered. **Common positions include:** Accountant; Administrative Assistant; AS400 Programmer Analyst; Biological Scientist; Chemist; Computer Programmer; Computer Technician; Controller; Database Administrator; Draftsperson; Electrical/Electronics Engineer; General Manager; Help-Desk Technician; Human Resources Manager; Industrial Engineer; Industrial Production Manager; Manufacturing Engineer; Mechanical Engineer; MIS Specialist; Operations Manager; Purchasing Agent/Manager; Quality Assurance Engineer; Quality Control Supervisor; Secretary; Technical Writer/Editor; Typist/Word Processor. **Corporate headquarters location:** Mansfield MA. **Other U.S. locations:** Nationwide. **International locations:** Worldwide. **Parent company:** Tyco International. **Operations at this facility include:** Manufacturing. **Listed on:** New York Stock Exchange. **Stock exchange symbol:** TYC. **President/CEO:** Rich Meelia. **Annual sales/revenues:** More than $100 million.

U.S. DEPARTMENT OF VETERANS AFFAIRS
BAY PINES VA MEDICAL CENTER
P.O. Box 5005, 10000 Bay Pines Boulevard, Bay Pines FL 33744. 727/398-6661. **Contact:** Human Resources. **World**

Wide Web address: http://www.va.gov. **Description:** A medical center operated by the U.S. Department of Veterans Affairs. The VA health care system includes 171 medical centers; more than 364 outpatient, community, and outreach clinics; 130 nursing home care units; and 37 domiciliaries. **Corporate headquarters location:** Washington DC. **Other U.S. locations:** Nationwide.

U.S. DEPARTMENT OF VETERANS AFFAIRS
MIAMI VA MEDICAL CENTER
1201 NW 16th Street, Miami FL 33125. 305/324-3155. **Contact:** Human Resources. **World Wide Web address:** http://www.va.gov/546miami. **Description:** A medical center operated by the U.S. Department of Veterans Affairs. From 54 hospitals in 1930, the VA health care system has grown to include 171 medical centers; more than 364 outpatient, community, and outreach clinics; 130 nursing home care units; and 37 domiciliaries. VA operates at least one medical center in each of the 48 contiguous states, Puerto Rico, and the District of Columbia. With approximately 76,000 medical center beds, VA treats nearly 1 million patients in VA hospitals; 75,000 in nursing home care units; and 25,000 in domiciliaries. VA's outpatient clinics register approximately 24 million visits per year. **Common positions include:** Dental Assistant/Dental Hygienist; Dietician/Nutritionist; EKG Technician; Licensed Practical Nurse; Medical Records Technician; Medical Technologist; Occupational Therapist; Pharmacist; Physical Therapist; Physician; Psychologist; Radiological Technologist; Recreational Therapist; Registered Nurse; Respiratory Therapist; Social Worker; Speech-Language Pathologist; Structural Engineer. **Corporate headquarters location:** Washington DC. **Other U.S. locations:** Nationwide. **Operations at this facility include:** Administration; Research and Development; Service. **Number of employees at this location:** 2,700.

UNIVERSITY COMMUNITY HOSPITAL
3100 East Fletcher Avenue, Tampa FL 33613. 813/615-7290. **Recorded jobline:** 813/615-7830. **Contact:** Bernadette Stypula, Human Resources Manager. **World Wide Web address:** http://www.uch.org. **Description:** A 431-bed, full-service, acute care hospital. **Common positions include:** Accountant/Auditor; Administrator; Biomedical Engineer; Buyer; Claim Representative; Computer Programmer; Credit Manager; Customer Service Rep.; Electrical/Electronics Engineer; Industrial Engineer; Purchasing Agent/Manager; Systems Analyst. **Office hours:** Monday - Friday, 8:00 a.m. -

5:00 p.m. **Operations at this facility include:** Administration; Service. **President:** Norm Stein. **Number of employees at this location:** 2,500.

UNIVERSITY HOSPITAL & MEDICAL CENTER
7201 North University Drive, Tamarac FL 33321. 954/721-2200. **Contact:** Scott Mazo, Director of Personnel. **World Wide Web address:** http://www.umhchealth.com. **Description:** A 317-bed hospital offering a full range of inpatient and outpatient health care services. Founded in 1974. **Number of employees at this location:** 1,550.

VISITING NURSE ASSOCIATION
2400 SE Monterey Road, Suite 300, Stuart FL 34996. 561/286-1844. **Contact:** Human Resources. **World Wide Web address:** http://www.visitingnurses.com. **Description:** A nonprofit home health agency that also offers rehabilitation and mental health services, home IV therapies, pre-op visits, private duty nurses, HIV/AIDS care, case management, and oncology care.

VISITING NURSE ASSOCIATION & HOSPICE
1111 36th Street, Vero Beach FL 32960. 561/567-5551. **Contact:** Human Resources. **World Wide Web address:** http://www.visitingnurses.com. **Description:** A nonprofit home health agency that also offers rehabilitation and mental health services, home IV therapies, pre-op visits, private duty nurses, HIV/AIDS care, case management, and oncology care.

WESTCHESTER GENERAL HOSPITAL, INC.
2500 SW 75th Avenue, Miami FL 33155. 305/264-5252. **Contact:** Human Resources. **Description:** A general acute care hospital.

WHITEHALL BOCA NURSING HOME
7300 Del Prado Circle South, Boca Raton FL 33433. 561/392-3000. **Contact:** Human Resources. **World Wide Web address:** http://www.whitehallboca.com. **Description:** A skilled nursing home that also offers some assisted living services.

WINDMOOR HEALTH CARE
11300 U.S. 19 North, Clearwater FL 33764. 727/541-2646. **Contact:** Human Resources. **World Wide Web address:** http://www.windmoorhealthcare.com. **Description:** A full-service hospital specializing in psychiatric treatment and chemical dependency therapy. The hospital provides both inpatient and outpatient services.

WINTER PARK MEMORIAL HOSPITAL
200 North Lakemont Avenue, Winter Park FL 32789. 407/646-7000. **Fax:** 407/646-7639. **Contact:** Human Resources. **World Wide Web address:** http://www.winterparkhospital.com. **Description:** A 334-bed medical/surgical hospital offering neonatal intensive care and oncology services. **Parent company:** Adventist Health System.

WINTER PARK TOWERS
1111 South Lakemont Avenue, Winter Park FL 32789. 407/647-4083. **Contact:** Human Resources. **Description:** A retirement community offering skilled nursing, assisted living, and independent living.

HOTELS AND RESTAURANTS

You can expect to find the following types of companies in this chapter:

Casinos
Dinner Theaters
Hotel/Motel Operators
Resorts
Restaurants

ATLANTIC COAST MANAGEMENT
P.O. Box 2066, Winter Park FL 32790. 407/647-4300. **Fax:** 407/647-5306. **Contact:** Joe Hayes, Vice President of Human Resources. **Description:** A restaurant management company. **Common positions include:** Management Trainee. **Corporate headquarters location:** This location. **Listed on:** Privately held.

BENIHANA INC.
8685 NW 53rd Terrace, Suite 201, Miami FL 33166. 305/593-0770. **Fax:** 305/592-6371. **Contact:** Human Resources. **E-mail address:** contact@benihana.com. **World Wide Web address:** http://www.benihana.com. **Description:** Owns and operates more than 60 Japanese steakhouses. Additional restaurants are operated by licensees. **Common positions include:** Accountant/Auditor; Data Entry Clerk; Purchasing Agent/Manager; Restaurant/Food Service Manager. **Corporate headquarters location:** This location. **Other U.S. locations:** Nationwide. **Subsidiaries include:** Rudy's Restaurant Group, Inc. **Listed on:** NASDAQ. **Stock exchange symbol:** BNHN. **Annual sales/revenues:** $21 - $50 million. **Number of employees nationwide:** 1,650.

CHECKERS DRIVE-IN RESTAURANTS, INC.
3300 West Cypress Street, Suite 600, Tampa FL 33607. 813/283-7000. **Contact:** Human Resources Department. **World Wide Web address:** http://www.checkers.com. **Description:** Develops, owns, operates, and franchises quick-service, drive-thru restaurants under the Checkers name. **Common positions include:** Restaurant/Food Service Manager. **Corporate headquarters location:** This location. **Listed on:** NASDAQ. **Stock exchange symbol:** CHKR. **Number of employees at this location:** 130. **Number of employees nationwide:** 12,000.

DARDEN RESTAURANTS, INC.
P.O. Box 593330, Orlando FL 32859-3330. 407/245-4000. **Contact:** Human Resources Department. **World Wide Web address:** http://www.darden.com. **Description:** Operates the Red Lobster, Olive Garden, and Bahama Breeze restaurant chains. **Corporate headquarters location:** This location. **Listed on:** New York Stock Exchange. **Stock exchange symbol:** DRI. **Annual sales/revenues:** More than $100 million. **Number of employees nationwide:** 122,000.

EXECUSTAY, INC.
3630 Park Central Boulevard North, Pompano Beach FL 33064. 954/975-0900. **Fax:** 954/975-0411. **Contact:** Human

Resources Department. **World Wide Web address:** http://www.execustay.com. **Description:** Specializes in providing corporations and executives with interim housing throughout south Florida. **Corporate headquarters location:** This location. **Parent company:** Marriott International, Inc.

FMS MANAGEMENT SYSTEMS, INC.
dba INTERNATIONAL HOUSE OF PANCAKES
2655 NE 189th Street, North Miami Beach FL 33180. 305/931-5454. **Fax:** 305/933-3300. **Contact:** Carol Boettcher, Director of Human Resources. **World Wide Web address:** http://www.ihop.com. **Description:** Operates International House of Pancakes (IHOP) restaurants. **Common positions include:** Accountant/Auditor; Administrative Manager; Controller; Vice President. **Other U.S. locations:** Nationwide. **International locations:** Canada. **Listed on:** New York Stock Exchange. **Stock exchange symbol:** IHP.

FAMOUS AMOS RESTAURANTS, INC.
2765 Clydo Road, Jacksonville FL 32207. 904/731-3396. **Contact:** Human Resources. **Description:** Operates a chain of 10 area restaurants. **Corporate headquarters location:** This location.

H.I. DEVELOPMENT, INC.
111 West Fortune Street, Tampa FL 33602. 813/229-6686. **Contact:** David Callen, President. **Description:** A hotel management and consulting firm. **Common positions include:** Accountant/Auditor; Administrative Worker/Clerk; Advertising Clerk; General Manager; Hotel Manager; Human Resources Manager; Marketing Specialist. **Corporate headquarters location:** This location. **Operations at this facility include:** Regional Headquarters.

HYATT REGENCY ORLANDO INTERNATIONAL AIRPORT
9300 Airport Boulevard, Orlando FL 32827. 407/825-1310. **Fax:** 407/825-1341. **Contact:** Human Resources. **World Wide Web address:** http://www.hyatt.com. **Description:** A full-service hotel that offers two restaurants, recreational facilities, air line tickets, car rental services, and meeting and banquet facilities. **Common positions include:** Accountant/Auditor; Credit Manager; Electrician; General Manager; Hotel Manager; Purchasing Agent/Manager; Restaurant/Food Service Manager. **Corporate headquarters location:** Chicago IL. **Other U.S. locations:** Nationwide. **International locations:** Worldwide. **Parent company:** Hyatt Hotel Corporation. **Operations at this facility include:** Service. **Listed on:** Privately held. **Number of**

employees at this location: 400. Number of employees nationwide: 40,000.

HYATT REGENCY PIER SIXTY-SIX
2301 SE 17th Street Causeway, Fort Lauderdale FL 33316. 954/728-3580. **Fax:** 954/728-3509. **Contact:** Human Resources. **World Wide Web address:** http://www.hyatt.com. **Description:** A full-service hotel that offers six restaurants, multiple recreational facilities, and extensive meeting and banquet facilities. **Common positions include:** Accountant/Auditor; Customer Service Representative; General Manager; Hotel Manager; Human Resources Manager; Restaurant/Food Service Manager. **Special programs:** Internships. **Operations at this facility include:** Administration; Divisional Headquarters; Sales. **Listed on:** Privately held. **Number of employees at this location:** 500.

KING PROVISION CORPORATION
P.O. Drawer U, Jacksonville FL 32203. 904/725-4122. **Contact:** Human Resources. **World Wide Web address:** http://www.kingprovision.com. **Description:** A distributor that provides food and supplies to Burger King Restaurants. **Common positions include:** General Manager; Management Trainee; Restaurant/Food Service Manager. **Corporate headquarters location:** This location.

LA CRUISE CASINO
4738 Ocean Street, Jacksonville FL 32233. 904/241-7200. **Contact:** Human Resources. **World Wide Web address:** http://www.lacruise.com. **Description:** A 24-hour casino cruise ship. La Cruise Dockside (also at this location) is a family-style restaurant.

OUTBACK STEAKHOUSE, INC.
2202 North West Shore Boulevard, 5th Floor, Tampa FL 33607. 813/282-1225. **Fax:** 813/282-1209. **Contact:** Trudy Cooper, Vice President of Training and Development. **World Wide Web address:** http://www.outbacksteakhouse.com. **Description:** The company operates Outback Steakhouse Restaurants. Outback Steakhouses, Inc. also owns and operates several Carraba's Italian Grill and Fleming's Prime Steakhouse and Wine Bar restaurants. **Listed on:** New York Stock Exchange. **Stock exchange symbol:** OSI. **Number of employees nationwide:** 8,800.

POPEYE'S
906 Lee Road, Orlando FL 32810. 407/628-0393. **Fax:**
407/628-8311. **Contact:** Human Resources. **World Wide Web
address:** http://www.popeyes.com. **Description:** Operates
more than 60 Popeye's restaurant franchises in central and
northern Florida. **Common positions include:** General
Manager; Management Trainee; Restaurant/Food Service
Manager. **Corporate headquarters location:** Macon GA.
Operations at this facility include: Divisional Headquarters.
Listed on: Privately held. **Number of employees nationwide:**
2,500.

RENAISSANCE MIAMI BISCAYNE BAY HOTEL
1601 Biscayne Boulevard, Miami FL 33132. 305/374-0000.
Fax: 305/374-8065. **Contact:** Human Resources. **World Wide
Web address:** http://www.marriott.com. **Description:** A 528-
room hotel that is located atop a shopping mall. **Common
positions include:** Administrative Assistant; General Manager;
Human Resources Manager; Sales Manager.

RESTAURANT ADMINISTRATION SERVICES
2699 Lee Road, Suite 200, Winter Park FL 32789. 407/645-
4811. **Fax:** 407/629-0641. **Contact:** Dale Lucas, Director of
Personnel and Training. **Description:** Operates quick-service
restaurants. **Common positions include:** Management Trainee;
Restaurant/Food Service Manager. **Corporate headquarters
location:** This location. **Listed on:** Privately held. **Number of
employees at this location:** 1,200.

SUN INTERNATIONAL, INC.
1415 East Sunrise Boulevard, Suite 800, Fort Lauderdale FL
33304. 954/713-2500. **Contact:** Human Resources. **World
Wide Web address:** http://www.sunint.com. **Description:**
Owns and operates casinos, resorts, and hotel facilities.
Common positions include: Accountant/Auditor;
Administrative Manager; Computer Programmer; Customer
Service Representative; Hotel Manager; Human Service
Worker; Management Trainee; Systems Analyst. **Corporate
headquarters location:** This location. **Number of employees at
this location:** 200. **Number of employees nationwide:** 15,000.

THE WESTIN INNISBROOK RESORT
36750 U.S. Highway 19 North, Palm Harbor FL 34684.
727/942-2000. **Fax:** 727/942-5268. **Contact:** Human
Resources. **World Wide Web address:** http://www.westin-
innisbrook.com. **Description:** A 221-room hotel and resort that
offers four golf courses, six restaurants, full-service recreational

facilities, and three convention centers. **NOTE:** Entry-level positions and second and third shifts are offered. **Company slogan:** People make the difference. **Common positions include:** Accountant; Administrative Assistant; Assistant Manager; Controller; Customer Service Representative; Electrician; General Manager; Human Resources Manager; Marketing Manager; MIS Specialist; Operations Manager; Project Manager; Public Relations Specialist; Purchasing Agent/Manager; Sales Executive; Sales Manager; Sales Representative; Secretary. **Special programs:** Internships; Training; Summer Jobs. **Corporate headquarters location:** Seattle WA. **Other U.S. locations:** Nationwide. **International locations:** Worldwide. **Listed on:** Privately held. **Number of employees at this location:** 1,600. **Number of employees worldwide:** 22,000.

WYNDHAM ORLANDO RESORT

8001 International Drive, Orlando FL 32819. 407/351-2420. **Fax:** 407/352-7054. **Contact:** Human Resources. **World Wide Web address:** http://www.wyndhamorlandohotels.com. **Description:** A hotel that offers five restaurants, recreational facilities, and business and meeting accommodations. **Common positions include:** Accountant/Auditor; Credit Manager; Electrical/Electronics Engineer; Human Resources Manager; Restaurant/Food Service Manager. **Corporate headquarters location:** Washington DC. **Parent company:** Wyndham International. **Operations at this facility include:** Administration; Sales. **Listed on:** New York Stock Exchange. **Stock exchange symbol:** WYN.

INSURANCE

**You can expect to find the following types of
companies in this chapter:**

*Commercial and Industrial Property/Casualty Insurers
Health Maintenance Organizations (HMOs)
Medical/Life Insurance Companies*

AAA (AMERICAN AUTOMOBILE ASSOCIATION)
1000 AAA Drive, Mailstop 70, Heathrow FL 32746-5063. 407/444-7537. **Fax:** 407/444-7504. **Contact:** Personnel. **World Wide Web address:** http://www.aaasouth.com. **Description:** A nonprofit organization that provides insurance, travel services, and related benefits to its members. **Common positions include:** Accountant/Auditor; Administrative Assistant; Advertising Clerk; Architect; Attorney; Blue-Collar Worker Supervisor; Branch Manager; Budget Analyst; Buyer; Claim Representative; Clerical Supervisor; Computer Programmer; Counselor; Credit Manager; Customer Service Representative; Draftsperson; Economist; Editor; Education Administrator; Financial Analyst; General Manager; Human Resources Manager; Insurance Agent/Broker; Librarian; Library Technician; Management Trainee; Public Relations Specialist; Purchasing Agent/Manager; Restaurant/Food Service Manager; Services Sales Representative; Statistician; Systems Analyst; Technical Writer/Editor; Travel Agent; Underwriter/Assistant Underwriter. **Corporate headquarters location:** This location. **Other U.S. locations:** Nationwide. **Number of employees at this location:** 1,100. **Number of employees nationwide:** 3,700.

ASSURANT GROUP
11222 Quail Roost Drive, Miami FL 33157. 305/253-2244. **Contact:** Human Resources Department. **World Wide Web address:** http://www.assurant.com. **Description:** A holding company. Through its major subsidiaries, the company sells unemployment, accident, health, credit card, mortgage, and homeowners insurance. **Corporate headquarters location:** This location. **Number of employees at this location:** 2,100.

BLUE CROSS AND BLUE SHIELD OF FLORIDA
4800 Deerwood Campus Parkway, Building 100, Jacksonville FL 32246. 904/791-6111. **Fax:** 888/310-4797. **Contact:** Director of Human Resources. **World Wide Web address:** http://www.bcbsfl.com. **Description:** A nonprofit health care insurance organization providing managed health care plans to both individuals and groups. Blue Cross and Blue Shield offers Point-of-Service, individual health, PPO, and HMO plans, as well as life insurance, dental insurance, worker's compensation, accidental death and dismemberment, and short- and long-term disability. **Common positions include:** MIS Specialist; Registered Nurse; Sales Representative; Systems Analyst; Underwriter/Assistant Underwriter. **Special programs:** Internships.

BROWN & BROWN INSURANCE
401 East Jackson Street, Suite 1700, Tampa FL 33602. 813/222-4100. **Contact:** Human Resources Department. **World Wide Web address:** http://www.brown-n-brown.com. **Description:** An independent insurance agency that provides a variety of insurance products and services to corporate, institutional, professional, and individual clients. Products and services fall into four major categories: National Programs specializes in liability and property insurance programs; Retail Operations provides property, casualty, life, and health insurance; Brokerage Operations provides property and casualty products; and Service Operations provides claims administration. **Common positions include:** Accountant; Administrative Assistant; Attorney; Chief Financial Officer; Computer Operator; Computer Programmer; Computer Support Technician; Customer Service Representative; Human Resources Manager; Marketing Manager; Marketing Specialist; Network/Systems Administrator; Systems Analyst; Typist/Word Processor; Underwriter/Assistant Underwriter; Webmaster. **Office hours:** Monday - Friday, 8:00 a.m. - 5:00 p.m. **Corporate headquarters location:** Daytona Beach FL. **Other U.S. locations:** Nationwide. **Operations at this facility include:** Administration; Sales; Service. **Listed on:** New York Stock Exchange. **Stock exchange symbol:** BRO. **Number of employees at this location:** 250. **Number of employees nationwide:** 1,000.

CAROLINA CASUALTY INSURANCE COMPANY
P.O. Box 2575, Jacksonville FL 32203. 904/363-0900. **Contact:** Catherine Steckner, Human Resources Manager. **World Wide Web address:** http://www.carolinacas.com. **Description:** A primary insurance company.

CRAWFORD & COMPANY
P.O. Box 48370, Jacksonville FL 32247-8370. 904/398-0551. **Contact:** Ronald J. Hayes, Branch Manager. **World Wide Web address:** http://www.crawford-thg.com. **Description:** A branch office of a regional insurance adjuster. **Corporate headquarters location:** Atlanta GA.

HEALTH PLAN SERVICES
3501 East Frontage Road, Tampa FL 33607. 813/289-1000. **Contact:** Human Resources Department. **World Wide Web address:** http://www.healthplan.com. **Description:** A third-party administrator and marketer of small group life and health insurance.

HUMANA
3501 SW 167th Avenue, Miramar FL 33027. 305/267-6633.
Contact: Human Resources. **World Wide Web address:**
http://www.humana.com. **Description:** A managed health care
company that provides comprehensive services through its
health maintenance organizations, and administrative services
through its workers' compensation third-party administration.
Listed on: New York Stock Exchange. **Stock exchange symbol:**
HUM.

METROPOLITAN LIFE INSURANCE COMPANY
4100 Boy Scout Boulevard, Tampa FL 33607. 813/870-8000.
Contact: Human Resources Department. **World Wide Web
address:** http://www.metlife.com. **Description:** This location is
the Southeast regional headquarters. Overall, Metropolitan Life
Insurance is an international insurance and financial services
company. **NOTE:** Positions are offered in the Metropolitan
Executive Training Program for professionals with MBAs and
JDs.

WARD NORTH AMERICA, INC.
1211 Semoran Boulevard, Suite 127, Casselberry FL 32707.
407/660-2222. **Contact:** Human Resources. **World Wide Web
address:** http://www.wardnorthamerica.com. **Description:** An
insurance adjuster. **Other U.S. locations:** Nationwide.
International locations: Canada.

LEGAL SERVICES

You can expect to find the following types of companies in this chapter:

Law Firms
Legal Service Agencies

CARLTON FIELDS

P.O. Box 3239, Tampa FL 33601. 813/223-7000. **Contact:** Deborah Jensen, Director of Human Resources. **World Wide Web address:** http://www.carltonfields.com. **Description:** A law firm specializing in real estate and construction. **Common positions include:** Accountant/Auditor; Attorney; Paralegal; Secretary. **Corporate headquarters location:** This location. **Operations at this facility include:** Administration; Service. **Number of employees at this location:** 420.

FOLEY & LARDNER

200 North Laura Street, Jacksonville FL 32202. 904/359-2000. **Contact:** Human Resources Department. **World Wide Web address:** http://www.foleylardner.com. **Description:** A law firm specializing in real estate, tax, corporate, securities, and individual planning. Founded in 1842.

FOWLER, WHITE, GILLEN, BAGGS, VILLAREAL, BANKER

P.O. Box 1438, Tampa FL 33601. **Physical address:** 501 East Kennedy Boulevard, Suite 1700, Tampa FL 33602. 813/228-7411. **Contact:** Human Resources. **World Wide Web address:** http://www.fowlerwhite.com. **Description:** A law firm specializing in corporate, business, and real estate law.

GREENBERG TRAURIG

1221 Brickell Avenue, 21st Floor, Miami FL 33131. 305/579-0500. **Fax:** 305/579-0717. **Contact:** Rosalyn Friedman, Director of Human Resources Department. **World Wide Web address:** http://www.gtlaw.com. **Description:** A business law firm specializing in corporate and securities, entertainment, information technology, litigation, real estate, and telecommunications.

MARKS, GRAY, CONROY & GIBBS

P.O. Box 447, Jacksonville FL 32201. 904/398-0900. **Contact:** Office Administrator. **Description:** A law firm. **Common positions include:** Attorney; Paralegal; Secretary. **Corporate headquarters location:** This location. **Number of employees at this location:** 60.

McGUIREWOODS

50 North Laura Street, Suite 3300, Jacksonville FL 32202. 904/798-3200. **Contact:** Human Resources. **World Wide Web address:** http://www.mcguirewoods.com. **Description:** A law firm specializing in environmental, estate trust, and labor law.

MANUFACTURING: MISCELLANEOUS CONSUMER

You can expect to find the following types of companies in this chapter:

Art Supplies
Batteries
Cosmetics and Related Products
Household Appliances and Audio/Video Equipment
Jewelry, Silverware, and Plated Ware
Miscellaneous Household Furniture and Fixtures
Musical Instruments
Tools
Toys and Sporting Goods

APPLICA INCORPORATED

5980 Miami Lakes Drive East, Miami Lakes FL 33014. 305/362-2611. **Contact:** Dave Warren, Director of Human Resources. **E-mail address:** careers@applicamail.com. **World Wide Web address:** http://www.applicainc.com. **Description:** Manufactures small beauty appliances including hair dryers and curling irons. **Listed on:** NASDAQ. **Stock exchange symbol:** APN.

ELIZABETH ARDEN, INC.

14100 NW 60th Avenue, Miami Lakes FL 33014. 305/818-8000. **Toll-free phone:** 800/227-2445. **Contact:** Human Resources Department. **World Wide Web address:** http://www.elizabetharden.com. **Description:** A leading global marketer and manufacturer of prestige beauty products. **Common positions include:** Computer Programmer; Industrial Engineer. **Corporate headquarters location:** This location. **Listed on:** NASDAQ. **Stock exchange symbol:** RDEN. **Number of employees at this location:** 150.

FISKARS POTTERY AND OUTDOOR LEISURE PRODUCTS

3000 West Orange Avenue, Apopka FL 32703. 407/889-5533. **Toll-free phone:** 800/621-4253. **Contact:** Human Resources. **World Wide Web address:** http://www.fiskars.com. **Description:** A manufacturer of plastic lawn and garden items. The company specializes in plastic flowerpots and shade structures. **Parent company:** Fiskars Consumer Products, Inc. **Number of employees at this location:** 400.

FLORIDA FURNITURE INDUSTRIES, INC.

P.O. Box 610, Palatka FL 32178. 386/328-3444. **Contact:** Human Resources Department. **World Wide Web address:** http://www.floridafurniture.com. **Description:** Manufactures wooden bedroom furniture.

LOREN INDUSTRIES, INC.

2801 Greene Street, Hollywood FL 33020. 800/772-8085. **Contact:** Human Resources Department. **World Wide Web address:** http://www.loren.com. **Description:** A manufacturer of jewelry. **Number of employees at this location:** 185.

MACHO PRODUCTS INC.

10045 102nd Terrace, Sebastian FL 32958. 561/388-9892. **Contact:** Human Resources Department. **World Wide Web address:** http://www.macho.com. **Description:** Manufactures protective foam gear and padding for use in martial arts instruction. **Number of employees at this location:** 155.

MOLTECH POWER SYSTEMS, INC.

P.O. Box 147114, Gainesville FL 32614-7114. 386/462-4719. **Contact:** Ms. Gerry Bryant, Human Resources. **World Wide Web address:** http://www.moltechpower.com. **Description:** A manufacturer of rechargeable batteries. **Common positions include:** Chemical Engineer; Electrical/Electronics Engineer; Mechanical Engineer; Metallurgical Engineer. **Special programs:** Internships. **Corporate headquarters location:** This location. **Operations at this facility include:** Administration; Manufacturing; Research and Development. **Number of employees at this location:** 1,300.

PARLUX FRAGRANCES, INC.

3725 SW 30th Avenue, Fort Lauderdale FL 33312. 954/316-9008x103. **Fax:** 954/316-8155. **Contact:** Tania Espinosa, Human Resources Administrator. **World Wide Web address:** http://www.parlux.com. **Description:** A manufacturer and international distributor of fragrances and cosmetics. The company's product line includes Perry Ellis Cosmetics, Fred Hayman Beverly Hills, Animale Parfums, and Phantom of the Opera. **Corporate headquarters location:** This location. **International locations:** Paris, France. **Listed on:** NASDAQ. **Stock exchange symbol:** PARL.

RECOTON CORPORATION

2950 Lake Emma Road, Lake Mary FL 32746. 407/333-0900. **Contact:** Human Resources. **World Wide Web address:** http://www.recoton.com. **Description:** Designs, manufactures, and markets consumer electronics, car stereo speakers, and loudspeakers. **Listed on:** NASDAQ. **Stock exchange symbol:** RCOT.

REVLON

P.O. Box 37557, Jacksonville FL 32236. 904/693-1200. **Fax:** 904/693-1259. **Contact:** Human Resources. **World Wide Web address:** http://www.revlon.com. **Description:** This location manufactures hair care products. Overall, Revlon manufactures a wide variety of cosmetics and personal care products. **Common positions include:** Accountant/Auditor; Blue-Collar Worker Supervisor; Buyer; Cashier; Chemical Engineer; Chemist; Clerical Supervisor; Computer Operator; Computer Programmer; Credit Clerk and Authorizer; Credit Manager; Dispatcher; Electrical/Electronics Engineer; Electrician; Human Resources Manager; Industrial Engineer; Machinist; Mechanical Engineer; Order Clerk; Payroll Clerk; Secretary; Systems Analyst. **Corporate headquarters location:** New York NY. **Operations at this facility include:** Administration;

Manufacturing; Research and Development. **Listed on:** New York Stock Exchange. **Stock exchange symbol:** REV. **Number of employees at this location:** 550.

SUNBEAM CORPORATION

2381 Executive Center Drive, Boca Raton FL 33431. 561/912-4100. **Contact:** Human Resources Department. **World Wide Web address:** http://www.sunbeam.com. **Description:** A designer, manufacturer, and marketer of consumer products. The company is divided into several business groups. Outdoor Products includes propane, natural gas, electric, and charcoal barbecue grills; aluminum lawn and patio furniture and related accessories; and wrought iron and wood furniture. Household Products includes electric and conventional blankets, comforters, heated throws, heating pads, bath scales, health monitoring systems, vaporizers, humidifiers, irons, steamers, and dental and hair care products. Small Kitchen Appliances includes hand mixers, blenders, food processors, juice extractors, toasters, can openers, waffle makers, and other culinary accessories. Sunbeam also produces barber and beauty products, personal care products, and animal products, as well as clocks, timers, thermometers, and weather instruments. **Corporate headquarters location:** This location. **International locations:** Worldwide.

TRAVELPRO LUGGAGE

700 Banyan Trail, Boca Raton FL 33431. 561/998-2824. **Contact:** Human Resources Department. **World Wide Web address:** http://www.travelpro.com. **Description:** Manufactures and distributes luggage.

TUPPERWARE WORLD HEADQUARTERS

P.O. Box 2353, Orlando FL 32802-2353. 407/826-5050. **Fax:** 407/826-4453. **Recorded jobline:** 407/826-4496. **Contact:** Human Resources. **E-mail address:** resume@tupperware.com. **World Wide Web address:** http://www.tupperware.com. **Description:** Manufactures plastic food storage and service containers. **Common positions include:** Accountant/Auditor; Adjuster; Administrative Assistant; Attorney; Budget Analyst; Buyer; Customer Service Rep.; Designer; Draftsperson; Economist; Editor; Electrician; Environmental Engineer; Financial Analyst; Human Resources Manager; Purchasing Agent/Manager; Travel Agent; Underwriter/Assistant Underwriter. **Corporate headquarters location:** This location. **Other U.S. locations:** Nationwide. **International locations:** Worldwide. **Operations at this facility include:** Administration; Divisional Headquarters; Research and

Development. **Listed on:** New York Stock Exchange. **Stock exchange symbol:** TUP. **CEO:** E. Goings. **Number of employees nationwide:** 7,000.

ZODIAC POOL CARE, INC.
2028 NW 25th Avenue, Pompano Beach FL 33069. 800/416-7665. **Contact:** Human Resources. **World Wide Web address:** http://www.zodiacpoolcare.com. **Description:** A manufacturer of automatic swimming pool vacuums and purification systems under the brand name Baracuda. **NOTE:** Applicants should indicate department of interest when sending a resume.

MANUFACTURING: MISCELLANEOUS INDUSTRIAL

You can expect to find the following types of companies in this chapter:

Ball and Roller Bearings
Commercial Furniture and Fixtures
Fans, Blowers, and Purification Equipment
Industrial Machinery and Equipment
Motors and Generators/Compressors and Engine Parts
Vending Machines

AEROTRON-REPCO SYSTEMS, INC.
4602 Parkway Commerce Boulevard, Orlando FL 32808. 407/856-1953. **Toll-free phone:** 800/950-5633. **Fax:** 407/856-1960. **Contact:** Ted McDonald, Human Resources Manager. **World Wide Web address:** http://www.aerotron-repco.com. **Description:** A manufacturer of communications equipment including wireless modems and hand-held radios. **Corporate headquarters location:** This location. **Listed on:** Privately held. **Number of employees at this location:** 55.

ALPINE ENGINEERED PRODUCTS, INC.
P.O. Box 2225, Pompano Beach FL 33061. 954/781-3333. **Contact:** Human Resources. **World Wide Web address:** http://www.alpeng.com. **Description:** A manufacturer of metal connector plates for floors and roofs. Alpine Engineered Products also manufactures wood-handling equipment and saws. **Parent company:** Dorbyl Ltd. (Johannesburg, South Africa).

BAIRNCO CORPORATION
300 Primera Boulevard, Suite 432, Lake Mary FL 32746. 407/875-2222. **Contact:** Human Resources Department. **World Wide Web address:** http://www.bairnco.com. **Description:** A holding company. **NOTE:** Hiring is done primarily through individual operating divisions. **Common positions include:** Accountant/Auditor; Chemist; Computer Programmer; Electrical/Electronics Engineer; Financial Analyst; General Manager; Human Resources Manager; Industrial Engineer; Mechanical Engineer; Operations/Production Manager; Supervisor. **Corporate headquarters location:** This location. **Subsidiaries include:** Kasco Corporation manufactures and services equipment for the supermarket industry; Arlon Inc. manufactures coated and laminated materials for industrial and commercial use. Markets include civilian and military communications, radar and computer systems, electronic testing, and other industrial, scientific, automotive, and military applications. **Listed on:** New York Stock Exchange. **Stock exchange symbol:** BZ. **Number of employees at this location:** 15. **Number of employees nationwide:** 900.

CROWN CORK & SEAL COMPANY, INC.
P.O. Box 770369, Winter Garden FL 34777-0369. 407/654-0225. **Contact:** Human Resources Department. **World Wide Web address:** http://www.crowncork.com. **Description:** This location manufactures two-piece aluminum soda cans and three-piece steel coffee cans. Overall, Crown Cork & Seal

Company is a worldwide manufacturer and distributor of a wide range of crowns, seals, and aluminum/steel cans including aerosol and beverage cans. Crown Cork & Seal Company also manufactures bottling equipment. **Listed on:** New York Stock Exchange. **Stock exchange symbol:** CCK.

ECC INTERNATIONAL CORPORATION
2001 West Oak Ridge Road, Orlando FL 32809. 407/859-7410. **Toll-free phone:** 800/327-1020. **Fax:** 407/855-4840. **Contact:** Human Resources Department. **World Wide Web address:** http://www.eccic.com. **Description:** This location manufactures training simulators for the government. Overall, ECC International Corporation has two major business segments: military training and simulation, and vending machine design and manufacture. ECC provides training systems and services to the United States Department of Defense and to armed forces in over 25 countries. ECC systems are used for familiarization and maintenance training, weapons systems operation, and gunnery training. ECC's Instructional Systems Design Group also designs computer-based training systems for nonmilitary markets. **Common positions include:** Accountant/Auditor; Commercial Artist; Computer Programmer; Cost Estimator; Draftsperson; Electrical/Electronics Engineer; Graphic Artist; Industrial Engineer; Machinist; Mechanical Engineer; Precision Assembler; Purchasing Agent/Manager; Receptionist; Secretary; Sheet-Metal Worker; Software Engineer; Systems Analyst; Technical Writer/Editor; Typist/Word Processor; Welder. **Subsidiaries include:** ECC Simulation Limited. **Number of employees at this location:** 780.

EVA-TONE
P.O. Box 7020, Clearwater FL 33758. 727/572-7000. **Fax:** 727/540-0088. **Contact:** Department of Human Resources. **E-mail address:** nancy.lewis@eva-tone.com. **World Wide Web address:** http://www.evatone.com. **Description:** Produces audio materials, CDs, CD-ROMs, and cassettes for business and marketing applications. The company also provides commercial printing, mailing, and packaging services. **Common positions include:** Factory Worker; Production Worker. **Corporate headquarters location:** This location. **Operations at this facility include:** Administration; Manufacturing; Research and Development; Sales. **Listed on:** Privately held. **Number of employees at this location:** 400.

FMC CORPORATION
400 Fairway Avenue, Lakeland FL 33801. 863/683-5411. **Contact:** Mary Lou Polin, Human Resources. **World Wide Web address:** http://www.fmc.com. **Description:** This location manufactures citrus fruit processing machinery. Overall, FMC Corporation is one of the world's leading producers of chemicals and machinery for the performance chemicals, industrial chemicals, machinery and equipment, defense systems, and precious metals markets. **Corporate headquarters location:** Chicago IL. **Listed on:** New York Stock Exchange. **Stock exchange symbol:** FMC. **Number of employees worldwide:** 6,000.

GENCOR INDUSTRIES INC.
5201 North Orange Blossom Trail, Orlando FL 32810. 407/290-6000. **Fax:** 407/578-0577. **Contact:** Personnel. **World Wide Web address:** http://www.gencor.com. **Description:** Manufactures combustion systems and related electronic heat process controls.

HI-RISE RECYCLING SYSTEMS, INC.
8505 NW 74th Street, Miami FL 33166. 305/597-0243. **Fax:** 305/594-4228. **Contact:** Human Resources. **World Wide Web address:** http://www.hiri.com. **Description:** Sells, installs, and services the patented Hi-Rise Recycling System for use in residential and industrial buildings. Founded in 1990. **Corporate headquarters location:** This location. **Subsidiaries include:** Wilkinson Company Inc. (Stow OH) manufactures recycling, trash, and linen chutes for high-rise apartment buildings, condominiums, and hotels. **Listed on:** NASDAQ. **Stock exchange symbol:** HIRI.

INVENSYS METERING SYSTEMS
9495 Delegates Drive, Orlando FL 32837. 407/851-4470. **Contact:** Department of Human Resources. **World Wide Web address:** http://www.invensys.com. **Description:** This division manufactures water meters. Overall, Invensys manufactures temperature control products, energy management systems, and mechanical services for the commercial marketplace. **Common positions include:** Accountant/Auditor; Administrative Manager; Budget Analyst; Credit Manager; Materials Engineer; Mechanical Engineer; Metallurgical Engineer; Purchasing Agent/Manager; Structural Engineer. **Operations at this facility include:** Administration; Manufacturing; Research and Development; Sales; Service.

MARTIN ELECTRONICS, INC.
10625 Puckett Road, Perry FL 32348. 850/584-2634. **Fax:** 850/584-2044. **Contact:** Human Resources. **World Wide Web address:** http://www.martin-electronics.com. **Description:** Manufactures pyrotechnic and explosive devices for ordnance applications. **Common positions include:** Chemical Engineer; Manufacturing Engineer; Production Manager. **Corporate headquarters location:** This location. **Parent company:** MEI Holdings, Inc. **Operations at this facility include:** Manufacturing. **Listed on:** Privately held. **Number of employees at this location:** 250.

PALL AEROPOWER
5775 Rio Vista Drive, Clearwater FL 33760. 727/539-8448. **Contact:** Laurel Dinan, Personnel Director. **World Wide Web address:** http://www.pall.com. **Description:** Manufactures high-technology filtration components for hydraulic systems, fuel systems, and lubrication systems. **Common positions include:** Accountant/Auditor; Administrator; Aerospace Engineer; Buyer; Computer Programmer; Draftsperson; Human Resources Manager; Machinist; Mechanical Engineer; Operations/Production Manager; Purchasing Agent/Manager; Quality Control Supervisor; Systems Analyst. **Corporate headquarters location:** East Hills NY. **Parent company:** Pall Corporation is a world leader in filtration end separation. The company's business is organized into three segments: Health Care, Aeropower, and Fluid Processing. In the fluid clarification market, Pall sells disposable cartridges that fit into filter houses they have sold to clients. In the separations market, the company sells complete systems, which include both semipermanent filters that are replaced rarely and systems that regularly consume disposable cartridges. **Listed on:** New York Stock Exchange. **Stock exchange symbol:** PLL.

PALL AEROPOWER
10540 Ridge Road, New Port Richey FL 34654. 727/849-9999. **Fax:** 727/848-5719. **Contact:** Human Resources. **World Wide Web address:** http://www.pall.com. **Description:** Manufactures high-technology filtration components for hydraulic systems, fuel systems, and lubrication systems. **Common positions include:** Aerospace Engineer; Aircraft Mechanic/Engine Specialist; Buyer; Chemist; Cost Estimator; Designer; Electrician; Human Resources Manager; Industrial Engineer; Mechanical Engineer; Operations/Production Manager; Purchasing Agent/Manager; Quality Control Supervisor. **Corporate headquarters location:** East Hills NY. **Other U.S. locations:** NJ. **Parent company:** Pall Corporation is a world

leader in filtration end separation. The company's business is organized into three segments: Health Care, Aeropower, and Fluid Processing. In the fluid clarification market, Pall sells disposable cartridges that fit into filter houses they have sold to clients. In the separations market, the company sells complete systems, which include both semipermanent filters that are replaced rarely and systems that regularly consume disposable cartridges. **Operations at this facility include:** Manufacturing. **Listed on:** New York Stock Exchange. **Stock exchange symbol:** PLL.

PARKSON CORPORATION
2727 NW 62nd Street, Fort Lauderdale FL 33309. 954/974-6610. **Contact:** Oti Wooster, Human Resources Manager. **World Wide Web address:** http//:www.parkson.com. **Description:** A water and wastewater treatment equipment manufacturer. Founded in 1971.

SIEMENS WESTINGHOUSE POWER CORPORATION
261 Litton Circle, Orlando FL 32824. 407/736-5900. **Recorded jobline:** 407/736-2500. **Contact:** Human Resources. **World Wide Web address:** http://www.siemenswestinghouse.com. **Description:** Manufactures steam turbine generators. **Parent company:** Siemens AG (Berlin, Germany). **Number of employees worldwide:** 26,500.

STAINLESS INC.
One Stainless Plaza, Deerfield Beach FL 33441. 954/421-4290x224. **Toll-free phone:** 800/877-5177. **Fax:** 954/421-4464. **Contact:** Elizabeth Mountcastle, Human Resources. **World Wide Web address:** http://www.stainless.com. **Description:** Manufactures and distributes dining room, kitchen, and playground equipment and accessories. **Common positions include:** Accountant/Auditor; Administrator; Architectural Engineer; Blue-Collar Worker Supervisor; Buyer; Computer Programmer; Credit Manager; Customer Service Representative; Department Manager; Draftsperson; Human Resources Manager; Manufacturer's/Wholesaler's Sales Rep.; Operations/Production Manager; Quality Control Supervisor; Transportation/Traffic Specialist. **Corporate headquarters location:** This location. **Operations at this facility include:** Administration; Manufacturing; Sales. **CEO:** Rob Kassab.

USNR
P.O. Box 40666, Jacksonville FL 32203. 904/354-2301. **Contact:** Lynn Adams, Department of Human Resources. **Description:** Manufactures wood-drying kilns. **World Wide**

Web address: http://www.usnr.com. **Common positions include:** Customer Service Representative; Draftsperson; Manufacturer's/Wholesaler's Sales Representative; Mechanical Engineer. **Operations at this facility include:** Divisional Headquarters.

UNIWELD PRODUCTS, INC.
2850 Ravenswood Road, Fort Lauderdale FL 33312. 954/584-2000. **Contact:** Erin Mumford, Human Resources Department. **World Wide Web address:** http://www.uniweld.com. **Description:** Manufactures gas welding, cutting, and pressure gauge equipment and accessories. **Common positions include:** Accountant/Auditor; Buyer; Commercial Artist; Credit Manager; Customer Service Representative; Draftsperson; Human Resources Manager; Industrial Engineer; Manufacturer's/Wholesaler's Sales Representative; Mechanical Engineer; Purchasing Agent/Manager; Quality Control Supervisor. **Corporate headquarters location:** This location. **Operations at this facility include:** Administration; Manufacturing; Research and Development; Sales; Service. **Other U.S. locations:** NV; TX. **International locations:** Canada; Ecuador; Lebanon; Singapore.

MINING/GAS/PETROLEUM/ENERGY RELATED

You can expect to find the following types of companies in this chapter:

Anthracite, Coal, and Ore Mining
Mining Machinery and Equipment
Oil and Gas Field Services
Petroleum and Natural Gas

ASCOM ENERGY SYSTEMS

One Pine Lakes Parkway North, Palm Coast FL 32137-3608. 386/445-0311. **Fax:** 386/445-0322. **Contact:** Louann Hamacher, Human Resources. **World Wide Web address:** http://www.ascom-usa.com. **Description:** Manufactures power packs for the computer and telecommunications industries. **NOTE:** Entry-level positions and second and third shifts are offered. **Common positions include:** Account Manager; Administrative Assistant; Buyer; Computer Operator; Computer Programmer; Controller; Customer Service Representative; Design Engineer; Finance Director; Human Resources Manager; Industrial Engineer; Manufacturing Engineer; MIS Specialist; Project Manager; Purchasing Agent/Manager; Quality Control Supervisor; Sales Engineer; Sales Executive; Sales Manager; Sales Representative; Secretary; Software Engineer; Telecommunications Manager; Vice President of Operations. **Special programs:** Internships; Training; Co-ops. **Number of employees at this location:** 160.

FLORIDA ROCK INDUSTRIES

P.O. Box 4667, Jacksonville FL 32201. 904/355-1781. **Contact:** Bob Banks, Director of Human Resources. **Description:** Manufactures concrete aggregates. Florida Rock & Tank Lines (also at this location) transports oil and gasoline. Sunbelt Transport (also at this location) is a flatbed transportation company. **Common positions include:** Accountant/Auditor; Administrator; Civil Engineer; Credit Manager; Department Manager; General Manager; Geologist/Geophysicist; Mining Engineer; Systems Analyst. **Corporate headquarters location:** This location. **Operations at this facility include:** Administration. **Listed on:** New York Stock Exchange. **Stock exchange symbol:** FRK.

IMC PHOSPHATES

P.O. Box 2000, Mulberry FL 33860. 863/428-2500. **Contact:** Human Resources. **Description:** Engaged in the production of phosphate rock and related surface mining activities. **Special programs:** Apprenticeships. **Parent company:** IMC Fertilizer Group, Inc. (Mundelein IL) produces oil; natural gas; sulfur deposits; and uranium oxide, a chemical which is used in nuclear power plant fuel.

SEMINOLE ELECTRIC COOPERATIVE INC.

P.O. Box 272000, Tampa FL 33688-2000. 813/963-0994. **Toll-free phone:** 800/321-6274. **Fax:** 813/264-7906. **Contact:** Faye Rampolla, Human Resources Analyst. **E-mail address:** frampolla@seminole-electric.com. **World Wide Web address:**

http://www.seminole-electric.com. **Description:** A nonprofit company that owns power plants that provide electricity to utility companies. **Common positions include:** Accountant; Administrative Assistant; Auditor; Budget Analyst; Chief Financial Officer; Civil Engineer; Computer Programmer; Database Administrator; Design Engineer; Draftsperson; Economist; Electrical/Electronics Engineer; Environmental Engineer; Financial Analyst; Fund Manager; General Manager; Human Resources Manager; Internet Services Manager; Intranet Developer; Network/Systems Administrator; Purchasing Agent/Manager; Secretary; Systems Analyst; Technical Support Manager; Telecommunications Manager; Typist/Word Processor; Webmaster; Website Developer. **Special programs:** Co-ops. **Corporate headquarters location:** This location. **Other area locations:** Palatka FL. **Operations at this facility include:** Divisional Headquarters. **Executive Vice-President:** Richard J. Midulla. **Annual sales/revenues:** More than $100 million.

TOWNLEY MANUFACTURING
P.O. Box 221, Candler FL 32111. 352/687-3001. **Contact:** Human Resources Department. **World Wide Web address:** http://www.townley.net. **Description:** Manufactures heavy machinery and equipment for the mining industry as well as smaller components such as pumps, valves, and rubber hoses used in the company's products. **Other U.S. locations:** AZ; IL; TX; VA.

WORLD FUEL SERVICES, INC.
700 South Royal Poinciana Boulevard, Suite 800, Miami Springs FL 33166. 305/884-2001. **Contact:** Ileana Garcia, Director of Human Resources. **World Wide Web address:** http://www.wfscorp.com. **Description:** Engaged in aviation fuel services for air carriers and provides used oil recycling services in the southeastern United States. **Common positions include:** Accountant/Auditor; Biological Scientist; Chemist; Credit Manager; Geologist/Geophysicist; Petroleum Engineer; Services Sales Representative. **Corporate headquarters location:** This location. **Operations at this facility include:** Administration; Sales. **Listed on:** New York Stock Exchange. **Stock exchange symbol:** INT. **Annual revenues:** More than $100 million.

PAPER AND WOOD PRODUCTS

You can expect to find the following types of companies in this chapter:

Forest and Wood Products and Services
Lumber and Wood Wholesale
Millwork, Plywood, and Structural Members
Paper and Wood Mills

CAUSEWAY LUMBER COMPANY

2601 South Andrews Avenue, Fort Lauderdale FL 33316. 954/763-1224. **Contact:** Human Resources. **World Wide Web address:** http://www.causewaylumber.com. **Description:** A lumber company that offers commercial hardware, doors, lumber and plywood, roof and floor trusses, and home improvement products and accessories.

COASTAL LUMBER COMPANY

P.O. Box 1128, Havana FL 32333. 850/539-6432. **Contact:** Rita Taylor, Human Resources Manager. **World Wide Web address:** http://www.coastallumber.com. **Description:** This location manufactures, treats, and markets a variety of lumber products including decking, hardwood tiles, landscape timbers, posts, and split rail fencing. Overall, Coastal Lumber offers lumber, lumber products, and related services. The company is also involved in environmental preservation. **Common positions include:** Accountant/Auditor; Blue-Collar Worker Supervisor; Forester/Conservation Scientist; General Manager; Operations Manager; Production Manager; Supervisor. **Corporate headquarters location:** Weldon NC. **Operations at this facility include:** Manufacturing.

CONSTANTINE'S WOOD CENTER OF FLORIDA

1040 East Oakland Park Boulevard, Fort Lauderdale FL 33334. 954/561-1716. **Contact:** Human Resources. **World Wide Web address:** http://www.constantine.com. **Description:** Sells tools, lumber, veneer, and related wood products.

FLORIDA PLYWOODS, INC.

P.O. Box 458, Greenville FL 32331. 850/948-2211. **Contact:** Arthur Maultsby, Personnel Manager. **World Wide Web address:** http://www.flply.com. **Description:** Manufactures particleboard for drawer sides, kitchen cabinets, laminated shelves, and hardwood plywood. **Common positions include:** Accountant/Auditor; Blue-Collar Worker Supervisor; Electrical/Electronics Engineer; General Manager; Machine Operator; Mechanical Engineer; Purchasing Agent/Manager. **Operations at this facility include:** Manufacturing; Sales.

GEORGIA-PACIFIC CORPORATION

P.O. Box 919, Palatka FL 32178. 386/325-2001. **Contact:** Michael Eichorn, Human Resources Manager. **World Wide Web address:** http://www.gp.com. **Description:** Manufactures pulp, paper, building materials, and related chemicals. **Other U.S. locations:** Nationwide. **Listed on:** New York Stock Exchange. **Stock exchange symbol:** GP. **CEO:** Pete Correll.

GULF STREAM LUMBER COMPANY
1415 South Federal Highway, Boynton Beach FL 33435. 561/732-9763. **Contact:** Department of Human Resources. **Description:** Manufactures lumber, trusses, and doors.

MAC PAPERS INC.
P.O. Box 5369, Jacksonville FL 32247. 904/396-5312. **Physical address:** 3350 Philips Highway, Jacksonville FL 32207. **Contact:** Ms. Darnell Babbit, Director of Human Resources Department/Corporate Office. **World Wide Web address:** http://www.macpapers.com. **Description:** Distributes envelops, graphic supplies, and printing paper to commercial printers, reproduction departments, commercial businesses, and graphic artists and designers.

RAYONIER INC.
50 North Laura Street, Jacksonville FL 32202. 904/357-9100. **Contact:** Human Resources. **World Wide Web address:** http://www.rayonier.com. **Description:** A leading international forest products company primarily engaged in the trading, merchandising, and manufacturing of logs, timber, and wood products and in the production and sale of specialty pulps. Rayonier owns, buys, and harvests timber stumpage and purchases delivered logs, primarily in North America and New Zealand, for subsequent sale into export markets (primarily to Japan, Korea, and China), as well as to domestic lumber and pulp mills. Rayonier also produces dimension and specialty products for residential construction and industrial uses. **Corporate headquarters location:** This location. **Listed on:** New York Stock Exchange. **Stock exchange symbol:** RYN. **Number of employees worldwide:** 2,300.

ROBBINS MANUFACTURING COMPANY
P.O. Box 17939, Tampa FL 33682. 813/971-3030. **Fax:** 813/972-3980. **Contact:** Human Resources. **World Wide Web address:** http://www.robbinslumber.com. **Description:** A lumber mill. **Common positions include:** Blue-Collar Worker Supervisor; Branch Manager; Buyer; Clerical Supervisor; Computer Programmer; Credit Manager; Customer Service Representative; Draftsperson; Human Resources Manager; Manufacturer's/Wholesaler's Sales Rep.; Mechanical Engineer; Operations/Production Manager; Software Engineer; Systems Analyst; Wholesale and Retail Buyer. **Corporate headquarters location:** This location. **Other U.S. locations:** CA; NC; TX; WA. **Listed on:** Privately held. **Number of employees at this location:** 250. **Number of employees nationwide:** 400.

SMURFIT-STONE CONTAINER CORPORATION
P.O. Box 2000, Fernandina Beach FL 32035. 904/261-5551. **Contact:** Human Resources. **World Wide Web address:** http://www.smurfit-stone.com. **Description:** This location manufactures kraft paper and corrugated shipping containers. Overall, Smurfit-Stone Container Corporation is one of the world's leading paper-based packaging companies. The company's main products include corrugated containers, folding cartons, and multiwall industrial bags. The company is also one of the world's largest collectors and processors of recycled products that are then sold to a worldwide customer base. Smurfit-Stone Container Corporation also operates several paper tube, market pulp, and newsprint production facilities. **Corporate headquarters location:** Chicago IL. **Other area locations:** Jacksonville FL. **Other U.S. locations:** Nationwide. **International locations:** Worldwide. **Listed on:** NASDAQ. **Stock exchange symbol:** SSCC.

SMURFIT-STONE CONTAINER CORPORATION
300 Alton Box Road, Jacksonville FL 32218. 904/757-1192. **Contact:** Human Resources. **World Wide Web address:** http://www.smurfit-stone.com. **Description:** This location is an industrial packing plant. Overall, Smurfit-Stone Container Corporation is one of the world's leading paper-based packaging companies. The company's main products include corrugated containers, folding cartons, and multiwall industrial bags. The company is also one of the world's largest collectors and processors of recycled products that are then sold to a worldwide customer base. Smurfit-Stone Container Corporation also operates several paper tube, market pulp, and newsprint production facilities. **Other area locations:** Fernandina Beach FL. **Corporate headquarters location:** Chicago IL. **Other U.S. locations:** Nationwide. **International locations:** Worldwide. **Listed on:** NASDAQ. **Stock exchange symbol:** SSCC.

PRINTING AND PUBLISHING

You can expect to find the following types of companies in this chapter:

Book, Newspaper, and Periodical Publishers
Commercial Photographers
Commercial Printing Services
Graphic Designers

ADD INC. PUBLICATIONS

1560 Kingsley Avenue, Suite 1, Orange Park FL 32073. 904/264-3200. **Fax:** 904/264-3285. **Contact:** Beth Plotner, Human Resources. **E-mail address:** addinc@earthlink.net. **Description:** Publishes four local newspapers including *Jacksonville Shopping Guide* and *Clay Today*. **NOTE:** Entry-level positions are offered. **Common positions include:** Account Representative; Accountant; Administrative Assistant; Advertising Executive; Controller; Customer Service Representative; Editor; General Manager; Human Resources Manager; Managing Editor; Production Manager; Reporter; Sales Executive; Secretary; Telecommunications Manager. **Special programs:** Internships. **Corporate headquarters location:** Waupaca WI. **Other U.S. locations:** Nationwide. **Publisher:** Joyce Lyndon. **Facilities Manager:** Tim Kult. **Annual sales/revenues:** Less than $5 million. **Number of employees at this location:** 50.

AMERICAN MEDIA, INC.

5401 NW Broken Sound Boulevard, Boca Raton FL 33487. 561/997-7733. **Contact:** Human Resources. **Description:** Publishes tabloid newspapers including the *National Enquirer, Star, Weekly World News, Country Weekly,* and *Soap Opera Magazine,* with an aggregate weekly circulation of approximately 7 million. **Common positions include:** Computer Programmer; Editor; Layout Specialist; Reporter; Systems Analyst. **Corporate headquarters location:** This location. **Subsidiaries include:** Distribution Services, Inc. arranges for the placement of its periodicals in approximately 180,000 locations in North America. **Operations at this facility include:** Administration; Research and Development; Service. **President/CEO:** David J. Pecker. **Annual sales/revenues:** More than $100 million.

BBF

10950 Belcher Road, Largo FL 33777. 727/545-8703. **Fax:** 727/548-0711. **Recorded jobline:** 727/545-8703x208. **Contact:** Eric Kemerer, Human Resources Department. **E-mail address:** hrmanager@bbfprinting.com. **World Wide Web address:** http://www.bbfprinting.com. **Description:** Supplies a full line of custom-printed forms, labels, envelopes, commercial printing, computer supplies, and promotional products. Founded in 1960. **NOTE:** Entry-level positions and second and third shifts are offered. **Common positions include:** Account Representative; AS400 Programmer Analyst; Customer Service Representative; Desktop Publishing Specialist; Press Operator. **Special programs:** Training. **Office**

hours: Monday - Friday, 8:00 a.m. - 5:00 p.m. **Corporate headquarters location:** This location. **Listed on:** Privately held. **President/CEO:** Joseph P. Baker. **Annual sales/revenues:** $51 - $100 million. **Number of employees nationwide:** 400.

BAILEY PUBLISHING & COMMUNICATIONS INC.
P.O. Box 1769, Jacksonville FL 32201. 904/356-2466. **Fax:** 904/353-2628. **Contact:** James F. Bailey, Jr., Publisher. **World Wide Web address:** http://www.baileypub.com. **Description:** Publishes several specialty newspapers including the *Financial News, Daily Record, FOCUS, GOLF News,* and the *Realty/Builder Connection.* **Common positions include:** Advertising Clerk; Editor; Reporter; Services Sales Representative. **Corporate headquarters location:** This location.

BOCA RATON NEWS
5801 North Congress Avenue, Boca Raton FL 33487. 561/893-6400. **Contact:** Human Resources. **World Wide Web address:** http://www.bocanews.com. **Description:** A daily newspaper.

THE BRADENTON HERALD
P.O. Box 921, Bradenton FL 34206. 941/748-0411x6801. **Contact:** Barbara Ferg, Director of Human Resources. **E-mail address:** bferg@bradentonherald.com. **World Wide Web address:** http://www.bradenton.com. **Description:** Publisher of a daily newspaper. **Common positions include:** Account Representative; Accountant/Auditor; Administrative Assistant; Advertising Clerk; Advertising Executive; Chief Financial Officer; Commercial Artist; Computer Operator; Computer Programmer; Computer Support Technician; Computer Technician; Credit Manager; Customer Service Representative; Editor; Editorial Assistant; Graphic Artist; Graphic Designer; Help-Desk Technician; Human Resources Manager; Managing Editor; Market Research Analyst; Marketing Manager; MIS Manager; Network Administrator; Operations/Production Manager; Photographer/Camera Operator; Reporter; Sales Manager; Sales Representative; Services Sales Representative; Systems Manager. **Corporate headquarters location:** San Jose CA. **Parent company:** Knight-Ridder. **Number of employees at this location:** 250.

BREEZE NEWSPAPERS
P.O. Box 151306, Cape Coral FL 33910. 941/574-1110. **Fax:** 941/574-1984. **Contact:** Scott Blonde, Account Manager. **World Wide Web address:** http://www.flguide.com. **Description:** Publishes over a dozen community newspapers

and other publications including the *Cape Coral Daily Breeze,
Fort Myers Beach Observer, Island Reporter, Sanibel-Captiva
Islander, Sanibel-Captiva Chronicle, Captiva Current, Gulf
Coast Woman, Lehigh Acres Citizen, Fort Myers Beach
Bulletin,* and *Gasparilla Gazette.* **Common positions include:**
Accountant/Auditor; Advertising Clerk; Public Relations
Specialist; Reporter; Services Sales Representative. **Corporate
headquarters location:** Wheeling WV. **Operations at this
facility include:** Sales. **Number of employees at this location:**
200.

CAPE PUBLICATIONS, INC.
P.O. Box 419000, Melbourne FL 32941-9000. 321/242-3753.
Contact: Human Resources. **World Wide Web address:**
http://www.floridatoday.com. **Description:** Publishes *Florida
Today,* a daily newspaper that serves Brevard County. Cape
Publications also publishes five weekly and four monthly
community newspapers. Founded in 1966. **Common positions
include:** Advertising Clerk; Credit Clerk and Authorizer;
Customer Service Representative; Editor; Reporter; Services
Sales Representative. **Special programs:** Internships. **Corporate
headquarters location:** Arlington VA. **Parent company:**
Gannett Company, Inc. **Operations at this facility include:**
Divisional Headquarters; Manufacturing; Sales. **Listed on:** New
York Stock Exchange. **Stock exchange symbol:** GSI. **Number
of employees at this location:** 600.

CENTRAL FLORIDA PRESS, L.C.
4560 L.B. McLeod Road, Orlando FL 32811. 407/843-5811.
Contact: Human Resources Department. **Description:** Engaged
in promotional printing services. **Parent company:** Cadmus
Communications Corporation (Richmond VA) is a graphic
communications company offering specialized products and
services in three broad areas: printing, marketing, and
publishing. Cadmus is one of the largest graphic
communications companies in North America. Product lines
include annual reports, catalogs, direct marketing financial
printing, point-of-sale marketing, promotional printing,
publishing, research journals, specialty magazines, and
specialty packaging. Subsidiaries of Cadmus Communications
include Cadmus Color Center, Inc. (Sandston VA); Cadmus
Consumer Publishing (Richmond VA); Cadmus Custom
Publishing (Boston MA); Cadmus Direct Marketing, Inc.
(Charlotte NC); Cadmus Interactive (Tucker GA); Cadmus
Journal Services (Linthicum MD; Easton MD; Richmond VA);
Cadmus Marketing Services (Atlanta GA); Expert Brown
(Sandston VA); Graftech Corporation (Charlotte NC); 3Score,

Inc. (Tucker GA); Washburn Graphics, Inc. (Charlotte NC); and The William Byrd Press (Richmond VA).

CONSTRUCTION DATA CORPORATION
2770 Indian River Boulevard, Suite 400, Vero Beach FL 32960. 561/770-6003. **Toll-free phone:** 800/652-0008. **Fax:** 561/231-7247. **Contact:** Human Resources. **World Wide Web address:** http://www.cdcnews.com. **Description:** Publishes semiweekly construction project newspapers that include planned and upcoming projects available for bid. The company's primary subscribers are general contractors, subcontractors, and construction suppliers in the commercial, residential, industrial, and highway construction markets. **Common positions include:** Accountant/Auditor; Clerk; Sales Representative; Secretary; Typist/Word Processor. **Corporate headquarters location:** This location. **Other U.S. locations:** Rockland MA; Lawrenceville NJ; Austin TX. **Listed on:** Privately held. **Annual sales/revenues:** $11 - $20 million. **Number of employees at this location:** 75. **Number of employees nationwide:** 175.

DARTNELL CORPORATION
360 Hiatt Drive, Palm Beach Gardens FL 33410. **Toll-free phone:** 800/621-5463. **Contact:** Personnel. **World Wide Web address:** http://www.dartnellcorp.com. **Description:** Dartnell publishes motivational books and newsletters that are used by companies to improve teamwork and employee morale, resolve conflicts, and increase motivation.

EVA-TONE
P.O. Box 7020, Clearwater FL 33758. 727/572-7000. **Fax:** 727/540-0088. **Contact:** Human Resources Department. **E-mail address:** nancy.lewis@eva-tone.com. **World Wide Web address:** http://www.evatone.com. **Description:** Produces audio materials, CDs, CD-ROMs, and cassettes for business and marketing applications. The company also provides commercial printing, mailing, and packaging services. **Common positions include:** Factory Worker; Production Worker. **Corporate headquarters location:** This location. **Operations at this facility include:** Administration; Manufacturing; Research and Development; Sales. **Listed on:** Privately held. **Number of employees at this location:** 400.

FLORIDA SENTINEL BULLETIN
2207 East 21st Avenue, Tampa FL 33605. 813/248-1921. **Contact:** Human Resources. **World Wide Web address:** http://www.flsentinel.com. **Description:** A newspaper.

THE FLORIDA STAR
P.O. Box 40629, Jacksonville FL 32203. 904/766-8834. **Contact:** Human Resources. **World Wide Web address:** http://www.thefloridastar.com. **Description:** A newspaper.

THE FLORIDA TIMES-UNION
FLORIDA PUBLISHING COMPANY
P.O. Box 1949, Jacksonville FL 32231. 904/359-4600. **Physical address:** One Riverside Avenue, Jacksonville FL 32202. **Fax:** 904/359-4695. **Recorded jobline:** 904/359-4588. **Contact:** Sherwin Pulmano, Human Resources Manager. **World Wide Web address:** http://www.jacksonville.com. **Description:** Florida Publishing Company publishes the *Florida Times-Union,* a daily newspaper in Jacksonville, and provides other products and services in northeastern Florida and southeastern Georgia. **Common positions include:** Advertising Clerk; Blue-Collar Worker Supervisor; Branch Manager; Commercial Artist; Customer Service Representative; Editor; Reporter; Services Sales Representative. **Special programs:** Internships. **Corporate headquarters location:** Augusta GA. **Parent company:** Morris Communications Corporation. **Operations at this facility include:** Administration; Manufacturing; Research and Development; Sales; Service. **Listed on:** Privately held. **Number of employees at this location:** 1,200.

FORT PIERCE TRIBUNE
600 Edwards Road, Fort Pierce FL 34982. 561/461-2050. **Contact:** Human Resources. **World Wide Web address:** http://www.tcpalm.com. **Description:** A daily newspaper. Founded in 1920. **Parent company:** E.W. Scripps Company.

THE GAINESVILLE SUN
P.O. Box 147147, Gainesville FL 32614-7147. 352/374-5000. **Recorded jobline:** 352/335-3500. **Contact:** Eva Del Rio, Human Resources Manager. **World Wide Web address:** http://www.gainesvillesun.com. **Description:** A newspaper with a daily circulation of approximately 52,550, and a Sunday circulation of 60,600.

GRAPHLINE COMPANY

5701 NW 94th Avenue, Tamarac FL 33321. **Toll-free phone:** 800/998-3200. **Contact:** Director of Human Resources. **World Wide Web address:** http://www.graphline.com. **Description:** Distributes graphic arts equipment, and provides service repairs to graphic arts equipment. **Common positions include:** Accountant/Auditor; Advertising Clerk; Buyer; Computer Programmer; Credit Clerk and Authorizer; Customer Service Representative; Financial Manager; Management Trainee; Payroll Clerk; Receptionist; Secretary; Services Sales Representative; Stock Clerk. **Corporate headquarters location:** This location. **Operations at this facility include:** Administration; Sales; Service. **Number of employees at this location:** 85. **Number of employees nationwide:** 125.

JACKSONVILLE BUSINESS JOURNAL

1200 Riverplace Boulevard, Suite 201, Jacksonville FL 32207. 904/396-3502. **Contact:** Operations Director. **World Wide Web address:** http://www.bizjournals.com/jacksonville. **Description:** Publishes a business newspaper.

KEY WEST CITIZEN

P.O. Box 1800, Key West FL 33041. 305/294-6641. **Fax:** 305/294-0768. **Contact:** Human Resources. **World Wide Web address:** http://www.keysnews.com. **Description:** A daily newspaper. **Parent company:** Thomson Florida Keys Media Group.

KNIGHT-RIDDER

One Herald Plaza, Miami FL 33132. 305/376-3800. **Contact:** Human Resources Department. **World Wide Web address:** http://www.kri.com. **Description:** The second largest newspaper publisher in the United States, it owns 32 dailies and operates the Real Cities network of 58 Regional Websites. **Corporate headquarters location:** San Jose CA. **Subsidiaries include:** Knight-Ridder also has interests in the information distribution market through Knight-Ridder Information, Inc.; Knight-Ridder Financial; and Technimetrics. Knight-Ridder's online information retrieval serves the business, scientific, technology, medical, and education communities in more than 100 countries. Knight-Ridder Financial provides real-time financial news and pricing information through primary products MoneyCenter, Digital Datafeed, ProfitCenter, and TradeCenter. Knight-Ridder also has interests in cable television and other businesses. TKR Cable, a 50-50 joint venture with Liberty Media Corporation, serves 344,000 basic subscribers in New Jersey and New York and manages

Kentucky systems with 277,000 subscribers. Through TKR Cable Partners, Knight-Ridder owns a 15 percent share of TCI/TKR L.P. Cable Systems with 867,000 subscribers in five states. Other interests include partial ownership of the Seattle Times Company, two paper mills, a newspaper advertising sales company, and SCI Holdings.

LAKE CITY REPORTER
P.O. Box 17109, Lake City FL 32056. 386/752-1293. **Fax:** 386/752-9400. **Contact:** Human Resources Department. **World Wide Web address:** http://www.lakecityreporter.com. **Description:** A newspaper published Monday through Friday. **Parent company:** The New York Times Company.

THE LEDGER
P.O. Box 408, Lakeland FL 33802. 863/802-7000. **Contact:** Cindy Moates, Personnel Director. **World Wide Web address:** http://www.theledger.com. **Description:** A newspaper for Polk County Florida. **Parent company:** The New York Times Company. **Number of employees at this location:** 415.

MAGNUM DIGITAL SERVICES
6601 Lyons Road, Suite D-2, Coconut Creek FL 33073. 954/570-7877. **Fax:** 954/428-5349. **Contact:** Human Resources. **Description:** A printer of digital graphic images for banners, billboards, and bus displays. The company is also a Scotchprint manufacturer. **Corporate headquarters location:** This location. **Number of employees at this location:** 10.

THE MIAMI HERALD PUBLISHING COMPANY
EL NUEVO HERALD
One Herald Plaza, Miami FL 33132. **Toll-free phone:** 800/437-2535. **Fax:** 305/995-8021. **Recorded jobline:** 305/376-2880. **Contact:** Department of Human Resources. **Description:** Publishes a regional daily newspaper in both English and Spanish. **NOTE:** Entry-level positions and second and third shifts are offered. **Common positions include:** Account Manager; Account Rep.; Accountant; Administrative Assistant; Administrative Manager; Advertising Clerk; Advertising Executive; Assistant Manager; Budget Analyst; Customer Service Rep.; Editor; Editorial Assistant; Financial Analyst; Graphic Artist; Graphic Designer; Human Resources Manager; Market Research Analyst; Marketing Manager; Marketing Specialist; Online Content Specialist; Operations Manager; Production Manager; Sales Executive; Sales Manager; Sales Representative; Systems Analyst; Systems Manager; Technical Writer/Editor; Typist/Word Processor; Webmaster. **Special**

programs: Internships. **Corporate headquarters location:** This location. **Parent company:** Knight-Ridder. **Operations at this facility include:** Administration; Sales. **Number of employees at this location:** 2,200.

MIAMI TIMES
900 NW 54th Street, Miami FL 33127. 305/757-1147. **Contact:** Human Resources. **Description:** Publishes a weekly newspaper. **Common positions include:** Advertising Clerk; Clerical Supervisor; Customer Service Representative; Editor; General Manager; Manufacturer's/Wholesaler's Sales Rep.; Reporter; Services Sales Representative. **Special programs:** Internships. **Corporate headquarters location:** This location. **Number of employees at this location:** 20.

MIAMI TODAY
P.O. Box 1368, Miami FL 33131. 305/358-2663. **Contact:** Human Resources Department. **World Wide Web address:** http://www.miamitodaynews.com. **Description:** Publishes a weekly newspaper that focuses on the business community. Founded in 1983. **NOTE:** Entry-level positions are offered. **Common positions include:** Advertising Executive; Advertising Manager; Department Manager; Management Trainee; Marketing Specialist; Reporter. **Special programs:** Internships. **Office hours:** Monday - Friday, 8:30 a.m. - 5:30 p.m. **Corporate headquarters location:** This location. **Operations at this facility include:** Administration; Production; Sales. **Sales Manager:** Kristine Cartwright. **Number of employees at this location:** 30.

THE NAPLES DAILY NEWS
P.O. Box 7009, Naples FL 34101. 941/262-3161. **Contact:** Human Resources Department. **World Wide Web address:** http://www.naplesnews.com. **Description:** Publishes a daily newspaper.

NEWS HERALD
P.O. Box 1940, Panama City FL 32402-1940. 850/747-5000. **Contact:** Lorraine Grimes, Human Resources Manager. **World Wide Web address:** http://www.newsherald.com. **Description:** A daily newspaper. **Parent company:** Freedom Communications.

NEWS PRESS
2442 Martin Luther King Boulevard, Fort Myers FL 33901. 941/335-0421. **Fax:** 941/335-0297. **Contact:** Human Resources. **World Wide Web address:** http://www.news-

press.com. **Description:** A newspaper with a daily circulation of 89,950 and a Sunday circulation of 104,000. **Common positions include:** Accountant/Auditor; Advertising Clerk; Computer Programmer; Credit Manager; Customer Service Representative; Editor; Electrical/Electronics Engineer; Human Resources Manager; Librarian; Purchasing Agent/Manager; Quality Control Supervisor; Systems Analyst. **Special programs:** Internships. **Corporate headquarters location:** Arlington VA. **Parent company:** Gannett Company, Inc. **Listed on:** Privately held. **Number of employees at this location:** 650. **Number of employees nationwide:** 38,000.

NEWS-JOURNAL CORPORATION
P.O. Box 2831, Daytona Beach FL 32120-2831. 904/252-1511. **Contact:** Human Resources. **Description:** Publishes a daily newspaper, the *News-Journal,* with a circulation of over 100,000.

THE NORTHWEST FLORIDA DAILY NEWS
P.O. Box 2949, Fort Walton Beach FL 32549. 850/863-1111. **Contact:** Human Resources. **World Wide Web address:** http://www.nfwdailynews.com. **Description:** A newspaper publisher. **Corporate headquarters location:** Atlanta GA. **Parent company:** The New York Times Company.

OCALA STAR-BANNER
P.O. Box 490, Ocala FL 34478. 352/867-4010. **Fax:** 352/867-4018. **Contact:** Ernestine Johnson, Human Resources Director. **World Wide Web address:** http://www.theozone.com. **Description:** A daily newspaper with a circulation of 50,000.

ORLANDO BUSINESS JOURNAL
315 East Robinson Street, Suite 250, Orlando FL 32801-4323. 407/649-8470. **Fax:** 407/420-1625. **Contact:** Pat Beall. **World Wide Web address:** http://www.bizjournals.com/orlando. **Description:** A weekly business newspaper. **Common positions include:** Accountant/Auditor; Advertising Executive; Commercial Artist; Customer Service Representative; Department Manager; Editor; Manufacturer's/Wholesaler's Sales Rep.; Operations/Production Manager; Reporter. **Corporate headquarters location:** This location. **Parent company:** American City Business Journals. **Operations at this facility include:** Administration; Sales; Service.

ORLANDO SENTINEL COMMUNICATIONS COMPANY
633 North Orange Avenue, Orlando FL 32801. 407/420-6253. **Fax:** 407/420-5766. **Recorded jobline:** 407/872-7200x9121. **Contact:** Human Resources. **World Wide Web address:** http://www.orlandosentinel.com. **Description:** Publishes the *Orlando Sentinel* newspaper and various niche publications. Other company divisions include interactive, direct mail, signage, and teleservices. The company is also involved in a joint venture with Time Warner Communications to produce a local 24-hour cable news channel. **Common positions include:** Account Representative; Accountant; Administrative Assistant; Advertising Executive; Applications Engineer; Broadcast Technician; Budget Analyst; Computer Engineer; Computer Operator; Computer Technician; Content Developer; Customer Service Representative; Database Administrator; Desktop Publishing Specialist; Editor; Editorial Assistant; Electrician; Financial Analyst; Graphic Artist; Graphic Designer; Market Research Analyst; Network/Systems Administrator; Purchasing Agent/Manager; Radio/TV Announcer/Broadcaster; Reporter; Sales Representative; Secretary; Systems Analyst; Webmaster. **Special programs:** Internships; Co-ops. **Corporate headquarters location:** Chicago IL. **Other U.S. locations:** Nationwide. **Parent company:** Tribune Company. **Number of employees at this location:** 1,500.

THE ORLANDO TIMES
4403 Vineland Road, Suite B5, Orlando FL 32811. 407/841-3052. **Contact:** Human Resources. **World Wide Web address:** http://www.orlando-times.com. **Description:** Publishes a weekly newspaper.

THE PALATKA DAILY NEWS
P.O. Box 777, Palatka FL 32178. 386/312-5200. **Fax:** 386/312-5209. **Contact:** Human Resources. **World Wide Web address:** http://www.palatkadailynews.com. **Description:** A newspaper publisher. **Common positions include:** Accountant/Auditor; Advertising Clerk; Editor; Reporter. **Corporate headquarters location:** Atlanta GA. **Parent company:** The New York Times Company. **Operations at this facility include:** Administration; Sales. **Number of employees at this location:** 50.

PALM BEACH NEWSPAPERS, INC.
P.O. Box 24700, West Palm Beach FL 33416-4700. 561/820-4190. **Fax:** 561/820-4192. **Recorded jobline:** 561/820-4511x1090. **Contact:** Linda Murphy, Vice President of Human Resources. **World Wide Web address:** http://www.gopbi.com. **Description:** A newspaper and shopper publisher of such titles

as the *Palm Beach Post, Palm Beach Daily News,* and *Florida Pennysaver.* **Common positions include:** Accountant/Auditor; Advertising Clerk; Blue-Collar Worker Supervisor; Clerical Supervisor; Commercial Artist; Computer Programmer; Editor; Electrician; Librarian; Library Technician; Management Trainee; Manufacturer's/Wholesaler's Sales Rep.; Marketing Specialist; Public Relations Specialist; Reporter; Systems Analyst. **Special programs:** Internships. **Corporate headquarters location:** Atlanta GA. **Parent company:** Cox Enterprises, Inc. **Operations at this facility include:** Administration; Manufacturing; Sales. **Listed on:** Privately held. **Number of employees at this location:** 1,300. **Number of employees nationwide:** 22,000.

PENSACOLA NEWS JOURNAL
P.O. Box 12710, Pensacola FL 32574. 850/435-8500. **Contact:** Kimberly Wheeler, Employment Manager. **World Wide Web address:** http://www.pensacolanewsjournal.com. **Description:** Publishes *Pensacola News Journal,* a newspaper with a daily circulation of 66,000, a Saturday circulation of 82,000, and a Sunday circulation of 92,000.

PRINTING HOUSE LTD.
1066 Strong Road, Quincy FL 32351. 850/875-1500. **Fax:** 850/574-9609. **Contact:** Human Resources. **World Wide Web address:** http://www.theprintinghouse.com. **Description:** The fourth largest printing company in Florida. **Number of employees at this location:** 250.

ROSE PRINTING COMPANY, INC.
2503 Jackson Bluff Road, Tallahassee FL 32304. 850/576-4151. **Toll-free phone:** 800/227-3725. **Fax:** 850/576-4153. **Contact:** Human Resources. **World Wide Web address:** http://www.roseprinting.com. **Description:** A complete in-house book manufacturer.

ST. AUGUSTINE RECORD
P.O. Box 1630, St. Augustine FL 32085. 904/829-6562. **Contact:** Human Resources. **World Wide Web address:** http://www.staugustine.com. **Description:** A newspaper. **NOTE:** Please indicate department of interest when applying. **Parent company:** Morris Communications Corporation.

ST. IVES INC.
2025 McKinley Street, Hollywood FL 33020. 954/920-7300. **Fax:** 954/929-9061. **Contact:** Human Resources. **World Wide Web address:** http://www.st-ives-hwd.com. **Description:**

Performs a variety of prepress and printing services. **Other U.S. locations:** Cleveland OH. **Parent Company:** St. Ives plc. **President/CEO:** Wayne Angstrom. **Number of employees at this location:** Over 350.

SANFORD HERALD
P.O. Box 1667, Sanford FL 32772-1667. **Physical address:** 300 North French Avenue, Sanford FL 32771. 407/322-2611. **Contact:** Human Resources. **World Wide Web address:** http://sanfordherald.com. **Description:** A newspaper publisher. **NOTE:** Please indicate department of interest when applying.

SOUTH FLORIDA BUSINESS JOURNAL
1000 East Hillsboro Boulevard, Suite 103, Deerfield Beach FL 33441. 954/949-7600. **Contact:** Human Resources. **World Wide Web address:** http://www.bizjournals.com/southflorida. **Description:** A publisher of a weekly business journal. **Common positions include:** Services Sales Representative. **Corporate headquarters location:** Charlotte NC. **Operations at this facility include:** Administration; Production; Sales.

THE STUART NEWS
P.O. Box 9009, Stuart FL 34995. 561/464-8414. **Recorded jobline:** 877/690/6397. **Physical address:** 1939 South Federal Highway, Stuart FL 34994. **Contact:** Human Resources. **World Wide Web address:** http://www.tcpalm.com/stuart. **Description:** A community newspaper. **Parent company:** E.W. Scripps Company.

THE SUN-SENTINEL
200 East Las Olas Boulevard, Fort Lauderdale FL 33301-2293. 954/356-4000. **Contact:** Human Resources. **World Wide Web address:** http://www.sun-sentinel.com. **Description:** A south Florida newspaper with a daily circulation of 274,000 and a Sunday circulation of 392,000. **NOTE:** Please send resumes to: Human Resources, 333 SW 12th Avenue, Deerfield Beach FL 33442. **Parent company:** The Tribune Company.

THE TALLAHASSEE DEMOCRAT
P.O. Box 900, Tallahassee FL 32302. 850/599-2128. **Physical address:** 277 North Magnolia Drive, Tallahassee FL 32301. 850/599-2128. **Contact:** Karen Sheffield, Employment Services Administrator. **E-mail address:** resumes@knightridder.com. **World Wide Web address:** http://www.tallahassee.com. **Description:** A daily newspaper. **Common positions include:** Accountant/Auditor; Advertising Clerk; Cashier; Computer Operator; Computer Programmer; Credit Manager; Customer

Service Representative; Dispatcher; Editor; Education Administrator; Employment Interviewer; Graphic Artist; Librarian; Payroll Clerk; Photographer/Camera Operator; Receptionist; Reporter; Secretary; Services Sales Rep.; Systems Analyst; Truck Driver. **Corporate headquarters location:** Miami FL. **Parent company:** Knight Ridder. **Operations at this facility include:** Manufacturing.

TAMPA TRIBUNE

P.O. Box 191, Tampa FL 33601. 813/259-7711. **Contact:** Human Resources Department. **World Wide Web address:** http://www.tampatrib.com. **Description:** A daily newspaper.

TIMES PUBLISHING COMPANY, INC.

P.O. Box 1121, St. Petersburg FL 33731. 727/893-8404. **Fax:** 727/892-2990. **Contact:** Human Resources. **E-mail address:** resumes@sptimes.com. **World Wide Web address:** http://www.sptimes.com. **Description:** Publishes the *St. Petersburg Times* newspaper. **Common positions include:** Accountant/Auditor; Administrative Manager; Advertising Clerk; Blue-Collar Worker Supervisor; Budget Analyst; Buyer; Clerical Supervisor; Computer Programmer; Counselor; Credit Manager; Customer Service Manager; Editor; Electrical/Electronics Engineer; Electrician; Human Service Worker; Librarian; Library Technician; Management Analyst/Consultant; Manufacturer's/Wholesaler's Sales Rep.; Operations/Production Manager; Quality Control Supervisor; Reporter; Securities Sales Representative; Services Sales Representative; Software Engineer; Systems Analyst; Technical Writer/Editor; Transportation/Traffic Specialist; Wholesale and Retail Buyer. **Corporate headquarters location:** This location. **Operations at this facility include:** Administration; Divisional Headquarters; Manufacturing; Sales; Service. **CEO:** Andy Barnes. **Number of employees nationwide:** 3,600.

TRADER PUBLISHING COMPANY

P.O. Box 9003, Clearwater FL 33758. 727/530-5656. **Physical address:** 14549 62nd Street North, Clearwater FL 33760. **Fax:** 727/531-1748. **Recorded jobline:** 727/535-3077. **Contact:** Human Resources Department. **World Wide Web address:** http://www.traderonline.com. **Description:** One of the nation's largest publishers devoted to classified and photo guide advertising. **Common positions include:** Administrative Assistant; Customer Service Representative; General Manager; Operations Manager; Production Manager; Sales Manager; Sales Representative. **Corporate headquarters location:** Norfolk VA. **Other U.S. locations:** Nationwide. **Number of**

employees at this location: 300. **Number of employees nationwide:** 4,000.

USA TODAY
3375 Commerce Parkway, Miramar FL 33025. 954/432-6229. **Fax:** 703/854-2027. **Contact:** Human Resources. **E-mail address:** jobs@usatoday.com. **World Wide Web address:** http://www.usatoday.com. **Description:** Regional office of the national newspaper. **NOTE:** Mail your resume to: USA Today Human Resources, 7950 Jones Branch Drive, 7th Floor, McLean VA 22108. Always include the title of the position that you are applying for. **Parent company:** Gannett Co. Inc. **Listed on:** New York Stock Exchange. **Stock exchange symbol:** GCI. **President:** Tom Curley.

WARNER BROTHERS PUBLICATIONS
15800 NW 48th Avenue, Miami FL 33014. 305/620-1500. **Contact:** Maria Cruz, Director of Human Resources. **World Wide Web address:** http://www.warnerbrospublications.com. **Description:** A printer and publisher of sheet music. **Common positions include:** Accountant/Auditor; Credit Manager; Customer Service Representative; Department Manager; Editor; Musician/Musical Arranger; Operations/Production Manager; Services Sales Representative. **Special programs:** Internships. **Corporate headquarters location:** This location. **Parent company:** AOL Time Warner. **Operations at this facility include:** Administration; Manufacturing; Sales; Service. **Listed on:** New York Stock Exchange. **Stock exchange symbol:** AOL.

REAL ESTATE

You can expect to find the following types of companies in this chapter:

Land Subdividers and Developers
Real Estate Agents, Managers, and Operators
Real Estate Investment Trusts

AVATAR HOLDINGS INC.
201 Alhambra Circle, 12th Floor, Coral Gables FL 33134. 305/442-7000. **Contact:** Human Resources. **World Wide Web address:** http://www.avatarhomes.com. **Description:** A real estate company that develops residential, resort, and recreational properties. **Listed on:** NASDAQ. **Stock exchange symbol:** AVTR.

BLUEGREEN CORPORATION
4960 100 Conference Way North, Suite 100, Boca Raton FL 33431. 561/912-8000. **Contact:** Human Resources. **World Wide Web address:** http://www.bluegreen-corp.com. **Description:** A national real estate company specializing in rural land acquisitions and sales. Bluegreen Corporation also serves as a mortgage broker. **Common positions include:** Accountant/Auditor; Advertising Clerk; Computer Programmer; Human Resources Manager; Systems Analyst. **Corporate headquarters location:** This location. **Other U.S. locations:** Nationwide. **Operations at this facility include:** Administration. **Listed on:** New York Stock Exchange. **Stock exchange symbol:** BXG. **Number of employees at this location:** 70. **Number of employees nationwide:** 400.

CB RICHARD ELLIS
12651 McGregor Boulevard, Suite 1-101, Fort Myers FL 33919. 941/481-3800. **Fax:** 941/481-9950. **Contact:** Human Resources. **World Wide Web address:** http://www.cbre.com. **Description:** A real estate services company offering property sales and leasing, property and facility management, mortgage banking, and investment management services. **Corporate headquarters location:** Los Angeles CA. **Other U.S. locations:** Nationwide. **Listed on:** New York Stock Exchange. **Stock exchange symbol:** CBG. **Number of employees worldwide:** 9,000.

CB RICHARD ELLIS
225 Water Street, Suite 110, Jacksonville FL 32202. 904/634-1200. **Contact:** Human Resources. **World Wide Web address:** http://www.cbre.com. **Description:** A real estate services company offering property sales and leasing, property and facility management, mortgage banking, and investment management services. **Corporate headquarters location:** Los Angeles CA. **Other U.S. locations:** Nationwide. **Listed on:** New York Stock Exchange. **Stock exchange symbol:** CBG. **Number of employees worldwide:** 9,000.

CB RICHARD ELLIS
200 South Biscayne Boulevard, Suite 1150, Miami FL 33131. 305/533-1214. **Fax:** 305/533-1211. **Contact:** Human Resources. **World Wide Web address:** http://www.cbre.com. **Description:** A real estate services company offering property sales and leasing, property and facility management, mortgage banking, and investment management services. **Corporate headquarters location:** Los Angeles CA. **Other U.S. locations:** Nationwide. **Listed on:** New York Stock Exchange. **Stock exchange symbol:** CBG. **Number of employees worldwide:** 9,000.

CB RICHARD ELLIS
Signature Plaza, 201 South Orange Avenue, Suite 1500, Orlando FL 32801-3494. 407/843-4020. **Fax:** 407/839-3171. **Contact:** Human Resources Department. **World Wide Web address:** http://www.cbre.com. **Description:** A real estate services company offering property sales and leasing, property and facility management, mortgage banking, and investment management services. **Corporate headquarters location:** Los Angeles CA. **Other U.S. locations:** Nationwide. **Listed on:** New York Stock Exchange. **Stock exchange symbol:** CBG. **Number of employees worldwide:** 9,000.

CB RICHARD ELLIS
The Plaza, 5355 Town Center Road, Suite 701, Boca Raton FL 33486. 561/394-2100. **Fax:** 561/393-1650. **Contact:** Human Resources. **World Wide Web address:** http://www.cbre.com. **Description:** A real estate services company offering property sales and leasing, property and facility management, mortgage banking, and investment management services. **Corporate headquarters location:** Los Angeles CA. **Other U.S. locations:** Nationwide. **Listed on:** New York Stock Exchange. **Stock exchange symbol:** CBG. **Number of employees worldwide:** 9,000.

CB RICHARD ELLIS
First American Plaza, 201 East Kennedy Boulevard, Suite 1121, Tampa FL 33602-5172. 813/229-3111. **Fax:** 813/223-7144. **Contact:** Human Resources Department. **World Wide Web address:** http://www.cbre.com. **Description:** A real estate services company offering property sales and leasing, property and facility management, mortgage banking, and investment management services. **Corporate headquarters location:** Los Angeles CA. **Other U.S. locations:** Nationwide. **Listed on:** New York Stock Exchange. **Stock exchange symbol:** CBG. **Number of employees worldwide:** 9,000.

COLDWELL BANKER
423 St. Armands Circle, Sarasota FL 34236-1483. 941/388-3966. **Contact:** Sharon Krueger, Human Resources Manager. **World Wide Web address:** http://www.coldwellbanker.com. **Description:** One of the largest residential real estate companies in the United States and Canada. Coldwell Banker also provides relocation services to businesses worldwide. **Corporate headquarters location:** Mission Viejo CA. **Other U.S. locations:** Nationwide. **Parent company:** Cendant Corporation. **Listed on:** New York Stock Exchange. **Stock exchange symbol:** CD.

COLDWELL BANKER
5971 Cattleridge Boulevard, Suite 202, Sarasota FL 34232. 941/927-3990. **Contact:** Human Resources. **World Wide Web address:** http://www.coldwellbanker.com. **Description:** One of the largest residential real estate companies in the United States and Canada. Coldwell Banker also provides relocation services to businesses worldwide. **Corporate headquarters location:** Mission Viejo CA. **Other U.S. locations:** Nationwide. **Parent company:** Cendant Corporation. **Listed on:** New York Stock Exchange. **Stock exchange symbol:** CD.

DELTONA CORPORATION
999 Brickell Avenue, Suite 700, Miami FL 33131. 305/579-0999. **Contact:** Department of Human Resources. **E-mail address:** corporate@deltona.com. **World Wide Web address:** http://www.deltona.com. **Description:** Develops community housing. Founded in 1962.

FIRST AMERICAN REAL ESTATE SOLUTIONS
1800 NW 66th Avenue, Fort Lauderdale FL 33313. 954/792-2000. **Contact:** Human Resources. **World Wide Web address:** http://www.firstamres.com. **Description:** Maintains credit reports and provides information services for the real estate industry. **NOTE:** Please send resumes to: Human Resources, 5601 East La Palma Avenue, Anaheim CA 92802. **Common positions include:** Accountant/Auditor; Adjuster; Assistant Manager; Bindery Worker; Blue-Collar Worker Supervisor; Computer Operator; Computer Programmer; Construction and Building Inspector; Construction Trade Worker; Customer Service Representative; Department Manager; Draftsperson; Electrical/Electronics Engineer; Electrician; General Manager; Graphic Artist; Human Resources Manager; Industrial Engineer; Machinist; Market Research Analyst; Marketing Manager; Marketing Specialist; Mechanical Engineer; Operations/Production Manager; Printing Press Operator;

Receptionist; Services Sales Representative; Software Engineer; Stock Clerk; Surveyor; Systems Analyst; Truck Driver; Typist/Word Processor. **Operations at this facility include:** Administration; Manufacturing; Regional Headquarters; Research and Development; Sales; Service. **Number of employees at this location:** 320. **Number of employees nationwide:** 1,200.

J.I. KISLAK MORTGAGE CORPORATION
7900 Miami Lakes Drive West, Miami Lakes FL 33016. 305/364-4116. **Contact:** Human Resources Department. **Description:** A mortgage banking and real estate firm. **Common positions include:** Accountant/Auditor; Bank Officer/Manager; Branch Manager; Claim Representative; Computer Programmer; Customer Service Representative; Department Manager; Financial Analyst; Human Resources Manager; Industrial Agent/Broker; Loan Officer; Marketing Specialist; Systems Analyst; Underwriter/Assistant Underwriter. **Corporate headquarters location:** This location.

LENNAR CORPORATION
700 NW 107th Avenue, Miami FL 33172. 305/559-4000. **Contact:** Carol Burgin, Personnel Manager. **World Wide Web address:** http://www.lennar.com. **Description:** Builds and sells homes, develops and manages commercial and residential properties, and provides real estate-related financial services. The Homebuilding Division constructs and sells single-family attached and detached multifamily homes. These activities also include the purchase, development, and sale of residential land. The company is one of the nation's largest homebuilders with operations in Florida, Arizona, and Texas. The Investment Division is involved in the development, management, leasing, acquisition, and sale of commercial and residential properties. **Corporate headquarters location:** This location. **Subsidiaries include:** Lennar Financial Services, Inc. invests in rated portions of commercial real estate mortgage-backed securities for which Lennar's investment division is the servicer, and an investor in the unrated portion of those securities. **Operations at this facility include:** Service. **Listed on:** New York Stock Exchange. **Stock exchange symbol:** LEN. **Number of employees nationwide:** 1,300.

THE ST. JOE COMPANY
DuPont Center, 1650 Prudential Drive, Suite 400, Jacksonville FL 32207. 904/396-6600. **Fax:** 905/858-5265. **Contact:** Human Resources Department. **World Wide Web address:** http://www.joe.com. **Description:** A full-service real estate

company engaged in the development, building, operation, and sale of commercial and residential real estate. The company also offers real estate financial services including brokerage, financial management, and representation. **Corporate headquarters location:** This location. **Listed on:** New York Stock Exchange. **Stock exchange symbol:** JOE.

WATERMARK COMMUNITIES, INC. (WCI)

P.O. Box 5698, Sun City Center FL 33571. 813/634-3311. **Contact:** Sharon May, Director of Human Resources. **World Wide Web address:** http://www.wcicommunities.com. **Description:** Develops, builds, and manages resort communities. **Corporate headquarters location:** This location. **Operations at this facility include:** Resort/Support Functions. **Number of employees at this location:** 3,600.

RETAIL

You can expect to find the following types of companies in this chapter:

Catalog Retailers
Department Stores; Specialty Stores
Retail Bakeries
Supermarkets

B&B CORPORATE HOLDINGS, INC.
P.O. Box 1808, Tampa FL 33601. 813/621-6411. **Contact:** Linda Toledo, Director of Human Resources. **World Wide Web address:** http://www.usave.com. **Description:** Operates a chain of supermarkets and convenience stores under the USave name. Founded in 1923. **Common positions include:** Accountant/Auditor; Advertising Clerk; Blue-Collar Worker Supervisor; Human Resources Manager; Management Trainee. **Corporate headquarters location:** This location. **Subsidiaries include:** U-Save Supermarkets. **Operations at this facility include:** Administration.

W.S. BADCOCK CORPORATION
P.O. Box 497, Mulberry FL 33860. 863/425-4921. **Contact:** Jim Vernon, Director of Personnel. **World Wide Web address:** http://www.badcock.com. **Description:** Operates a chain of retail furniture stores. **Corporate headquarters location:** This location.

BARNES & NOBLE BOOKSTORES
23654 U.S. 19 North, Clearwater FL 34625. 727/669-1688. **Contact:** Manager. **World Wide Web address:** http://www.bn.com. **Description:** A bookstore chain. This location also has a cafe and a music department.

BARNES & NOBLE BOOKSTORES
2790 North University Drive, Coral Springs FL 33325. 954/344-6291. **Contact:** Manager. **World Wide Web address:** http://www.bn.com. **Description:** A bookstore chain. This location also has a cafe and a music department.

BARNES & NOBLE BOOKSTORES
1900 West International Speedway Boulevard, Suite 100, Daytona Beach FL 32120. 386/238-1118. **Contact:** Manager. **World Wide Web address:** http://www.bn.com. **Description:** A bookstore chain. This location also has a cafe.

BARNES & NOBLE BOOKSTORES
13751 South Tamiami Trail, Fort Myers FL 33912. 941/437-0654. **Contact:** Manager. **World Wide Web address:** http://www.bn.com. **Description:** A bookstore chain. This location also has a cafe and a music department.

BARNES & NOBLE BOOKSTORES
4170 Oakwood Boulevard, Hollywood FL 33020. 954/923-1738. **Contact:** Manager. **World Wide Web address:**

http://www.bn.com. **Description:** A bookstore chain. This location also has a cafe and a music department.

BARNES & NOBLE BOOKSTORES
9282 Atlantic Boulevard, Jacksonville FL 32225. 904/721-2446. **Contact:** Manager. **World Wide Web address:** http://www.bn.com. **Description:** A bookstore chain. This location also has a cafe and a music department.

BARNES & NOBLE BOOKSTORES
11112 San Jose Boulevard, Suite 8, Jacksonville FL 32223. 904/886-9904. **Contact:** Manager. **World Wide Web address:** http://www.bn.com. **Description:** A bookstore chain. This location also has a cafe and a music department.

BARNES & NOBLE BOOKSTORES
3001 NW Federal Highway, Jensen Beach FL 34957. 561/692-2270. **Contact:** Manager. **World Wide Web address:** http://www.bn.com. **Description:** A bookstore chain. This location also has a cafe and a music department.

BARNES & NOBLE BOOKSTORES
11802 North Dale Mayberry Highway, Tampa FL 33624. 813/962-6446. **Contact:** Manager. **World Wide Web address:** http://www.bn.com. **Description:** A bookstore chain. This location also has a cafe and a music department.

BEALL'S DEPARTMENT STORES
P.O. Box 25207, Bradenton FL 34206. 941/747-2355. **Contact:** Human Resources. **World Wide Web address:** http://www.beallsinc.com. **Description:** Operates a department store chain. **Corporate headquarters location:** This location.

BODY SHOP OF AMERICA, INC.
6225 Powers Avenue, Jacksonville FL 32217-2215. 904/737-0811. **Contact:** Judy Anderson, Assistant Controller. **Description:** A retail store offering apparel for juniors.

BURDINES
22 East Flagler Street, 4th Floor, Miami FL 33131. 305/577-1998. **Contact:** Human Resources. **World Wide Web address:** http://www.burdinesflorida.com. **Description:** Operates a retail department store chain. **Office hours:** Monday - Friday, 10:00 a.m. - 5:00 p.m. **Corporate headquarters location:** This location. **Parent company:** Federated Department Stores, Inc.

BURDINES
19503 Biscayne Boulevard, Aventura FL 33180. 305/792-6300x5. **Contact:** Employment Manager. **World Wide Web address:** http://www.burdinesflorida.com. **Description:** A retail department store. **Common positions include:** Branch Manager; Buyer; Claim Representative; Credit Manager; Customer Service Rep.; Department Manager; General Manager; Human Resources Manager; Operations/Production Manager. **Special programs:** Internships. **Corporate headquarters location:** Miami FL. **Parent company:** Federated Department Stores, Inc. **Operations at this facility include:** Administration; Sales; Service.

CED (CONSOLIDATED ELECTRICAL DISTRIBUTORS, INC.)
4910A Adamo Drive, Tampa FL 33605. 813/248-6699. **Contact:** Manager. **World Wide Web address:** http://www.ced.com. **Description:** A retail store that specializes in the sale of electrical supplies.

CHAMPS SPORTS
311 Manatee Avenue West, Bradenton FL 34205. 941/741-7158. **Fax:** 941/741-7170. **Contact:** Sue Campbell, Vice President of Human Resources. **World Wide Web address:** http://www.champssports.com. **Description:** A specialty sporting goods retailer. Products include hard goods, apparel, footwear, and accessories. **Common positions include:** Advertising Clerk; Buyer; Clerical Supervisor; Computer Programmer; Customer Service Representative; General Manager; Human Resources Manager; Management Trainee; Merchandiser; Operations Research Analyst; Purchasing Agent/Manager; Services Sales Representative; Systems Analyst. **Special programs:** Internships. **Corporate headquarters location:** This location. **Other U.S. locations:** Nationwide. **Parent company:** Foot Locker Inc. **Listed on:** New York Stock Exchange. **Stock exchange symbol:** Z. **Number of employees at this location:** 115.

CHICO'S FAS
11215 Metro Parkway, Fort Myers FL 33912. 941/277-6200. **Fax:** 941/277-7035. **Contact:** Human Resources. **E-mail address:** humanresources@chicos.com. **World Wide Web address:** http://www.chicos.com. **Description:** A manufacturer and retailer of women's apparel and accessories. Founded in 1983. **Corporate headquarters location:** This location. **Other U.S. locations:** Nationwide. **Listed on:** NASDAQ. **Stock exchange symbol:** CHS. **Annual sales/revenues:** More than $100 million.

CLAIRE'S ACCESSORIES
11401 Pines Boulevard, Pembroke Pines FL 33026. 954/437-1693. **Contact:** Manager. **World Wide Web address:** http://www.claires.com. **Description:** A specialty store offering women's accessories with over 2,200 locations in the United States and Canada. **NOTE:** For corporate positions, call human resources at 847/765-1100.

DILLARD'S DEPARTMENT STORES, INC.
6990 Tyrone Square, St. Petersburg FL 33710. 727/341-6000. **Contact:** Human Resources. **World Wide Web address:** http://www.dillards.com. **Description:** This location is the Florida divisional headquarters. Overall, Dillard's Department Stores operates over 220 stores in 20 states. Dillard's offers a full line of fashion apparel and home furnishings. Founded in 1938. **Common positions include:** Customer Service Representative; Retail Sales Worker; Sales Manager; Services Sales Representative. **Corporate headquarters location:** Little Rock AR. **Operations at this facility include:** Sales. **Listed on:** New York Stock Exchange. **Stock exchange symbol:** DDS. **Annual sales/revenues:** More than $100 million.

ECKERD CORPORATION
8201 Chancellor Drive, Orlando FL 32809. 407/858-4000. **Contact:** Human Resources. **World Wide Web address:** http://www.eckerd.com. **Description:** This location is a distribution center. Overall, Eckerd is one of the largest drug store chains in the United States, with over 1,715 stores in 13 states. The stores feature general merchandise, prescription and over-the-counter drugs, and photo development services. Nonpharmacy merchandise at Eckerd stores includes health and beauty aids, greeting cards, and other convenience products. The Eckerd Vision Group operates 47 optical superstores and 30 optical centers with one-hour service. Insta-Care Pharmacy Service centers provide prescription drugs and offer patient record and consulting services to health care institutions. **Common positions include:** Assistant Manager; Department Manager; Management Trainee. **Office hours:** Monday - Friday, 8:00 a.m. - 4:30 p.m. **Corporate headquarters location:** Clearwater FL. **Parent company:** JCPenney. **Listed on:** New York Stock Exchange. **Stock exchange symbol:** JCP. **Annual Revenue:** More than $100 million. **Number of employees nationwide:** 75,000.

ECKERD CORPORATION
P.O. Box 4689, Clearwater FL 33758. 727/395-6000. **Physical address:** 833 Bryan Dairy Road, Largo FL 33777. **Recorded**

jobline: 727/395-6443. **Contact:** Human Resources. **World Wide Web address:** http://www.eckerd.com. **Description:** One of the largest drug store chains in the United States, with over 1,715 stores in 13 states. The stores feature general merchandise, prescription and over-the-counter drugs, and photo development services. Nonpharmacy merchandise at Eckerd stores includes health and beauty aids, greeting cards, and other convenience products. The Eckerd Vision Group operates 47 optical superstores and 30 optical centers with one-hour service. Insta-Care Pharmacy Service centers provide prescription drugs and offer patient record and consulting services to health care institutions. **Common positions include:** Accountant/Auditor; Attorney; Buyer; Human Resources Manager; Operations/Production Manager; Paralegal; Pharmacist; Transportation/Traffic Specialist. **Special programs:** Internships. **Corporate headquarters location:** This location. **Parent company:** JCPenney. **Operations at this facility include:** Administration; Research and Development. **Listed on:** New York Stock Exchange. **Stock exchange symbol:** JCP. **Number of employees at this location:** 1,000. **Number of employees nationwide:** 75,000.

FARM STORES
5800 NW 74th Avenue, Miami FL 33166. 305/471-5141. **Contact:** Human Resources. **World Wide Web address:** http://www.farmstores.com. **Description:** Operates a regional chain of convenience stores. **Corporate headquarters location:** This location.

GOLDEN BEAR GOLF INC.
11780 U.S. Highway 1, Suite 400, North Palm Beach FL 33408. 561/626-3900. **Contact:** Linda Clark, Personnel Administrator. **World Wide Web address:** http://www.nicklaus.com. **Description:** Franchises golf practice and instruction facilities, operates golf schools, constructs golf courses through Weitz Golf International (also at this location), and sells consumer golf products and apparel. **Common positions include:** Accountant/Auditor; Administrator; Architect; Civil Engineer; Marketing Specialist. **Corporate headquarters location:** This location. **Operations at this facility include:** Service. **Listed on:** NASDAQ. **Stock exchange symbol:** JACK.

HOME SHOPPING NETWORK, INC.
One HSN Drive, St. Petersburg FL 33729. 727/872-1000. **Contact:** Human Resources Department. **World Wide Web address:** http://www.homeshoppingnetwork.com. **Description:** A holding company that owns and operates Home Shopping Club, Inc. (HSC), which offers jewelry, hard goods, soft goods, cosmetics, and other items via live television presentations; the Internet Shopping Network, which delivers online shopping; and HSN Direct division, which produces and airs infomercials and distributes infomercial products. **Corporate headquarters location:** This location. **Parent company:** USA Networks Inc. **Listed on:** NASDAQ. **Stock exchange symbol:** USAi. **Number of employees nationwide:** 4,500.

KANE FURNITURE
5700 70th Avenue North, Pinellas Park FL 33781. 727/545-9555. **Fax:** 727/548-0552. **Contact:** Human Resources. **World Wide Web address:** http://www.kanefurniture.com. **Description:** A furniture retailer. **Common positions include:** Accountant/Auditor; Administrative Manager; Clerical Supervisor; Customer Service Representative; Designer; Management Trainee; Services Sales Representative. **Corporate headquarters location:** This location. **Operations at this facility include:** Administration. **Listed on:** Privately held. **Number of employees at this location:** 250. **Number of employees nationwide:** 750.

KASH 'N KARRY FOOD STORES
6401A Harney Road, Tampa FL 33610. 813/620-1139. **Contact:** Human Resources. **World Wide Web address:** http://www.kashnkarry.com. **Description:** An operator of retail food and liquor stores. **Corporate headquarters location:** This location. **Number of employees nationwide:** 8,400.

LEVITZ FURNITURE CORPORATION
7887 North Federal Highway, Boca Raton FL 33487. 516/496-9560. **Contact:** Nicholas Masullo, Vice President of Human Resources. **World Wide Web address:** http://www.levitz.com. **Description:** Operates a national furniture store chain. **Corporate headquarters location:** This location. **Other U.S. locations:** Nationwide.

MARTINE'S CORPORATION
120 East Main Street, Suite A, Pensacola FL 32501. 850/429-8640. **Contact:** Human Resources. **Description:** Operates fast-food establishments, liquor stores, and shopping centers.

MAYORS JEWELERS
14051 NW 14th Street, Sunrise FL 33323. 954/846-8000. **Fax:** 954/846-2787. **Recorded jobline:** 800/223-6964x5408. **Contact:** Human Resources Department. **World Wide Web address:** http://www.mayors.com. **Description:** A retailer, merchandiser, and distributor of jewelry, watches, sunglasses, fragrances, and collectibles. **Common positions include:** Accountant/Auditor; Blue-Collar Worker Supervisor; Buyer; Computer Programmer; Customer Service Representative; Department Manager; Financial Analyst; Graphic Artist; Human Resources Manager; Order Clerk; Payroll Clerk; Receptionist; Stock Clerk; Systems Analyst; Wholesale and Retail Buyer. **Corporate headquarters location:** This location. **Other U.S. locations:** Nationwide. **Operations at this facility include:** Administration; Distribution. **Number of employees at this location:** 500.

OFFICE DEPOT
2200 Old Germantown Road, Delray Beach FL 33445. 561/278-4800. **Contact:** Human Resources. **World Wide Web address:** http://www.officedepot.com. **Description:** Operates a chain of large-volume office-products warehouse stores that sell brand name office merchandise primarily to small and medium-sized businesses. The retail locations also serve the growing home office market. Major merchandise categories include general office supplies, office furniture, computer hardware and software, copiers, telephones and fax machines, paper, writing instruments, briefcases, accounting supplies, and back-to-school supplies. **Corporate headquarters location:** This location. **Other U.S. locations:** Nationwide. **International locations:** Canada. **Listed on:** New York Stock Exchange. **Stock exchange symbol:** ODP. **Number of employees nationwide:** 33,000.

THE PANTRY, INC.
P.O. Box 23180, Jacksonville FL 32241. 904/464-7200. **Contact:** Manager. **World Wide Web address:** http://www.thepantry.com. **Description:** A chain of retail grocery and convenience stores. Stores operate under the names Depot, ETNA, Express Stop, Food Chief, Handy-Way, Kangaroo, Lil' Champ, Quick Stop, Smokers Express, Sprint, The Pantry, Wicker Mart, and Zip Mart. **Corporate headquarters location:** This location. **Listed on:** NASDAQ. **Stock exchange symbol:** PTRY.

POTAMKIN SOUTH

21111 South Dixie Highway, Miami FL 33189. 305/238-0000. **Contact:** General Manager. **World Wide Web address:** http://www.potamkinsouth.com. **Description:** An automobile dealership. **Common positions include:** Accountant/Auditor; Automotive Mechanic. **Special programs:** Internships. **Other U.S. locations:** Nationwide. **Operations at this facility include:** Administration; Sales; Service. **Listed on:** Privately held. **Number of employees at this location:** 115.

PUBLIX SUPER MARKETS, INC.

9786 West Beaver Street, Jacksonville FL 32220. 904/781-8600. **Recorded jobline:** 904/693-6172. **Contact:** Human Resources Department. **World Wide Web address:** http://www.publix.com. **Description:** Part of a regional chain of retail supermarkets with 691 stores in Alabama, Florida, Georgia, and South Carolina. The company also produces dairy, delicatessen, and bakery items through four plants and conducts distribution operations through more than eight facilities in Florida and Georgia. **Company slogan:** Where shopping is a pleasure. **Corporate headquarters location:** Lakeland FL. **Listed on:** Privately held. **Annual sales/revenues:** More than $100 million. **Number of employees nationwide:** 122,000.

PUBLIX SUPER MARKETS, INC.

P.O. Box 407, Lakeland FL 33802-0407. 863/688-1188. **Physical address:** 1936 George Jenkins Boulevard, Lakeland FL 33815. **Recorded jobline:** 863/680-5265. **Contact:** Human Resources. **World Wide Web address:** http://www.publix.com. **Description:** Operates a chain of retail supermarkets with 691 stores in Alabama, Florida, Georgia, and South Carolina. The company also produces dairy, delicatessen, and bakery items through four plants and conducts distribution operations through more than eight facilities in Florida and Georgia. Founded in 1930. **Company slogan:** Where shopping is a pleasure. **Special programs:** Summer Jobs. **Corporate headquarters location:** This location. **Other U.S. locations:** AL; FL; GA; SC. **Listed on:** Privately held. **CEO:** Howard Jenkins. **Annual sales/revenues:** More than $100 million. **Number of employees at this location:** 5,000. **Number of employees nationwide:** 122,000.

RECREATION USA

3337 Bartlett Boulevard, Orlando FL 32819. 407/363-9211. **Fax:** 800/732-0512. **Contact:** Human Resources. **World Wide Web address:** http://www.recusa.com. **Description:** One of the largest retailers of recreational vehicles and boats in the United States. **Corporate headquarters location:** This location. **Other U.S. locations:** CA; GA; SC. **Operations at this facility include:** Divisional Headquarters; Sales; Service. **Listed on:** NASDAQ. **Stock exchange symbol:** RVEE.

ROBB & STUCKY

13170 South Cleveland Avenue, Fort Myers FL 33907. 941/936-8541. **Fax:** 941/437-6286. **Contact:** Sharon Dill, Director of Human Resources Department. **E-mail address:** personnel@robbstuckey.net. **World Wide Web address:** http://www.robbstucky.com. **Description:** One location of a chain of furniture stores that also offers interior design services.

SEARS, ROEBUCK & CO.

9501 Arlington Expressway, Jacksonville FL 32225. 904/727-3255. **Contact:** Human Resources Department. **World Wide Web address:** http://www.sears.com. **Description:** One location of the nationwide department store chain. **Corporate headquarters location:** Chicago IL. **Listed on:** New York Stock Exchange. **Stock exchange symbol:** S.

SOUND ADVICE, INC.

301 East Las Olas Boulevard, Suite 300, Ft. Lauderdale FL 33301. 954/922-4434. **Contact:** Human Resources. **E-mail address:** hr@soundadvice-fl.com. **World Wide Web address:** http://www.wegivesoundadvice.com. **Description:** Operates retail stores that sell and service audio and video equipment for the home and automobile markets. **Corporate headquarters location:** This location.

WINN-DIXIE STORES, INC.

P.O. Box 585200, Orlando FL 32858. 407/578-4000. **Physical address:** 3015 Coastline Drive, Orlando FL 32808. **Fax:** 407/294-4225. **Contact:** Human Resources Department. **E-mail address:** hr@winn-dixie.com. **World Wide Web address:** http://www.winn-dixie.com. **Description:** This location is the headquarters of the Orlando division of a chain of supermarkets. Overall, Winn-Dixie is one of the largest supermarket operators in the 14 Sunbelt states. Winn-Dixie stores operate under the names Winn-Dixie, Marketplace, and Buddies. Winn-Dixie also operates 20 warehousing and distribution centers and a host of manufacturing and processing facilities. A subsidiary of the company operates 12 stores in the Bahamas. **Corporate headquarters location:** Jacksonville FL. **Listed on:** New York Stock Exchange. **Stock** exchange symbol: WIN. **President/CEO:** Al Rowland. **Number of employees nationwide:** 120,000.

WINN-DIXIE STORES, INC.
P.O. Box 44110, Jacksonville FL 32231-4110. 904/695-7840. **Physical address:** 5233 Commonwealth Avenue, Jacksonville FL 32254. Fax: 904/695-7843. **Contact:** Human Resources. **E-mail address:** hr@winn-dixie.com. **World Wide Web address:** http://www.winn-dixie.com. **Description:** Winn-Dixie is one of the largest supermarket operators in the 14 Sunbelt states. Overall, Winn-Dixie stores operate under the names Winn-Dixie, Marketplace, and Buddies. Winn-Dixie also operates 20 warehousing and distribution centers and a host of manufacturing and processing facilities. A subsidiary of the company operates 12 stores in the Bahamas. **Corporate headquarters location:** Jacksonville FL. **Listed on:** New York Stock Exchange. **Stock exchange symbol:** WIN **President/CEO:** Al Rowland. **Number of employees nationwide:** 120,000.

WINN-DIXIE STORES, INC.
P.O. Box B, Jacksonville FL 32203-0297. 904/783-5000. **Physical address:** 5050 Edgewood Court, Jacksonville FL 32254. **Fax:** 904/783-5235. **Contact:** Human Resources. **E-mail address:** hr@winn-dixie.com. **World Wide Web address:** http://www.winn-dixie.com. **Description:** Winn-Dixie is one of the largest supermarket operators in the 14 Sunbelt states. Winn-Dixie stores operate under the names Winn-Dixie, Marketplace, and Buddies. Winn-Dixie also operates 20 warehousing and distribution centers and a host of manufacturing and processing facilities. A subsidiary of the company operates 12 stores in the Bahamas. **Corporate headquarters location:** This location. **Listed on:** New York Stock Exchange. **Stock exchange symbol:** WIN. **President/CEO:** Al Rowland. **Number of employees nationwide:** 120,000.

STONE, CLAY, GLASS, AND CONCRETE PRODUCTS

You can expect to find the following types of companies in this chapter:

Cement, Tile, Sand, and Gravel
Crushed and Broken Stone
Glass and Glass Products
Mineral Products

AFGD, INC.
6600 Suemac Place, Jacksonville FL 32254. 904/786-6611. **Fax:** 904/781-9779. **Contact:** Stan Mesnik, Branch Manager. **World Wide Web address:** http://www.afgd.com. **Description:** Manufactures architectural insulated glass units and specializes in custom tempering. AFGD manufactures a complete line of insulated glass units for commercial and residential applications. Products include clear, tint, and reflective glass; wire glass; and equipment for the handling, storage, and transportation of glass. **Common positions include:** Blue-Collar Worker Supervisor; Branch Manager; Clerical Supervisor; Credit Manager; Customer Service Representative; Industrial Engineer; Industrial Production Manager; Management Trainee; Manufacturer's/Wholesaler's Sales Rep.; Mechanical Engineer; Metallurgical Engineer; Operations/Production Manager. **Corporate headquarters location:** Atlanta GA. **Other U.S. locations:** Nationwide. **Subsidiaries include:** AFGD Canada. **Parent company:** AFG Industries, Inc. **Operations at this facility include:** Manufacturing; Sales. **Number of employees at this location:** 75. **Number of employees nationwide:** 1,000.

ANCHOR GLASS CONTAINER CORPORATION
4343 Anchor Plaza Parkway, Tampa FL 33634. 813/884-0000. **Contact:** Human Resources. **Description:** Manufactures glassware, commercial and institutional chinaware, decorative and convenience hardware, glass containers, and metal and plastic closures. Operations encompass over 20 divisions and subsidiaries, with 40 plants and distribution centers worldwide. **Common positions include:** Accountant/Auditor; Administrator; Attorney; Buyer; Chemical Engineer; Civil Engineer; Computer Programmer; Credit Manager; Customer Service Representative; Department Manager; Draftsperson; Electrical/Electronics Engineer; Financial Analyst; General Manager; Human Resources Manager; Industrial Engineer; Management Trainee; Manufacturer's/Wholesaler's Sales Rep.; Mechanical Engineer; Metallurgical Engineer; Purchasing Agent/Manager; Quality Control Supervisor; Systems Analyst; Transportation/Traffic Specialist. **Corporate headquarters location:** This location. **Other area locations:** Jacksonville FL.

ANCHOR GLASS CONTAINER CORPORATION
2121 Huron Street, Jacksonville FL 32254. 904/786-1010. **Contact:** Human Resources. **Description:** Manufactures glassware, commercial and institutional chinaware, decorative and convenience hardware, glass containers, and metal and plastic closures. Operations encompass over 20 divisions and

subsidiaries, with 40 plants and distribution centers worldwide. **Common positions include:** Accountant/Auditor; Customer Service Representative; Department Manager; Electrical/Electronics Engineer; General Manager; Industrial Engineer; Manufacturer's/Wholesaler's Sales Rep.; Mechanical Engineer; Metallurgical Engineer; Operations/Production Manager; Purchasing Agent/Manager; Quality Control Supervisor; Transportation/Traffic Specialist. **Corporate headquarters location:** Tampa FL. **Number of employees nationwide:** 6,900.

FLORIDA CRUSHED STONE COMPANY
P.O. Box 490180, Leesburg FL 34749-0300. 352/787-0608. **Contact:** Human Resources. **World Wide Web address:** http://www.fcsco.com. **Description:** Manufactures construction materials including cement, aggregates, and pavement components.

FLORIDA ROCK INDUSTRIES
P.O. Box 4667, Jacksonville FL 32201. 904/355-1781. **Contact:** Bob Banks, Human Resources Director. **Description:** Manufactures concrete aggregates. Florida Rock & Tank Lines (also at this location) transports oil and gasoline. Sunbelt Transport (also at this location) is a flatbed transportation company. **Common positions include:** Accountant/Auditor; Administrator; Civil Engineer; Credit Manager; Department Manager; General Manager; Geologist/Geophysicist; Mining Engineer; Systems Analyst. **Corporate headquarters location:** This location. **Operations at this facility include:** Administration. **Listed on:** New York Stock Exchange. **Stock exchange symbol:** FRK.

HARDRIVES, INC.
2101 South Congress Avenue, Delray Beach FL 33445-7398. 561/278-0456. **Contact:** Human Resources Director. **World Wide Web address:** http://www.hardrivespaving.com. **Description:** Manufactures paving rouxes and related materials. **Common positions include:** Accountant/Auditor. **Number of employees at this location:** 400.

MONIERLIFETILE, INC.
135 NW 20th Street, Boca Raton FL 33431. 561/338-8200. **Toll-free phone:** 800/585-8453. **Contact:** Ferndo Padron, Human Resources Department. **World Wide Web address:** http://www.monierlifetile.com. **Description:** A manufacturer of concrete roof tile.

RMC-EWELL INDUSTRIES, INC.

P.O. Box 3858, Lakeland FL 33802. 863/688-5787. **Contact:** Human Resources Department. **World Wide Web address:** http://www.rmcewell.com. **Description:** Produces concrete products including ready-mix concrete and concrete piping. **Common positions include:** Accountant/Auditor; Administrator; Blue-Collar Worker Supervisor; Computer Programmer; Credit Manager; General Manager; Management Trainee; Manufacturer's/Wholesaler's Sales Representative; Operations/Production Manager; Purchasing Agent/Manager; Quality Control Supervisor; Systems Analyst. **Parent company:** RMC Industries Corporation. **Operations at this facility include:** Administration; Manufacturing; Sales; Service.

RINKER MATERIALS CORPORATION

1501 Belvedere Road, West Palm Beach FL 33406. 561/833-5555. **Toll-free phone:** 800/226-5521. **Contact:** Tim Dugan, Human Resources Manager. **World Wide Web address:** http://www.rinker.com. **Description:** Manufactures and supplies assorted concrete, cement, and aggregate products. **Common positions include:** Accountant/Auditor; Attorney; Buyer; Civil Engineer; Computer Programmer; Department Manager; Draftsperson; Electrical/Electronics Engineer; Human Resources Manager; Industrial Engineer; Management Trainee; Quality Control Supervisor. **Corporate headquarters location:** This location. **Parent company:** CSR America. **Operations at this facility include:** Administration.

UNITED STATES GYPSUM COMPANY

P.O. Box 9579, Jacksonville FL 32208. 904/768-2501. **Contact:** Gary Jones, Human Resources Manager. **World Wide Web address:** http://www.usg.com. **Description:** Manufactures gypsum wallboard, plasters, and agricultural gypsum. **Corporate headquarters location:** Chicago IL. **Other U.S. locations:** Nationwide. **International locations:** Worldwide. **Listed on:** New York Stock Exchange. **Stock exchange symbol:** USG. **President/CEO:** William C. Foote. **Number of employees worldwide:** 14,000.

WATER BONNET MANUFACTURING INC.

P.O. Box 180427, Casselberry FL 32718. 407/831-2122. **Contact:** Robin Bordirick, Human Resources. **Description:** Manufactures windshields for boats and Caterpillar tractors, as well as canvas tops for boats.

TRANSPORTATION/TRAVEL

You can expect to find the following types of companies in this chapter:

Air, Railroad, and Water Transportation Services
Courier Services
Local and Interurban Passenger Transit
Ship Building and Repair
Transportation Equipment Travel Agencies
Trucking
Warehousing and Storage

ALAMO RENT-A-CAR
200 South Andrews Avenue, Fort Lauderdale FL 33305. 954/320-4400. **Contact:** Human Resources Department. **World Wide Web address:** http://www.alamo.com. **Description:** One of the nation's leading car rental companies. **Common positions include:** Accountant/Auditor; Computer Programmer; Customer Service Representative; Financial Analyst; Secretary. **Corporate headquarters location:** This location. **Operations at this facility include:** Administration. **Listed on:** Privately held.

ALTERMAN TRANSPORT LINES
12805 NW 42nd Avenue, Opa-Locka FL 33054. 305/688-3571. **Contact:** Human Resources. **World Wide Web address:** http://www.alterman.com. **Description:** An interstate trucking company that specializes in the transport of perishable goods.

BLACKBEARD'S CRUISES
P.O. Box 66-1091, Miami FL 33266. 305/888-1226. **Contact:** Human Resources Department. **World Wide Web address:** http://www.blackbeard-cruises.com. **Description:** A cruise line that sails to the Bahamas. **Common positions include:** Automotive Mechanic; Chef/Cook/Kitchen Worker.

BUDGET GROUP, INC.
125 Basin Street, Suite 210, Daytona Beach FL 32114. 386/238-7035. **Contact:** Human Resources Department. **World Wide Web address:** http://www.bgi.com. **Description:** A holding company. **Corporate headquarters location:** This location. **Subsidiaries include:** Budget Airport Parking; Budget Car Sales, Inc.; Budget Rent A Car Corporation; Cruise America, Inc.; Premier Car Rental; Ryder TRS, Inc.; Van Pool Services, Inc.

CSX TRANSPORTATION
500 Water Street, Jacksonville FL 32202-4423. 904/359-3100. **Contact:** Human Resources. **World Wide Web address:** http://www.csxt.com. **Description:** A railroad company that transports a variety of products for the agricultural, automotive, mining, food, and consumer markets. **Parent company:** CSX Corporation.

CARNIVAL CORPORATION
CARNIVAL CRUISE LINES
Carnival Place, 3655 NW 87th Avenue, Miami FL 33178-2428. **Contact:** Human Resources. **World Wide Web address:** http://www.carnival.com. **Description:** A travel holding

company. **NOTE:** This firm does not accept unsolicited resumes. Please only respond to advertised openings. **Subsidiaries include:** Carnival Cruise Lines (also at this location) operates nine cruise ships serving the Caribbean and Mexican Riviera; Holland America Line operates seven cruise ships serving primarily the Caribbean and Alaska through the Panama Canal; Windstar Cruises operates three sail-powered vessels that call on locations inaccessible to larger ships; Holland America Westours markets sightseeing tours both separately and as a part of Holland America Line cruise/tour packages.

CELEBRITY CRUISES
1050 Caribbean Way, Miami FL 33132. 305/262-6677. **Contact:** Human Resources. **World Wide Web address:** http://www.celebrity-cruises.com. **Description:** Operates an ocean cruise line that sails to Alaska, Bermuda, the Caribbean Islands, Europe, Hawaii, and South America. **Corporate headquarters location:** This location.

COSTA CRUISE LINES
200 South Park Road, Hollywood, FL 33021. 954/266-5600. **Contact:** Claudia Juliao, Personnel Manager. **World Wide Web address:** http://www.costacruises.com. **Description:** An ocean cruise line.

CROWLEY AMERICAN TRANSPORT, INC.
P.O. Box 2110, Jacksonville FL 32203-2110. 904/727-2200. **Contact:** Human Resources Department. **World Wide Web address:** http://www.crowley.com. **Description:** An ocean freight company.

CUNARD LINE
6100 Blue Lagoon Drive, Suite 400, Miami FL 33126. 305/463-3000. **Toll-free phone:** 800/223-0764. **Fax:** 305/463-3035. **Contact:** Human Resources. **World Wide Web address:** http://www.cunard.com. **Description:** An ocean cruise line that calls at ports worldwide. **Corporate headquarters location:** This location. **Listed on:** New York Stock Exchange. **Stock exchange symbol:** CCL.

FLORIDA EAST COAST RAILWAY COMPANY
P.O. Box 1048, St. Augustine FL 32085-1048. 904/826-2320. **Contact:** Gloria S. Taylor, Director of Human Resources. **Description:** A railway transportation company. **Common positions include:** Clerk; Engineer; Human Resources Manager; Maintenance Technician; Training Specialist;

Transportation/Traffic Specialist. **Corporate headquarters location:** This location. **Operations at this facility include:** Administration. **Number of employees at this location:** 200. **Number of employees nationwide:** 1,000.

FLORIDA ROCK INDUSTRIES

P.O. Box 4667, Jacksonville FL 32201. 904/355-1781. **Contact:** Bob Banks, Director of Human Resources Department. **Description:** Manufactures concrete aggregates. Florida Rock & Tank Lines (also at this location) transports oil and gasoline. Sunbelt Transport (also at this location) is a flatbed transportation company. **Common positions include:** Accountant/Auditor; Administrator; Civil Engineer; Credit Manager; Department Manager; General Manager; Geologist/Geophysicist; Mining Engineer; Systems Analyst. **Corporate headquarters location:** This location. **Operations at this facility include:** Administration. **Listed on:** New York Stock Exchange. **Stock exchange symbol:** FRK.

LAND SPAN, INC.

P.O. Box 95007, Lakeland FL 33804. 863/688-1102. **Contact:** Human Resources Department. **World Wide Web address:** http://www.landspan.com. **Description:** An interstate trucking company that transports dry and refrigerated freight. **Common positions include:** Administrator; Computer Programmer; Credit Manager; Customer Service Representative; Department Manager; Human Resources Manager; Operations/Production Manager; Services Sales Representative; Transportation/Traffic Specialist. **Other U.S. locations:** Norcross GA; Chicago IL; Hagerstown MD; Charlotte NC; El Paso TX; Fort Worth TX. **Parent company:** Watkins Associated Industries, Inc. **Number of employees at this location:** 300.

LANDSTAR LIGON, INC.

P.O. Box 19137, Jacksonville FL 32245-9939. **Toll-free phone:** 800/235-4466. **Contact:** Susan Ramsey, Human Resources Director. **World Wide Web address:** http://www.landstar.com. **Description:** Landstar Ligon provides truckload transportation services through independent contractors and commissioned sales agents. **Parent company:** Landstar System, Inc. is divided into specialized freight transportation segments. Landstar is one of the only publicly traded trucking companies relying on independent owner-operators rather than salaried company drivers, with the company owning just 10 percent of the trucks in its fleet. Subsidiaries of Landstar System, Inc. include Landstar Expedited, Inc.; Landstar Express America, Inc.; Landstar Gemini, Inc.; Landstar Inway, Inc.; Landstar ITCO,

Inc.; Landstar Poole, Inc.; Landstar Ranger, Inc.; Landstar T.L.C., Inc.; Landstar Transportation Service, Inc. **Listed on:** NASDAQ. **Stock exchange symbol:** LSTR.

LANDSTAR SYSTEM, INC.
13410 Sutton Park Drive, Jacksonville FL 32224. 904/398-9232. **Toll-free phone:** 800/862-9232. **Contact:** Department of Human Resources. **World Wide Web address:** http://www.landstar.com. **Description:** Provides truckload transportation services through independent contractors and commissioned sales agents. **Corporate headquarters location:** This location. **Listed on:** NASDAQ. **Stock exchange symbol:** LSTR.

LUHRS CORPORATION
255 Diesel Road, St. Augustine FL 32084. 904/829-0500. **Fax:** 904/829-0683. **Contact:** Erica Stegerwald, Human Resources Manager. **World Wide Web address:** http://www.luhrs.com. **Description:** Manufactures fiberglass boats. **Common positions include:** Blue-Collar Worker Supervisor; Buyer; Carpenter; Customer Service Representative; Draftsperson; Electrician; Industrial Engineer; Mechanical Engineer. **Corporate headquarters location:** This location. **Operations at this facility include:** Administration; Manufacturing; Sales; Service. **Number of employees at this location:** 375.

MARITRANS INC.
302 Knights Run Avenue, Suite 1200, Tampa FL 33602. 813/209-0602. **Fax:** 813/221-3179. **Contact:** Human Resources Department. **E-mail address:** hr@maritrans.com. **World Wide Web address:** http://www.maritrans.com. **Description:** Maritrans provides marine transportation for petroleum and oil storage terminals. The company also offers a full package of oil distribution services including product exchanges, marine transportation, scheduling, terminal storage, and automated truck rack delivery systems. **Corporate headquarters location:** This location. **Listed on:** New York Stock Exchange. **Stock exchange symbol:** TUG.

McKENZIE TANK LINES, INC.
122 Appleyard Drive, Tallahassee FL 32304. 850/576-1221. **Contact:** Paulette McElroy, Director of Human Resources. **World Wide Web address:** http://www.mckenzietank.com. **Description:** An interstate trucking company.

NORWEGIAN CRUISE LINES

7665 NW 19th Street, Miami FL 33126. 305/436-4000. **Contact:** Human Resources Department. **World Wide Web address:** http://www.ncl.com. **Description:** An ocean cruise line.

REGAL MARINE INDUSTRIES, INC.

2300 Jetport Drive, Orlando FL 32809. 407/851-4360. **Fax:** 407/857-1256. **Contact:** Kim Evans, Director of Human Resources. **E-mail address:** regal@regalboats.com. **World Wide Web address:** http://www.regalboats.com. **Description:** Manufactures pleasure boats.

ROYAL CARIBBEAN

1050 Caribbean Way, Miami FL 33132. 305/379-2601. **Contact:** Human Resources. **World Wide Web address:** http://www.rccl.com. **Description:** An ocean cruise line that operates 22 ships sailing to the Caribbean, the Bahamas, Bermuda, Mexico, Alaska, the Mediterranean, Europe, the Greek Isles, Panama Canal, Hawaii, Scandinavia/Russia, and the Far East. **NOTE:** Job seekers are encouraged to submit their resume on-line, so that they may be considered for job opportunities as they become available. **Corporate headquarters location:** This location. **Listed on:** New York Stock Exchange. **Stock exchange symbol:** RCL. **CEO:** Richard D. Fain. **Number of employees nationwide:** 15,000.

RYDER SYSTEM, INC.

3600 NW 82nd Avenue, Miami FL 33166. 305/593-3726. **Contact:** Human Resources. **World Wide Web address:** http://www.ryder.com. **Description:** Leases trucks, hauls automobiles, provides contract carriage and logistics services, and provides school bus transportation. Truck leasing operations are conducted in the United States, Puerto Rico, United Kingdom, Germany, and Poland with over 78,000 vehicles. The company provides maintenance, leasing, and related supplies, and also maintains over 27,000 nonleased trucks. **Corporate headquarters location:** This location. **Other U.S. locations:** Nationwide. **International locations:** Canada; Continental Europe; England; Mexico; Singapore; South America. **Listed on:** NASDAQ. **Stock exchange symbol:** R. **Number of employees worldwide:** 30,000.

TNT LOGISTICS

P.O. Box 40083, Jacksonville, FL 32203. **Toll-free phone:** 888/LOG-ISTX. **Fax:** 904/928-1547. **Contact:** Human Resources. **World Wide Web address:** http://www.tnt-logistics.com. **Description:** A third party logistics provider. Founded in 1980. **NOTE:** Entry-level positions and second and third shifts are offered. **Common positions include:** Accountant; Administrative Assistant; Applications Engineer; AS400 Programmer Analyst; Attorney; Auditor; Clerical Supervisor; Computer Operator; Computer Programmer; Computer Technician; Cost Estimator; Credit Manager; Customer Service Manager; Database Administrator; Financial Analyst; Help-Desk Technician; Industrial Engineer; Internet Services Manager; Management Trainee; Network Engineer; Network/Systems Administrator; Operations Manager; Project Manager; Purchasing Agent/Manager; Quality Control Supervisor; Sales Executive; Secretary; Software Engineer; SQL Programmer; Systems Analyst; Systems Manager; Technical Support Manager; Transportation/Traffic Specialist; Website Developer. **Special programs:** Internships; Training. **Office hours:** Monday - Friday, 8:00 a.m. - 5:00 p.m. **Corporate headquarters location:** This location. **International locations:** Argentina; Brazil; Canada; Mexico; United Kingdom. **Listed on:** New York Stock Exchange. **Stock exchange symbol:** TP. **Annual sales/revenues:** More than $100 million. **Number of employees worldwide:** 116,000.

WELLCRAFT MARINE
1651 Whitfield Avenue, Sarasota FL 34243. 941/753-7811. **Contact:** Human Resources Department. **World Wide Web address:** http://www.wellcraft.com. **Description:** Manufactures a variety of boats including cruisers, fishing boats, sport boats, and high-performance speed boats. **Common positions include:** Accountant/Auditor; Administrator; Blue-Collar Worker Supervisor; Buyer; Computer Programmer; Customer Service Representative; Department Manager; Draftsperson; Electrical/Electronics Engineer; General Manager; Human Resources Manager; Industrial Engineer; Industrial Production Manager; Manufacturer's/Wholesaler's Sales Rep.; Marketing Specialist; Operations/Production Manager; Purchasing Agent/Manager; Quality Control Supervisor; Systems Analyst. **Corporate headquarters location:** Minneapolis MN. **Operations at this facility include:** Administration; Divisional Headquarters; Manufacturing; Research and Development; Sales; Service.

WINDJAMMER BAREFOOT CRUISES
P.O. Box 120, Miami Beach FL 33119. 305/672-6453. **Toll-free:** 800-327-2601. **Contact:** John Horn, Personnel Director. **World Wide Web address:** http://www.windjammer.com.

Description: A cruise line that operates six ships sailing to the Caribbean.

UTILITIES: ELECTRIC/GAS/WATER

You can expect to find the following types of companies in this chapter:

Gas, Electric, and Fuel Companies; Other Energy-Producing Companies
Public Utility Holding Companies
Water Utilities

FPL GROUP
700 Universe Boulevard, Juno Beach FL 33408. 561/694-4000. **Fax:** 305/552-3641. **Contact:** Human Resources. **World Wide Web address:** http://www.fplgroup.com. **Description:** One of the nation's largest providers of electricity-related services. **NOTE:** You may call the Recruiting Center at 800/892-2711. Job seekers should apply via the internet or by fax. Resumes will not be accepted at address listed. **Corporate headquarters location:** This location. **Subsidiaries include:** Florida Power and Light Company serves more than 7 million people along the eastern and southern coast of Florida; FPL Energy owns and operates power plants throughout the United States and abroad; FPL FiberNet, LLC sells fiber optic network capacity wholesale to telecommunications companies in Florida. **Listed on:** New York Stock Exchange. **Stock exchange symbol:** FPL. **Annual sales/revenues:** More than $100 million.

FLORIDA KEYS ELECTRIC COOPERATIVE
P.O. Box 377, Tavernier FL 33070. 305/852-2431. **Toll-free phone:** 800/858-8845. **Fax:** 305/852-4794. **Contact:** Donna Bosold, Manager of Human Resources Department. **E-mail address:** mail@fkec.com. **World Wide Web address:** http://www.fkec.com. **Description:** A nonprofit, electric utility company. Founded in 1940. **NOTE:** Entry-level positions are offered. **Common positions include:** Accountant; Auditor; Budget Analyst; Computer Engineer; Electrical/Electronics Engineer; Electrician; General Manager; Human Resources Manager; MIS Specialist; Purchasing Agent/Manager; Secretary. **Special programs:** Apprenticeships. **Other area locations:** Marathon FL.

FLORIDA PROGRESS ENERGY
P.O. Box 14042, St. Petersburg FL 33733. 727/824-6400. **Physical address:** One Progress Plaza, St. Petersburg FL 33701. **Contact:** Human Resources. **World Wide Web address:** http://www.progress-energy.com. **Description:** A diversified utility holding company. **Corporate headquarters location:** This location. **Other U.S. locations:** Raleigh NC. **Listed on:** NASDAQ. **Stock exchange symbol:** PGN.

GULF POWER COMPANY
One Energy Place, Pensacola FL 32520-0714. **Toll-free phone:** 800/225-5797. **Recorded jobline:** 800/457-2981. **Contact:** Human Resources Department. **World Wide Web address:** http://www.southernco.com. **Description:** A public utility company. **NOTE:** Entry-level positions are offered. The company only accepts resumes for open positions. Please call

the jobline for more information. **Common positions include:** Customer Service Representative; Systems Analyst; Typist/Word Processor. **Corporate headquarters location:** Atlanta GA. **Other area locations:** Fort Walton Beach FL; Panama City FL. **Parent company:** Southern Company Services. **Operations at this facility include:** Administration; Sales; Service. **Listed on:** New York Stock Exchange. **Stock exchange symbol:** SO. **Number of employees at this location:** 1,500.

MASTEC
3155 NW 77th Avenue, Miami FL 33122. 305/599-1800. **Contact:** Human Resources Department. **World Wide Web address:** http://www.mastec.com. **Description:** A water, sewer, and power service. **Listed on:** New York Stock Exchange. **Stock exchange symbol:** MTZ.

ORLANDO UTILITIES COMMISSION
500 South Orange Avenue, Orlando FL 32801. 407/423-9100. **Contact:** Human Resources. **World Wide Web address:** http://www.ouc.com. **Description:** Offers utility services to the Central Florida area.

TAMPA ELECTRIC
P.O. Box 111, Tampa FL 33601. 813/228-4111. **Contact:** Human Resources Department. **World Wide Web address:** http://www.tecoenergy.com. **Description:** Provides electricity to residents of Tampa and outlying areas. **Parent company:** TECO Energy. **Listed on:** New York Stock Exchange. **Stock exchange symbol:** TE. **CEO:** Robert D. Fagan.

MISCELLANEOUS WHOLESALING

You can expect to find the following types of companies in this chapter:

Exporters and Importers
General Wholesale Distribution Companies

BAKER DISTRIBUTING COMPANY
7892 Baymeadows Way, Jacksonville FL 32256. 904/733-9633. **Contact:** Doris Spears, Payroll Manager. **World Wide Web address:** http://www.bakerdist.com. **Description:** A wholesaler of industrial heating and cooling equipment.

CAIN AND BULTMAN, INC.
2145 Dennis Street, Jacksonville FL 32204. 904/356-4812. **Contact:** Human Resources. **World Wide Web address:** http://www.cain-bultman.com. **Description:** A wholesale distributor of carpets and vinyl floor coverings.

EDWARD DON & COMPANY
2200 SW 45th Street, Fort Lauderdale FL 33312. 954/983-3000. **Contact:** Human Resources. **Description:** Distributes furniture and equipment to restaurants, hotels, and schools. **World Wide Web address:** http://www.don.com. **Common positions include:** Buyer; Customer Service Representative; Sales Representative. **Operations at this facility include:** Administration; Divisional Headquarters; Sales. **Listed on:** Privately held. **Number of employees at this location:** 270. **Number of employees nationwide:** 1,200.

HUGHES SUPPLY INC.
P.O. Box 2273, Orlando FL 32802-2273. 407/841-4755. **Physical address:** 20 North Orange Avenue, Suite 200, Orlando FL 32801. **Contact:** Human Resources Director. **World Wide Web address:** http://www.hughessupply.com. **Description:** A wholesale distributor of electrical, plumbing, building, and pool supplies. **Corporate headquarters location:** This location. **Listed on:** New York Stock Exchange. **Stock exchange symbol:** HUG.

LINDER INDUSTRIAL MACHINERY COMPANY
P.O. Box 4589, Plant City FL 33564. 813/754-2727. **Contact:** Roxanne Taylor, Human Resources Coordinator. **World Wide Web address:** http://www.linderco.com. **Description:** A distributor of construction and mining equipment. **Number of employees at this location:** 200.

ACCOUNTING & MANAGEMENT CONSULTING

Arthur Andersen/51
Deloitte & Touche/51, 52
Ernst & Young LLP/52
KPMG/53
O'Sullivan Hicks Patton, LLP/53
PricewaterhouseCoopers/53, 54

ADVERTISING, MARKETING, AND PUBLIC RELATIONS

BBDO/56
Catalina Marketing Corporation/56
W.B. Doner & Company/56
Fitzgerald Advertising and Public
   Relations/57
Husk Jennings Advertising/57
Landers and Partners, Inc./57
Nationwide Advertising Service
   Inc./57
Shaker Advertising Agency/58
Tully-Menard, Inc./58
Val-Pak Direct Marketing/58
WestWayne, Inc./59
Yesawich, Pepperdine and
   Brown/59

AEROSPACE

ABA Industries/61
Aerosonic Corporation/61
Arrow Air, Inc./61
B/E Aerospace, Inc./61, 62
BAE SYSTEMS/63
Crestview Aerospace
   Corporation/63
Dayton-Granger, Inc./64
Eaton Corporation/64
Fort Lauderdale Jet Center/64
Gables Engineering, Inc./64
HEICO Aerospace Corporation/64
Honeywell/65
Hoover Industries Inc./65
Lockheed Martin Electronics &
   Missiles/65
Metric Systems Corporation/65
Microdyne Corporation/66
The New Piper Aircraft, Inc./67
Northrop Grumman
   Corporation/67
Pratt & Whitney/67
Rockwell Collins/67
Signature Flight Support/68
Sikorsky Aircraft Corporation/68
Unison Industries/68

United Space Alliance (USA)/69
World Fuel Services, Inc./69

APPAREL, FASHION, AND TEXTILES

American Woolen Company/71
Chico's Fas/71
Decorator Industries, Inc./71
Hollander Home Fashions
   Corporation/71
Injection Footwear Corporation/71
Superior Uniform Group/72
Tropical Sportswear
   International/72
Westpoint Stevens/73

ARCHITECTURE/ CONSTRUCTION/ ENGINEERING (MISC.)

AJT & Associates, Inc./75
ATC Associates/75
Aluma Systems/75
APAC Inc./75, 76
Ashley Aluminum, LLC/dba
   Cameron Ashley Building
   Products/76
Atlantic Marine, Inc./Atlantic Dry
   Dock Corporation/76
Bertram Yacht, Inc./76
Catalina Yachts/77
Centex Rooney/77
J.W. Conner & Sons, Inc./77
Devcon International
   Corporation/77
Exponent, Inc./77
Florida Crushed Stone Company/78
Florida Engineered Construction
   Products/78
The Haskell Company/78
Hubbard Construction Company/78
Misener Marine Construction
   Inc./79
Nobility Homes, Inc./79
Oriole Homes Corporation/79
Palmer Electric Company/
   Showcase Lighting/79
Post, Buckley, Schuh, and Jernigan,
   Inc./79
Reynolds, Smith, and Hills, Inc./80
Scotty's, Inc./80
Tri-City Electrical Contractors/80
Walt Disney Imagineering/80
Walter Industries/81
Watkins Engineers & Constructors,
   Inc./81

ARTS, ENTERTAINMENT, SPORTS, AND RECREATION

Alliance Entertainment
Corporation/83
Allied Vaughn/83
Brevard Zoo/83
Busch Gardens Tampa Bay/
Adventure Island/83
CPAmerica, Inc./84
Caribbean Gardens/84
Gatorland/84
Golden Bear Golf Inc./84
Gulf Breeze Zoo/84
International Speedway
Corporation/85
Lion Country Safari/85
Lowry Park Zoo/85
M.E. Productions/85
Manhattan Transfer Miami/86
Miami Metrozoo/86
Parrot Jungle and Gardens/86
Sea World of Florida/86
Tallahassee Museum of History &
Natural Science/86
Universal Studios Florida/87
Wet 'n Wild/87
Wildlife on Easy Street, Inc./87

AUTOMOTIVE

Autonation Inc./89
Breed Technologies, Inc./89
Discount Auto Parts, Inc./89
Dura Automotive Systems, Inc./89
Emergency One Inc./90
Hi-Stat Manufacturing Company,
Inc./90
Recoton Corporation/91
TI Group Automotive Systems/91
Wheeled Coach Industries, Inc./91

BANKING/SAVINGS & LOANS/ OTHER DEPOSITORY INSTITUTIONS (MISC.)

AmSouth Bank/93
Bank of America/93
BankAtlantic/93
CB Richard Ellis/Suntrust/94
Fidelity Federal Bank & Trust/94
First Union National Bank of
Florida/94, 95
Regions Bank/95
SouthTrust Bank/95
SunTrust Bank, Gulf Coast, N.A./96
SunTrust Bank, Miami, N.A./96

SunTrust Bank, Tampa Bay,
N.A./97
SunTrust Bank, Central Florida,
N.A./97
U.S. Federal Reserve Bank of
Florida/98
Wachovia Bank/98

BIOTECHNOLOGY/ PHARMACEUTICALS/ SCIENTIFIC R&D (MISC.)

ABC Research Corporation/100
Beckman Coulter, Inc./100
IVAX Corporation/100
IVAX Pharmaceuticals/101
The Monticello Company/101
North American Biologicals
Inc./101
Noven Pharmaceuticals, Inc./101
PharMerica/Pharmacy Management
Services, Inc. (PMSI)/102
Quest Diagnostics
Incorporated/102
Research Triangle Institute
(RTI)/102
Rexall Showcase International/103
Schering-Plough/103
Scientific Instruments, Inc./104

BUSINESS SERVICES/ NON-SCIENTIFIC RESEARCH

ADP Total Source/106
ARAMARK Corporation/106
Armor Holdings, Inc./106
First American Real Estate
Solutions/106
G&K Services, Inc./107
OSI Collection Services/107
Palm Coast Data Ltd./108
Spherion/108
Team Staff Rx/108
The Wackenhut Corporation/108,
109

CHARITIES/SOCIAL SERVICES

American Cancer Society/111
American Red Cross/111
Bayfront YMCA/111
Bradenton YMCA/111
Cathedral Residences/111
St. Augustine Family YMCA/112
St. Petersburg YMCA/112

CHEMICALS/RUBBER AND PLASTICS

Arizona Chemical/114
CF Industries, Inc./Plant City/114
CF Industries, Inc./Tampa/114
Cargill Fertilizer/114
Dayco Products/114
Hercules, Inc./115
International Flavors & Fragrances (IFF)/115
McNeel International Corporation/115
Reichhold Chemicals, Inc./115
Security Plastics Inc./116
U.S. Agri-Chemicals Corporation/116
Uniroyal Technology Corporation/116

COMMUNICATIONS: TELECOMMUNICATIONS/ BROADCASTING

API Media/118
Aerotron-Repco Systems, Inc./118
America II Electronics, Inc./118
Dictaphone Corporation/118
Dycom Industries, Inc./119
Harris Corporation/119
Harris Technical Services Corporation/119
Manhattan Transfer Miami/120
Motorola, Inc./120, 121
NBC 6 / WTVJ/121
Nextel Communications/121
NextiraOne/122
Paxson Communications Corporation/122
Protel, Inc./122
Siemens Business Communication Systems, Inc./122
Siemens Stromberg-Carlson/123
Symetrics Industries/123
WCTV/123

COMPUTERS (MISC.)

AGRA Baymont/125
Allen Systems Group Inc./125
American Ribbon & Toner Company/125
Analysts International Corporation (AiC)/125
Answerthink Consulting Group/125
Bell Microproducts Latin America//126

Benefit Technology Inc./126
Boca Research/126
CPA Software/126
CTG (Computer Task Group, Inc.)/126
CareCentric/127
Citel America, Inc./127
Citrix Systems, Inc./127
Colamco Inc./127
Compucom Systems, Inc./128
Computer Associates International, Inc./128
Comsys Inc./128
Concurrent Computer Corporation/128
Convergys/129
DMR Consulting Group/129
Dataco Derex Inc./129
ECI Telecom/129
Encore Real Time Computing, Inc./130
Equifax Payment Services/130
Executrain of Florida/130
FDP Corporation/130
Fischer International Systems Corporation/131
Fortel/131
GRC International, Inc./131
Geac AEC Business Solutions/131
HTE Inc./132
Harris Corporation/132
Harris Technical Services Corporation/132
Hummingbird, Inc./133
IBM Corporation/133
IKON Office Solutions Technology Services/133
ISYS/Biovation/134
Khameleon Software/134
Lockheed Martin Tactical Defense Systems/134
MacAcademy/Windows Academy/Florida Marketing International, Inc./135
McKessonHBOC/135
Modcomp Inc./135
Modis/136
Modus Operandi/136
Network Infoserve, Inc./136
NextiraOne/136
Oce Printing Systems USA/137
Paradyne Corporation/137
Paravant Computer Systems Inc./137
Payformance Corporation/137
PaySys International/137
Premio Computer/137

Pygmy Computer Systems Inc./138
Solution 6 Holdings Limited/138
Sun Microsystems, Inc./138
Tech Data Corporation/139
TigerDirect, Inc./139
Tingley Systems/140
Tybrin Corporation/140
Unisys Corporation/140
Veridian Inc./141
Veritas Software/141
Vicorp.com/141

EDUCATIONAL SERVICES

Edison Community College/143
Embry-Riddle Aeronautical
  University/143
Florida Atlantic University/143
Florida Community College at
  Jacksonville/144
Florida Memorial College/144
Florida State University/144
Hillsborough Community
  College/144
Lynn University/145
Miami-Dade Community College
  Kendall Campus/145
  Medical Center Campus/146
  Mitchell Wolfson Campus/146
  North Campus/146
Nova Southeastern University/146
Palm Beach Community
  College/146
Rollins College/147
St. Petersburg Junior College/147
University of Central Florida/147
University of Florida/147
University of Miami/148
University of North Florida/148
University of South Florida
  (USF)/148
University of West Florida/149

ELECTRONIC/INDUSTRIAL ELECTRICAL EQUIPMENT AND COMPONENTS

A-1 Components, Inc./151
ACR Electronics/151
ATK Integrated Defense
  Company/151
A.W. Industries/152
Artesyn Technologies/152
BAE SYSTEMS/152
Chromalloy Florida/153
Conax Florida Corporation/153
Concord Camera Corporation/153
Cypress Electronics/153
Danka Office Imaging/154
Dynalco Controls/154
Electro Corporation/154
Eltec Instruments Inc./154
GE Automation Services/155
Harris Corporation/155
Hi*Tech Electronic Displays/155
Lambda Novatronics Inc./156
Lighting Components & Design,
  Inc./156
Lockheed Martin Electronics &
  Missiles/156
Lockheed Martin Missiles and Fire
  Control/156
Lockheed Martin Tactical Defense
  Systems/157
Micro Systems, Inc./157
Northrop Grumman/158
Piezo Technology, Inc. (PTI)/158
Sensormatic Electronics
  Corporation/158
Signal Technology Corporation/159
Solectron/159
Solitron Devices, Inc./160
Sparton Electronics/160, 161
Titan Corporation/161
Titan Systems Corporation/162
TRAK Microwave Corporation/162

ENVIRONMENTAL & WASTE MANAGEMENT SERVICES

AJT & Associates, Inc./165
ATC Associates/165
Browning-Ferris Industries, Inc.
  (BFI)/165
Evans Environmental
  Corporation/165
Harding ESE/166
Munters Corporation/166
Severn Trent Laboratories, Inc./166

FABRICATED METAL PRODUCTS AND PRIMARY METALS

Ashley Aluminum, LLC/dba
  Cameron Ashley Building
  Products/169
Sonoco Products/169
VAW of America Inc./169

FINANCIAL SERVICES (MISC.)

Alliance Mortgage Company/172

First Union Securities Financial Network/172
Fiserv Inc./172
Raymond James and Associates/172
J.I. Kislak Mortgage Corporation/173
LBS Capital Management, Inc./173
MBNA Marketing Systems, Inc./173
Marshall & Ilsley Trust Company of Florida/173
Merrill Lynch/174
Prudential Securities, Inc./175
Quick and Reilly, Inc./175
Salomon Smith Barney/175
UBS PaineWebber Inc./176

FOOD AND BEVERAGES/ AGRICULTURE

ABC Fine Wine & Spirits/178
CF Industries, Inc./Plant City/178
CF Industries, Inc./Tampa/178
Cargill Fertilizer/178
Coca-Cola Bottling Company/178, 179
Florida Global Citrus Limited/179
Florida's Natural Growers/179
Fort Myers Coca-Cola Bottling Company/180
Gold Kist Poultry/180
Golden Gem Growers, Inc./180
Juice Bowl Products/180
Kendall Foods Corporation/181
McArthur Dairy/181
National Beverage Corporation/181
Okeelanta Corporation/181
Pepsi-Cola Bottling Company/181
Pepsi-Cola Company/182
Swisher International/182
Tropicana North America/183
Tyson Foods, Inc./183
U.S. Beverage/183
U.S. Foodservice/183
United States Sugar Corporation/184
George Weston Bakeries Inc./184

GOVERNMENT

Charlotte County Recording Department/186
Florida Department of Transportation/186
Hillsborough, County of/186
Jacksonville, City of/186
Jacksonville Port Authority/186
Lantana, Town of/187
Leon, County of/Board of County Commissioners/187
Naval Surface Warfare Center/187
North Lauderdale, City of/187
U.S. Postal Service/187

HEALTH CARE: SERVICES, EQUIPMENT, AND PRODUCTS (MISC.)

Alimed Home Infusion/189
Apria Healthcare Group Inc./189
Aso Corporation/189
Baptist St. Vincent's Health/ Systems/Baptist St. Vincent's Medical Center/190
Baptist St. Vincent's Visiting Nurses/190
Bausch & Lomb Pharmaceuticals, Inc./190
Baxter Healthcare Corporation/191
Bayfront Medical Center/191
Bon Secours-St. Joseph Hospital/192
Caladesi Animal Hospital/192
Care Medical Equipment/192
Charlotte Regional Medical Center/192
Cleveland Clinic Florida Hospital/193
Columbia New Port Richey Hospital/194
Coram Healthcare Corporation/194
Cordis Corporation/195
Cypress Village/195
Delray Medical Center/195
Essilor of America/195
Florida Infusion Services/196
Florida State Hospital/196
Freedom Square Retirement Center/196
Freedom Village/196
Gentiva Health Services/197
Gulf Coast Center/197
Health First/Holmes Regional Medical Center/Palm Bay Community Hospital/197
Health Management Associates, Inc./197
HealthSouth Doctors Hospital/198
Heartland Rehabilitation Center/198
Hospice By The Sea, Inc./198
Hospice of Northeast Florida/198
Indian River Memorial Hospital/199
Interim HealthCare Inc./199

Jackson Memorial Hospital/199
John Knox Village of Central
  Florida/199
John Knox Village of Florida/200
John Knox Village of Tampa
  Bay/200
Kelly Assisted Living Services/200
Kendall Medical Center/200
Kindred Healthcare/200
Kissimmee Good Samaritan
  Village/200
La Amistad Behavioral Health
  Services/201
Lee Memorial Health System/201
Life Care Services/201
Linvatec Corporation/202
Manatee Memorial Hospital/202
Martin Memorial Health Systems,
  Inc./202
Mayo Clinic/203
Medical Technology Systems/203
Medtronic Xomed Surgical
  Products, Inc./203
Memorial Hospital of Tampa/203
Miami Jewish Home &
  Hospital/204
Moorings Park/204
Morton Plant Hospital/204
Morton Plant Mease Health
  Care/204
Naples Medical Center/204
NuMED Home Health Care,
  Inc./205
Orlando Regional Healthcare/205
Orlando Regional Lucerne
  Hospital/206
Osceola Regional Medical
  Center/206
Plantation General Hospital/206
Prime Care Health Agency Inc./206
Ramsay Youth Services, Inc./207
RoTech Medical Corporation/207
S.H. Medical Corporation/207
Sacred Heart Health Systems/207
Skyway Animal Hospital/208
Smith Dental Labs/208
Star Multicare Services Inc./209
Sunrise Community, Inc./209
Swanholm Nursing and
  Rehabilitation/209
Tallahassee Community
  Hospital/209
Tampa General Hospital/209
Tender Loving Care/
  Staff Builders/210
3i (Implant Innovations, Inc.)/211
Transitions Optical Inc./211

Tyco Healthcare/Kendall/211
U.S. Dept. of Veterans Affairs
  Bay Pines VA Medical
  Center/211
U.S. Dept. of Veterans Affairs
  Miami VA Medical Center/212
University Community
  Hospital/212
University Hospital & Medical
  Center/213
Visiting Nurse Association/213
Visiting Nurse Association and
  Hospice/213
Westchester General Hospital,
  Inc./213
Whitehall Boca Nursing Home/213
Windmoor Health Care/213
Winter Park Memorial Hospital/214
Winter Park Towers/214

HOTELS AND RESTAURANTS

Atlantic Coast Management/216
Benihana Inc./216
Checkers Drive-In Restaurants,
  Inc./216
Darden Restaurants, Inc./216
Execustay, Inc./216
FMS Management Systems, Inc./dba
  International House of
  Pancakes/217
Famous Amos Restaurants, Inc./217
H.I. Development, Inc./217
Hyatt Regency Orlando
  International Airport/217
Hyatt Regency Pier Sixty-Six/218
King Provision Corporation/218
La Cruise Casino/218
Outback Steakhouse, Inc./218
Popeye's/219
Renaissance Biscayne Bay
  Hotel/219
Restaurant Administration
  Services/219
Sun International, Inc./219
The Westin Innisbrook Resort/219
Wyndham Orlando Resort/220

INSURANCE

AAA (American Automobile
  Association)/222
Assurant Group/222
Blue Cross and Blue Shield of
  Florida/222
Brown & Brown Insurance/223

Carolina Casualty Insurance
  Company/223
Crawford & Company/223
Health Plan Services/223
HUMANA/224
Metropolitan Life Insurance
  Company/224
Ward North America, Inc./224

LEGAL SERVICES

Carlton Fields/226
Foley & Lardner/226
Fowler, White, Gillen, Baggs,
  Villareal, Banker/226
Greenberg Traurig/226
Marks, Gray, Conroy & Gibbs/226
McGuireWoods/226

MANUFACTURING: MISCELLANEOUS CONSUMER

Applica Incorporated/228
Elizabeth Arden, Inc./228
Fiskars Pottery and Outdoor Leisure
  Products/228
Florida Furniture Industries,
  Inc./228
Loren Industries, Inc./228
Macho Products Inc./228
Moltech Power Systems, Inc./229
Parlux Fragrances, Inc./229
Recoton Corporation/229
Revlon/229
Sunbeam Corporation/230
TravelPro Luggage/230
Tupperware World
  Headquarters/230
Zodiac Pool Care, Inc./231

MANUFACTURING: MISCELLANEOUS INDUSTRIAL

Aerotron-Repco Systems, Inc./233
Alpine Engineered Products,
  Inc./233
Bairnco Corporation/233
Crown Cork & Seal Company/233
ECC International Corporation/234
Eva-tone/234
FMC Corporation/235
Gencor Industries Inc./235
Hi-Rise Recycling Systems, Inc./235
Invensys Metering Systems/235
Martin Electronics, Inc./236
Pall Aeropower/236
Parkson Corporation/237

Siemens Westinghouse Power
  Corporation/237
Stainless Inc./237
USNR/237
Uniweld Products, Inc./238

MINING/GAS/PETROLEUM/ ENERGY RELATED

Ascom Energy Systems/240
Florida Rock Industries/240
IMC Phosphates/240
Seminole Electric Cooperative
  Inc./240
Townley Manufacturing/241
World Fuel Services, Inc./241

PAPER AND WOOD PRODUCTS

Causeway Lumber Company/243
Coastal Lumber Company/243
Constantine's Wood Center of
  Florida/243
Florida Plywoods, Inc./243
Georgia-Pacific Corporation/243
Gulf Stream Lumber Company/244
Mac Papers Inc./244
Rayonier Inc./244
Robbins Manufacturing
  Company/244
Smurfit-Stone Container
  Corporation/245

PRINTING AND PUBLISHING

Add Inc. Publications/247
American Media Inc./247
BBF/247
Bailey Publishing &
  Communications Inc./248
Boca Raton News/248
The Bradenton Herald/248
Breeze Newspapers/248
Cape Publications, Inc./249
Central Florida Press, L.C./249
Construction Data Corporation/250
Dartnell Corporation/250
Eva-tone/250
Florida Sentinel Bulletin/251
The Florida Star/251
The Florida Times-Union/Florida
  Publishing Company/251
Fort Pierce Tribune/251
The Gainesville Sun/251
Graphline Company/252
Jacksonville Business Journal/252
Key West Citizen/252

Knight-Ridder/252
Lake City Reporter/253
The Ledger/253
Magnum Digital Services/253
The Miami Herald Publishing/
    El Nuevo Herald/253
Miami Times/254
Miami Today/254
The Naples Daily News/254
News Herald/254
News Press/254
News-Journal Corporation/255
The Northwest Florida Daily
    News/255
Ocala Star-Banner/255
Orlando Business Journal/255
Orlando Sentinel Communications
    Company/256
The Orlando Times/256
The Palatka Daily News/256
Palm Beach Newspapers, Inc./256
Pensacola News Journal/257
Printing House Ltd./257
Rose Printing Company, Inc./257
St. Augustine Record/257
St. Ives Inc./257
Sanford Herald/258
South Florida Business Journal/258
The Stuart News/258
The Sun-Sentinel/258
The Tallahassee Democrat/258
Tampa Tribune/259
Times Publishing Company,
    Inc./259
Trader Publishing Company/259
USA Today/260
Warner Brothers Publications/260

REAL ESTATE

Avatar Holdings Inc./262
Bluegreen Corporation/262
CB Richard Ellis/262, 263
Coldwell Banker/264
Deltona Corporation/264
First American Real Estate
    Solutions/264
J.I. Kislak Mortgage
    Corporation/265
Lennar Corporation/265
The St. Joe Company/265
Watermark Communities, Inc.
    (WCI)/266

RETAIL

B&B Corporate Holdings, Inc./268
W.S. Badcock Corporation/268
Barnes & Noble Bookstores/268,
    269
Beall's Department Stores/269
Body Shop of America, Inc./269
Burdines/269, 270
CED (Consolidated Electrical
    Distributors, Inc.)/270
Champs Sports/270
Chico's Fas/270
Claire's Accessories/271
Dillard's Department Stores,
    Inc./271
Eckerd Corporation/271
Farm Stores/272
Golden Bear Golf Inc./272
Home Shopping Network, Inc./273
Kane Furniture/273
Kash 'N Karry Food Stores/273
Levitz Furniture Corporation/273
Martine's Corporation/273
Mayors Jewelers/274
Office Depot/274
The Pantry, Inc./274
Potamkin South/275
Publix Super Markets, Inc./275
Recreation USA/275
Robb & Stucky/276
Sears, Roebuck & Co./276
Sound Advice, Inc./276
Winn-Dixie Stores, Inc./276

STONE, CLAY, GLASS, AND CONCRETE PRODUCTS

AFGD, Inc./279
Anchor Glass Container
    Corporation/279
Florida Crushed Stone
    Company/280
Florida Rock Industries/280
Hardrives, Inc./280
MonierLifetile, Inc./280
RMC-Ewell Industries, Inc./281
Rinker Materials Corporation/281
United States Gypsum
    Company/281
Water Bonnet Manufacturing
    Inc./281

TRANSPORTATION/TRAVEL

Alamo Rent-A-Car/283

Alterman Transport Lines/283
Blackbeard's Cruises/283
Budget Group, Inc./283
CSX Transportation/283
Carnival Corporation/
    Carnival Cruise Lines/283
Celebrity Cruises/284
Costa Cruise Lines/284
Crowley American Transport,
    Inc./284
Cunard Line/284
Florida East Coast Railway
    Company/284
Florida Rock Industries/285
Land Span, Inc./285
Landstar Ligon, Inc./285
Landstar System, Inc./286
Luhrs Corporation/286
Maritrans Inc./286
McKenzie Tank Lines, Inc./286
Norwegian Cruise Lines/287
Regal Marine Industries, Inc./287
Royal Caribbean/287
Ryder System, Inc./287
TNT Logistics/287
Wellcraft Marine/288
Windjammer Barefoot Cruises/288

UTILITIES: ELECTRIC/GAS/WATER

FPL Group/291
Florida Keys Electric
    Cooperative/291
Florida Progress Energy/291
Gulf Power Company/291
Mastec/292
Orlando Utilities Commission/292
Tampa Electric/292

MISC. WHOLESALING

Baker Distributing Company/294
Cain and Bultman, Inc./294
Edward Don & Company/294
Hughes Supply Inc./294
Linder Industrial Machinery
    Company/294